C000264748

Introduction

A: Legal and management

B: Health and welfare

C: General safety

D: High risk activities

E: Environment

F: Specialist activities

Introduction

Contents

Overview

Site supervision simplified (GE 706) is aimed at supervisors and first line managers, but also provides managers and owners of small construction companies with easy-to-understand information and practical guidance to help them implement, supervise and monitor the required standards of health, safety and the environment on construction sites.

This is the official reference book for the CITB Site Safety Plus *Site supervisors' safety training scheme* (SSSTS), a two-day course for first line managers and supervisors, and the one-day SSSTS refresher course. It is a supporting document not only on the courses but for reference purposes at work afterwards.

It is also a useful source of information on basic, site-based health, safety and environment issues for university undergraduates, college students on construction management courses and for those on other construction-focused courses.

Content provides the supervisor with advice on solutions, case studies and practical day-to-day guidance on what to do, as well as short, clear explanations on related legislation.

 It is recommended that owners of small and medium-sized companies also refer to *Construction site safety* (GE 700), which covers in more detail the legal duties placed on employers.

Acknowledgements

CITB wishes to acknowledge the assistance offered by the following organisations in the preparation of this edition of GE 706.

- ☑ Costain.
- ☑ GoakesSAFETY Ltd.
- ☑ Montpellier International Consulting Ltd.
- ☑ RED Scientific Ltd.
- ☑ Safety Training Services.
- ☑ Simian Risk Management Ltd.
- ☑ Thames Laboratories.

 This publication contains public sector information published by the Health and Safety Executive and licensed under the Open Government Licence.

Occupational health and safety

Occupational health deals with all aspects of workplace health and safety. The main focus is on prevention of hazards. To make sure the health of workers is not affected, employers have to protect people from risks at the workplace.

Some work activities, and some equipment, materials and chemicals used in the workplace, may carry risks that lead to accidents, musculoskeletal diseases (such as long-term spine or back problems), respiratory diseases (such as breathing problems from inhaling dusts or fumes), hearing loss, circulatory (blood) diseases, cancers, stress-related disorders, and many other conditions.

☑ *Occupational health* is the promotion and maintenance of the highest degree of physical, mental and social wellbeing of workers in all occupations. This means keeping workers as healthy as possible, by removing or preventing the hazards and risks than can cause harm to people at work.

☑ *Safety* is freedom from physical harm. (The condition of being protected from or unlikely to cause danger, risk or injury.)

When someone is injured, the effects are usually immediate (for example, a cut). However, some of the problems and conditions mentioned above cause harm inside the body for many years before their effects are known or felt. In some cases it can be up to 60 years before the person affected is diagnosed with a disease that has no cure, which was caused by breathing in harmful dusts or fibres as a teenager or young adult working in construction.

Work-related injuries and ill health statistics for the construction industry

☑ The construction sector is a major employer accounting for around 6% of the UK workforce.

☑ Construction includes three broad industry groups:

– civil engineering – covering general construction for civil engineering works, including road and railway construction, and utility projects

– the construction of buildings – covering general construction of buildings, including new work, repair, additions and alterations

– specialised construction activities – covering trades that are usually specialised in one aspect common to different structures (for example, demolition, electrical and plumbing installation, joinery installation, plastering, painting and glazing).

☑ The UK construction industry is made up of over 200,000 construction businesses, of which 90% employ fewer than 10 workers.

☑ Approximately 2.65 million people are employed in the UK construction industry. It covers activities including housing, utilities, repair and maintenance, refurbishment, demolition, roofing, shopfitting, mechanical and electrical, plumbing and highways maintenance.

☑ On average 39 construction workers are killed each year due to accidents.

☑ The biggest killer (around half) is falls from height, with an average of seven people dying each year as a result of falling through fragile roofs.

☑ The most common over seven-day injuries are due to manual handling or lifting accidents, followed by slips, trips and falls on the same level, falls from height and being struck by an object.

☑ The construction industry has the largest burden of occupational cancer. It accounts for over 40% of occupational cancer deaths and cancer registrations each year in Great Britain.

☑ The most significant carcinogen is past exposure to asbestos, followed by silica, solar radiation, and coals, tars and pitches.

☑ Approximately 5,000 people die each year due to past exposure to asbestos.

Introduction

- ☑ Work-related respiratory disease covers a range of illnesses that are caused or made worse by breathing in hazardous substances (such as construction dust) that damage the lungs.

- ☑ Silica is the biggest risk to construction workers after asbestos. Prolonged exposure to respirable crystalline silica can cause lung cancer and other serious respiratory diseases.

- ☑ Vibration white finger, carpal tunnel syndrome, noise-induced hearing loss and dermatitis are the most common non-lung diseases suffered by those in the construction industry.

- ☑ Around 0.4 million working days every year are lost through stress-related absence.

 Construction workers (just like you) could die due to work-related ill health, or as a result of an accident, if control measures are not followed.

 For in-depth statistical information visit the companion website.

Why so many accidents?

Reports of present day construction accidents and ill health make depressing reading because simple actions were not taken to prevent them. In many cases, those planning the jobs totally failed to consider the health, safety or welfare of the people carrying out the work (and possibly others who were affected) and to actively manage the situation.

Common examples of such events include the following.

- ☑ The increasing number of workers who suffer from cancers and life changing illnesses ranging from breathing difficulties to skin complaints – some of these force the sufferer to give up work, because exposure to dangerous substances, such as dust, was not even considered, let alone prevented or controlled.

- ☑ The deaths and serious injuries that occur because people fall from height – often basic safety actions (like using temporary work platforms on fragile roofs, installing edge protection or using a safety harness and lanyard clipped to a strong point) were not taken.

- ☑ Workers being buried in collapsed excavations because the sides were unstable and not supported.

- ☑ Workers being killed or injured by construction plant because pedestrians were not kept out of the plant operating area.

Achieving acceptable standards of on-site health and safety is not difficult. Where the work to be carried out is uncomplicated and familiar, the precautions that need to be taken are simple, requiring the application of common sense or a little investigation and research. The crucial decision for anyone with responsibility for health and safety is to know when they have reached the limits of their knowledge and capabilities and need the assistance of someone with specialist knowledge.

Caution should also be exercised when a job is not going to plan and there is the temptation to resort to improvised methods of working. If you are not at ease with the way that things are going, you should stop the job, step back and think things through carefully before deciding upon a course of action.

Research from the Health and Safety Executive (HSE) has shown that workers are most vulnerable during their first few days on site.

Setting out

Construction is an exciting industry. It is constantly changing as projects move on and jobs get done. As a result of this a building site is one of the most dangerous environments to work in. But many accidents that occur on sites can be avoided if everyone on site works together.

A free film *Setting out*, produced by the industry, sets out what the site must do and what you must do to stay healthy and safe at work.

This film is essential viewing for everyone involved in construction, and should be viewed before sitting the CITB *Health, safety and environment test*. The principles of the film form the basis for the behavioural case study questions, which are included at the beginning of all tests.

Working Well Together in construction

The Working Well Together (WWT) campaign is an industry-led initiative that helps support micro and small businesses in improving their health and safety performance. WWT has become the most successful health and safety initiative within the construction industry.

The campaign undertakes a variety of work, including health and safety awareness days, designer awareness days, breakfast and evening events, roadshows and regional WWT groups.

Working Well Together campaign posters

The following are aims of the WWT initiative.

☑ Improve health and safety knowledge and good practice and seek to continuously improve health, safety and welfare performance in the construction industry.

- ☑ Provide practical advice and assistance to the construction industry on the provision and maintenance of healthy and safe working environments.

- ☑ Encourage co-operation between members in relation to sharing knowledge of health and safety matters.

- ☑ Promote training and learning in health and safety.

- ☑ Provide free or low cost information, advice and training to employers and workers in the construction industry.

- ☑ Stage events where at least half the people who attend will be from small businesses (15 or fewer employees) and 20% from micro businesses (five or fewer employees).

 To find out how the WWT campaign can help you and your company visit its website.

How to use GE 706

GE 706 follows the standard structure that is used across all core CITB publications.

Section A: Legal and management

Section B: Health and welfare

Section C: General safety

Section D: High risk activities

Section E: Environment

Section F: Specialist activities

Each chapter begins with a summary list of the employer's responsibilities, together with a corresponding checklist for supervisors, to help them understand what they and their employer should be doing together to protect their workforce.

New for the 2018 edition

- ☑ Content has been reviewed and updated, where necessary, to ensure the information reflects current legislation and good practice.

- ☑ The health and safety management system information in Section A has been restructured and includes the HSE's recognised model for managing health and safety HSG65: plan, do, check and act. Section A also now includes a summary chart on health and safety law, provides a link to the CDM explainer video, and includes a table detailing the HSE's red, amber and green (RAG) lists.

- ☑ Information on so called legal highs within Section B has been updated in line with the Psychoactive Substances Act and a table has been included to outline the penalties for illegal drugs. Additional guidance, techniques and images have also been included in Section B to enhance the manual handling information.

- ☑ A case study has been included in Section D to highlight the consequences of dangerous working at height.

- ☑ Section E has enhanced information on ecology surveys, archaeology and heritage environments.

- ☑ A new specialist chapter, street works and road works, has been added to Section F.

Toolbox talks

Toolbox talks (GT 700) follows the same structure and chapter layout as *Site supervision simplified* (GE 706) in order to help supervisors prepare for a toolbox talk.

For example, if a supervisor wants to deliver a talk on concrete and silica, they can first look up the relevant GT 700 toolbox talk: B18 Silica dust, which is in Section B, under the Dust and fumes (Respiratory hazards) topic.

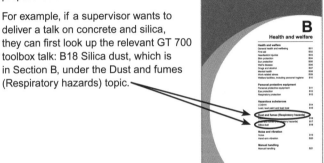

As each topic relates to a chapter within GE 706, further information to help prepare can easily be found within GE 706, Section B Health and welfare, 13 Dust and fumes (Respiratory hazards).

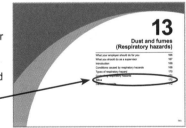

Use of icons

A set of icons emphasises important points within the text and also directs readers to further information. The icons are explained below.

 Website/further info

 Example

 Question

 Ideas

 Notes

 Favourite

 Important

 Good practice

 Poor practice

 Caution

 Consultation

 Guidance

 Case study

 Quote

 Definition

 Interactive checklists and forms

 Video

 Shopping basket

Companion website

A companion website supports *Site supervision simplified*. This is a free resource that provides updates to the current GE 706 publication, to keep it up to date.

It also supports the reader in progressing from the GE 706 book content to additional information available on the internet. Instead of having to type long website details into browsers, or searching on appropriate terms, the reader is directed to the companion website where all other sites of interest can be accessed by quick links.

The companion website contains up to date information on:

☑ any amendments or updates to the current edition

☑ news (such as legislation changes, industry guidance and good practice)

☑ web-links, phone numbers and addresses.

 This icon indicates that further information (such as useful websites and links) can be found on the companion website at citb.co.uk/GE706companion

 The companion website is regularly updated to ensure that the information is current.

 Save the companion website address to your favourites, so it is always available when you need it.

Steps to access a link

The content on the companion website is structured in the same way as the current edition of GE 706.

To access information from a link use the following steps to navigate the structure.

The example provided is for the **Drinkaware alcohol unit guidance website**, referenced in **B08 – Drugs and alcohol.**

Step 1	Open the companion website*	www.citb.co.uk/publications/ companion-websites/ge-706-companion/weblinks/
Step 2	Open the relevant section for the content required	**B: Health and welfare**
Step 3	Open the relevant chapter	**B08 Health and welfare**
Step 4	Select the relevant link	**B08 For further information on alcohol visit the Drinkaware website**
Step 5	Access the 3rd party referenced site	Drinkaware alcohol unit guidance site opens

* To access information from a link in the download or online edition click on the GE 706 companion link on the top left of each page, which will take you directly to the companion website.

Interactive checklists and forms

Interactive checklists and forms are available to download from the GE 700 companion website (identified by this icon).

To access an interactive checklist or form use the following steps to navigate the structure.

The example provided is for the **risk assessment form**, referenced in **A04 Risk assessments, method statements and permits to work.**

Step 1	Open the companion website	www.citb.co.uk/publications/ companion-websites/ge-700-companion/checklists-and-forms/
Step 2	Open the relevant section for the content required	**GA: Legal and management**
Step 3	Access the interactive PDF	Download the the **GA03: Risk assessment** form

You are able to complete individual or multiple forms on your computer before saving or printing them to use, as required. The forms are compatible with both PC and Mac operating systems. You can also print off blank copies of the forms and fill them in manually, if required.

The checklists and forms are user-friendly and quick to complete, making the recording of important information a simple process.

Augmented reality

Augmented reality (AR) technology is used in our publications to provide readers with additional digital content such as videos, images and web-links.

This technology has been used to connect you with extra, complementary content. This can be accessed via your mobile device using the Layar app.

[!] How to install and use the Layar app

☑ Go to the appropriate app store (Apple or Android) and download the Layar app (free of charge) to your mobile device.

☑ Look out for the AR logo (right), which indicates a Layar-friendly page or image.

☑ Open the Layar app and scan the Layar-friendly page or image (ensure that you have the whole page or the specific image in view whilst scanning).

☑ Wait for the page to activate on your device.

☑ Select one of the buttons, when they appear on screen, to access the additional content.

Where can I find augmented reality in this publication?

The table below identifies the pages in this publication that are compatible with augmented reality and the information that can be accessed when an active page is scanned.

Page	Content
Cover	Visit the GE 706 companion website
	Buy related products
5	Watch the *Setting out* film
26	Watch the *CDM 2015* video
159	Watch the short film *Simon's Story* – living with an asbestos related disease

Further supporting information from CITB

CITB has a wide range of products, publications and courses that could help to improve your health, safety and environment knowledge.

After reading this book or attending the CITB Site Safety Plus two-day *Site supervisors' safety training scheme* (SSSTS) you may wish to consider the next step in expanding your health, safety and environment knowledge and competence.

In due course, if you already are, or are about to become, responsible for planning, organising, monitoring, controlling and administering a workforce, you could consider deepening your understanding of health and safety by attending the CITB Site Safety Plus five-day *Site management safety training scheme* (SMSTS).

 Details of course training providers can be found on the CITB website.

Site Safety Plus courses

The Site Safety Plus scheme provides a number of courses that will enhance and develop your skills within the building, civil engineering and allied industries.

Courses give everyone, from operative to senior manager, the skills they need to progress.

 For further information on Site Safety Plus refer to their scheme rules.

01

Health and safety law

A 01

What your employer should do for you
1. Understand the duties imposed by the Health and Safety at Work etc. Act 1974.
2. Understand and put into practice the standards of compliance required.
3. Be aware of the implications of the duties imposed by the Corporate Manslaughter and Corporate Homicide Act.
4. Understand the legal status of health and safety regulations.
5. Be aware of their duties under the Construction (Design and Management) Regulations.
6. Make employees aware of their statutory duties and ensure understanding and compliance.
7. Understand the functions and powers of the Health and Safety Executive (HSE).
8. Ensure access to competent health and safety advice.

What you should do as a supervisor

Checklist	Yes	No	N/A
1. Put into practice your duties imposed by the company health and safety policy.			
2. Understand the standards of compliance required to ensure safety of your workers and others.			
3. Comply with your safety instructions and ensure your workers understand their duties and responsibilities.			
4. Supervise your workers to ensure their, and your, safety.			
5. Make sure that work equipment is in good condition, inspected and used correctly.			
6. Make sure correct personal protective equipment (PPE) is provided, correctly worn, used, maintained and replaced when defective.			
7. Co-operate with your employer so that they can carry out their legal duties.			
8. Report anything that you feel is unsafe.			

A
01

A
01

Introduction

The purpose of health and safety legislation is to protect the wellbeing of people at work and others (such as the general public) by ensuring work is carried out in a manner that is safe and free of risks to health for everyone who may be affected.

Everyone who goes to work has a right to return home uninjured and in a good state of health. Similarly, visitors to sites and passers-by have a right to the same level of protection of their health and safety.

If health and safety laws are broken, a criminal offence is committed. If the results are sufficiently serious the offence could be punishable by a fine or even imprisonment. The Health and Safety Executive (HSE) can issue enforcement notices and offer advice. After discovering a material breach of health and safety requirements, and in accordance with regulations, the HSE may charge for its time under the Health and Safety (Fees) Regulations. This is known as a **fee for intervention (FFI)**.

Whilst health and safety legislation is embedded in criminal law, in some circumstances civil legislation gives a person who has been injured, made ill or suffered a loss through a work-related activity the right to take legal action against the employer for compensation, through the civil courts.

 Employers can and must insure against civil liabilities but they cannot insure against criminal liabilities.

The primary focus of health and safety legislation is to put legal duties on employers (and the self-employed, who in many cases have the same legal duties as employers) to ensure that work is carried out safely and without risks to health.

In specific situations, legal duties are placed upon *duty holders*, as defined in the specific legislation. It should also be noted that some legislation places legal duties upon *employees*.

In many situations, site-based staff (such as supervisors, site managers or project managers) will be nominated by the employer to ensure that the employer's legal duties are complied with at site level. However, legal duties still lie with the employer who must resource and be confident in the ability and competence of their supervisors, managers and others to manage health and safety on their behalf.

Progress of health and safety law

☑ The Health and Safety at Work etc. Act is the basis for modern legislation and came into force in 1974, bringing with it protection for virtually everyone at work and consolidating much of the earlier industry-specific legislation under a single Act.

☑ Construction (Design and Management) Regulations (CDM) were originally drafted in 1994 to address an unacceptably high rate of accidents and ill health to construction workers. The CDM Regulations were revised in 2007. This revision reinforced the requirements for competence, co-operation and co-ordination, with a focus on the provision of 'the right information to the right people at the right time'.

☑ The coming into force of the Corporate Manslaughter and Corporate Homicide Act and the Health and Safety (Offences) Act 2008 demonstrated a hardening of Government's attitude with regard to serious breaches of health and safety legislation.

☑ Professor Ragnar Löfstedt's report, *Reclaiming health and safety for all: an independent review of health and safety legislation,* was published in 2011. The report considered ways in which health and safety legislation could be combined, simplified or reduced so that the burden on British businesses could be alleviated. It led to a review of a number of regulations, including the Reporting of Injuries, Diseases and Dangerous Occurrences Regulations (RIDDOR).

☑ In March 2015 the Legal Aid, Sentencing and Punishment of Offenders Act was amended. Prior to this date Magistrates' Courts were limited to fines of a maximum of £20,000 under Sections 2 to 6 of the Health and Safety at Work etc. Act 1974. This has now been amended to allow Magistrates' Courts to issue unlimited fines and up to 12 months imprisonment.

☑ In 2015 the CDM Regulations were revised to closer reflect the requirements of the European Directive on the implementation of minimum safety and health requirements at temporary or mobile construction sites and to support improved co-ordination, better value for money and improved efficiency.

Health and Safety at Work etc. Act 1974

The Health and Safety at Work etc. Act (HSWA) is the primary piece of health and safety legislation in the United Kingdom. The HSWA is an enabling Act, which allows the Government to make health and safety regulations that become part of the law. The requirements of the HSWA are very general and wide-ranging, such as in the example below.

It shall be the duty of every employer to ensure, so far as is reasonably practicable, the health, safety and welfare at work of all their employees.

This typical requirement does not specify any technical requirements or set any minimum standards of behaviour that can be measured, but it does clearly outline the requirement for safe places of work.

Health and safety regulations expand upon the legal requirements of the HSWA with regard to specific occupational activities, hazards and risks and include specific and technical requirements.

Health and safety regulations

Health and safety regulations are a part of UK law that place duties on employers, employees and other designated persons. It is a criminal offence to contravene them. Some regulations have been developed and introduced as a means of incorporating European Union directives into our domestic legal framework.

Health and safety regulations expand upon the legal requirements of the Health and Safety at Work etc. Act, with regard to specific occupational activities, hazards and risks, and include specific and technical requirements. Health and safety regulations are often supported by Approved Codes of Practice (ACoPs) and guidance notes.

Some sets of regulations apply to construction activities only.

Examples of legislation that have an effect on the building and construction industry are shown below.

Management of Health and Safety at Work Regulations
The main requirement on employers is to carry out a risk assessment. Employers with five or more employees need to record the significant findings of the risk assessment. Employers should use a hierarchy of preventative and protective measures to control risks, and carry out employee health surveillance, where required.

A
01

Construction (Design and Management) Regulations
(refer to Chapter A02)

There is a strong focus on duty holders having the necessary training, knowledge, qualifications, experience and skills and, where an organisation, organisational capability. To meet these criteria, an organisation or individual must possess the following.

- ☑ Have knowledge of the specific tasks to be undertaken and the hazards and risks that the work will entail.

- ☑ Take appropriate action in order to prevent harm to those carrying out construction work, or those affected by the work.

- ☑ Have sufficient experience, ability and resources to carry out their duties in relation to the project.

- ☑ Recognise and understand their limitations.

Work at Height Regulations *(refer to Chapter D24)*

Duty holders are required to ensure the following.

- ☑ Every employer and person in charge of a premises shall ensure that no work at height is carried out where it is reasonably practicable to carry out the work safely in another way.

- ☑ All work at height is properly planned and organised.

- ☑ All work at height takes due account of weather conditions that could endanger health and safety.

- ☑ The place where work at height is carried out is safe.

- ☑ The risks from fragile surfaces are properly controlled, as are the risks from falling objects.

- ☑ Those involved in work at height are trained and competent.

- ☑ Equipment for work at height is appropriately inspected.

Provision and Use of Work Equipment Regulations
(refer to Chapter C20)

Details the specific duties on people and companies who own, operate or have control over work equipment. Suitable and sufficient equipment must be provided, inspected, tested and properly maintained and operators must be properly trained in its use.

Electricity at Work Regulations *(refer to Chapter C18)*

Stipulates that people in control of electrical systems must ensure that the systems are safe to use and are maintained in a safe condition. Only a qualified electrician should install, maintain or alter an electrical distribution system.

Control of Asbestos Regulations *(refer to Chapter B12)*

The minimum standards for protecting workers and the general public from risks associated with exposure to asbestos. It requires the identification of asbestos-containing materials (ACMs) that may be present in the workplace, before any work is carried out. Those carrying out the work must be properly briefed as to the location of the asbestos or ACM, and be properly trained and adequately resourced.

Reporting of Injuries, Diseases and Dangerous Occurrences Regulations *(refer to Chapter A07)*

A legal duty is placed on employers, the self-employed and those in control of premises to report the following.

- ☑ Work-related deaths and specified injuries.

- ☑ Injuries resulting in an absence of more than seven days or the inability to perform normal work activities for a period of seven days.

- ☑ Work-related diseases or conditions.

☑ Specified dangerous occurrences.

☑ Exposure to carcinogenic, mutagenic, biological and chemical agents.

Approved Codes of Practice

ACoPs are written to support some health and safety regulations. They offer examples of good practice and have a special legal status. They are not compulsory, but if the ACoP guidance was not followed and an organisation was prosecuted, failure to comply with the ACoP guidance may be cited in court as a failure to comply with the law and may form part of the evidence in a health and safety prosecution.

Guidance

The HSE publishes or approves guidance on many subjects. The purpose of this is to help people understand what the law says, to help them comply with the requirements of the law and to provide technical advice. Following the guidance is not compulsory, but if the guidance is followed it would normally be seen as complying with the law, in respect of the matters the guidance relates to.

Standards of compliance

Within health and safety legislation specific words or phases are used to qualify or describe the standard of compliance that must be achieved with regard to some legal duties. The meanings of these are explained below.

It shall be the duty of an employer to... so far as is practicable
This means that the employer (or employer's representative) must, shall or will comply with the legal duty being described, regardless of time, effort and cost.

The words **shall**, **must** or **will** (if not qualified by the phrase 'so far as reasonably practicable' or the word 'practicable') leave no scope for not complying with the duty.

Practicable

Practicable means that there is no scope for taking cost and convenience into account; the duty must be complied with if it is capable of being carried out within current knowledge and technology (if it is technically possible there is no choice). If it can be done, it should be done, regardless of cost.

For example – Practicable
A worker has to use a disc-cutter to cut paving slabs to the required size. It is well known that mechanical cutting operations can create harmful levels of dust and that, where practicable, dust should be eliminated or controlled.

This means that appropriate techniques should be used to ensure dust does not become airborne, or is minimised to an acceptable level. This could be done by using on-tool dust extraction equipment or by adopting suitable wet-cutting techniques, such as a continuous water feed. In most cases, respiratory protective equipment (RPE) would still be required as on-tool extraction or wet cutting may not capture all of the airborne dust particles.

The law also requires the employer and the operator to ensure that the rotating blade of the machine is guarded to the extent that it is practicable to do so and that the guard be adjusted to expose enough blade to enable the job to be carried out safely, whilst providing the maximum degree of protection to the operator.

It is not an option not to use a guard at all or to dry cut and expose workers to harmful levels of dust, even if employing the additional safeguards causes additional cost or inconvenience.

It shall be the duty of every employer to... as far as is reasonably practicable

Where a requirement to carry out a specific legal duty is qualified by the phrase 'as far as is reasonably practicable', employers are allowed to exercise their judgement on the extent of the measures that need to be taken to ensure the health and safety of the person(s) carrying out the job and anyone else who may be affected by it.

Deciding what reasonably practicable measures to take should be based upon the findings of a risk assessment.

Reasonably practicable

Reasonably practicable means that the risks involved in carrying out the work may be balanced against the cost in terms of money, inconvenience and time.

Where the risks to health and safety in carrying out a job are found to be low in comparison to what would be disproportionately high costs to overcome the risks totally, the employer need only take the measures that are considered to be reasonably practicable.

For example – Reasonably practicable

It was necessary to provide access to working platforms of a scaffold at four different levels, the higher level being a narrow lift between two structures for a 12-week period. A decision had to be made on the best means of access.

Legislation on working at height requires 'every employer to ensure that work at height is carried out in a manner which is, so far as reasonably practicable, safe'.

In planning the job, the risk assessment showed the following.

- ☑ It would be necessary for tools and materials for various trades to be carried up to and down from the main working platform but not from the higher level lift.

- ☑ The ground was firm and level and there was plenty of space at the bottom of the scaffold.

- ☑ If a ladder was used, it could be securely tied to the scaffold and suitable handholds could be provided at the stepping-off point.

- ☑ The tools and materials would have to be hoisted up using a small electric hoist fixed to the scaffold.

- ☑ Various trades could be working together and at the same time.

- ☑ Only a means of access was required, not a place of work, to the higher level lift.

- ☑ There were no weather considerations that would make the use of a ladder unsafe.

Given the circumstances, it was decided that a ladder was not a reasonably practicable measure to prevent a fall with regard to accessing the main working platform where tools and materials were required. Therefore a stair tower was used. For access to the higher level a stair tower was considered to be suitable; this also offered quicker, safer and easier access.

Burden of proof

Many of the duties on employers are qualified with the phrases 'so far as is practicable' or 'so far as is reasonably practicable'. Generally, in a court of law a defendant is innocent until proven guilty. However, with regard to health and safety law, the burden of proof is reversed and so the defendant must prove that it was not practicable or reasonably practicable, as the case may be, to do more than was in fact done to mitigate the risks. In effect the defendant is assumed guilty until they prove their innocence. *(For further information refer to the HSWA Section 40.)*

Legal duties

The broad legal duties of employers and employees, as specified in the Health and Safety at Work etc. Act, are shown below.

Employers' responsibilities

An employer must, so far as is reasonably practicable:

- ☑ protect the health, safety and welfare at work of all their employees

- ☑ provide and maintain plant and systems of work that are safe and without risk to health

- ☑ have arrangements for ensuring safety and absence of risk to health in connection with the use, handling, storage and transport of articles and substances

- ☑ provide such information, instruction, training and supervision as is necessary to ensure the health and safety at work of employees

- ☑ maintain any place of work under their control in a condition that is safe and without risks to health, and with access to and egress from it, that are safe and without risks

- ☑ provide and maintain a working environment that is safe, without risks to health and adequate as regards the welfare of employees.

Employees' duties

It is the duty of every employee:

- ☑ to take reasonable care for the health and safety of themselves or others who may be affected by their acts or omissions

- ☑ to co-operate with the employer in all matters relating to health and safety

- ☑ to report anything that is thought to be dangerous

- ☑ to use anything provided by the employer in accordance with instructions

- ☑ not to intentionally or recklessly interfere with or misuse anything provided in the interests of health, safety and welfare. This is a general requirement that applies to all persons, including members of the public.

The requirement, on the employer, to do what is reasonably practicable to ensure the health, safety and welfare of employees at work is balanced by a requirement, on the employees, to comply with any necessary rules or instructions and to take reasonable care of themselves or others.

The above general legal duties are expanded upon and made more specific by the various sets of regulations that are relevant to construction industry activities.

These more specific duties will be explained at the appropriate places in this book.

A
01

Most chapters of this book outline legal duties placed on employers. These duties apply equally to self-employed persons, where their acts or omissions may affect other persons.

Corporate Manslaughter and Corporate Homicide Act

Since 6 April 2008, companies whose gross negligence leads to the death of individuals can face prosecution for manslaughter (homicide in Scotland) under the Corporate Manslaughter and Corporate Homicide Act.

Under this legislation, companies, organisations and Government bodies face an unlimited fine if they are found to have caused death due to their gross corporate health and safety failures. The legislation primarily came about as a result of the failure to identify 'the controlling mind' in companies with complex management structures during court cases, which followed several high profile disasters.

This Act offers employees of companies, consumers and other individuals greater protection against corporate negligence.

☑ It makes it easier to prosecute companies and other large organisations, including central and local government organisations, when gross failures in the management of health and safety leads to a death, by delivering a new, more effective basis for corporate liability.

☑ It means that both small and large companies and local government organisations can be held liable for manslaughter, where gross failures in the management of health and safety cause death, and not just be held responsible for health and safety violations.

☑ It complements the current law under which individuals can be prosecuted for gross negligence manslaughter and health and safety offences, where there is direct evidence of their culpability.

This Act uses the term *senior management* and defines it as meaning those persons who play a significant role in the management of the whole or a substantial part of the organisation's activities. This covers both those in the direct chain of management as well as those in, for example, strategic or regulatory compliance roles.

Enforcement of health and safety law

The enforcement of all health and safety law is carried out under the provisions of the Health and Safety at Work etc. Act. This means that methods of enforcement are the same throughout the country.

The maximum penalty imposed by a Magistrates' Court for breach of health and safety legislation is an unlimited fine for each offence, or 12 months' imprisonment, or both. For offences that are dealt with at a Crown Court, the maximum penalty is an unlimited fine and up to two years' imprisonment.

The HSE is responsible for maintaining a force of health and safety inspectors, some of whom specialise in construction industry activities.

A 01

Powers of HSE inspectors

- ☑ May enter any premises at any reasonable time, or at any time if they suspect a dangerous situation.

- ☑ Can examine and investigate as necessary.

- ☑ Can measure, or take photographs, samples or possession of anything, if required for evidence.

- ☑ Can inspect books and any other documents.

- ☑ Can insist that dangerous equipment is made safe.

- ☑ Can question people and require that they make a signed declaration as to the truth of answers given.

- ☑ Can demand that the scene of an accident remains undisturbed.

- ☑ Can call upon police to assist entry into premises if necessary.

 Health and safety inspectors can serve enforcement notices or initiate a prosecution against an employer, an employee, or both.

If it appears to a HSE inspector that there may be a contravention or breach of health and safety law, they may serve an **improvement notice** on an employer, requiring that improvements to the way health and safety matters are being managed are completed within a specified time.

If, in the opinion of the HSE inspector, a situation poses a risk of serious injury to any person, the HSE inspector may serve a **prohibition notice**, which immediately stops the work operation stated in the notice until remedial work is satisfactorily completed.

Where serious breaches of health and safety law have occurred, particularly where personal injury or death has resulted from unsafe working practices, the inspector conducting the investigation can instigate a **prosecution** of the alleged offender(s).

Employers have a right of appeal against any improvement or prohibition notices, which they must lodge within 21 days. When an appeal is lodged against an improvement notice, the requirements of the notice are suspended until the appeal is heard. However, if an appeal is lodged against a prohibition notice, the effects of the notice remain in force.

Whilst the HSE has the power to visit workplaces and take enforcement action where appropriate, it would rather offer advice and guidance to employers to prevent dangerous situations from occurring.

HSE inspectors can issue notices if they think it necessary

Fee for intervention

A fee for intervention (FFI) cost recovery scheme applies to businesses and individuals regulated by the HSE. FFI enables the HSE to recover costs incurred in carrying out its duties, where a material breach of health and safety law is discovered. The hourly FFI is charged from the time the HSE inspector arrives on site, not from the time they identified the material breach.

A material breach is where an HSE inspector is of the opinion that a breach of law is identifiable and serious enough to inform the duty holder in writing, notifying the duty holder what is wrong, why it is wrong and what the employer needs to do to comply with the law.

A
01

Health and safety law

Environmental law

The Environment Agency (EA) in England offers information and advice to assist companies in protecting and improving the environment and contributing to sustainable development. The same service is offered by the Scottish Environment Protection Agency (SEPA) and Natural Resources Wales (NRW). Environmental law is enforced by the EA, NRW and SEPA.

 For further information on environmental law refer to the individual websites for England, Scotland and Wales.

 For further information refer to:

☑ **Chapter E28 Environmental management**

☑ **Chapter E29 Waste management.**

Health and safety law

Common law (Duty of care)		
Statute law (Written)		
Types of statutory duty		
Absolute duty	Practicable	Reasonably practicable

Health and Safety at Work etc. Act 1974

The Act consists of four parts
Part 1. Health and safety of people at work and protection of others who may be affected
Part 2. Employment Medical Advisory Service
Part 3. Amends to previous law
Part 4. General and miscellaneous provisions

General duties for employers and employees

Health and safety regulations

Regulations require additional specific actions They can be concerning:
- health and safety management
- workplaces and dangerous substances
- machinery, handling and equipment
- specific areas of work or situations
- chemicals and hazardous substances

ACoPs Approved Codes of Practice

ACoPs explain what measures must be taken to comply with relevant regulations Following an ACoP (or an equivalent standard) is generally accepted as being legally compliant

HSE and industry guidance

HSE guidance notes Issued by the HSE, giving practical guidance on how regulations may be complied with

Industry guidance Practical guidance produced by industry associations, federations and training bodies

02

Construction (Design and Management) Regulations

A 02

What your employer should do for you

1. Explain what your duties are under the Construction (Design and Management) Regulations (CDM) 2015, and how they apply on construction projects.

2. Ensure that the construction phase is planned, managed, monitored and co-ordinated, and explain to the workforce how to implement it.

3. Plan the work, taking into account the general principles of prevention.

4. Provide all workers with a suitable induction.

5. Provide information, instruction, training and supervision relevant to the workforce and their existing level of skills, knowledge, training and experience and the level of risk.

6. Provide information on what action to take in the event of an emergency.

7. As a contractor, be aware of and explain company obligations to the principal contractor and provide information as required.

8. Ensure safe systems of work are in place and provide and explain relevant paperwork (risk assessments and method statements) to managers and supervisors.

9. Ensure designs for work have removed all reasonably practicable hazards.

10. Ensure workers are consulted with and engaged in discussions about health and safety.

11. Provide suitable and sufficient welfare facilities.

12. Ensure the site is safe and protect it from unauthorised access.

13. Display an up to date F10 notice in the construction site office, where required.

14. Co-operate with other duty holders to ensure the F10 notice is kept up to date and current.

What you should do as a supervisor

Checklist	Yes	No	N/A
1. Assist in implementing the construction phase plan and managing contractors and workers.			
2. Understand the health risks associated with the work and make sure that preventative controls are being followed and used.			
3. Ensure that any designs that require modification are checked before the work is carried out and recorded for the future.			
4. Put safe working methods into practice to ensure a safe place of work for your workforce.			
5. Ensure no-one starts work unless they have received a suitable and sufficient induction.			
6. Check risk assessments and method statements reflect the actual conditions and environment for the work being completed.			
7. Provide supervision and advice, taking into account the current level of skills, knowledge, training and experience of your workers in relation to the health and safety risks involved in the job.			
8. Ensure that workers are consulted on matters of health and safety, and advise your manager of items requiring attention.			
9. Ensure the welfare facilities are in a suitable state of cleanliness with adequate provision to match site needs.			
10. Ensure that inspections and tests are carried out and recorded.			
11. Display an up to date F10 notice in the construction site office, where required, and make sure all relevant parties are aware of it.			

A
02

Introduction

**A
02**

The Construction (Design and Management) Regulations (CDM) originally came into force in 1994, were revised in 2007 and again in 2015. The current revision (CDM 2015) came into force on 6 April 2015.

www. **The regulations are supported by six industry guidance documents, one for each duty holder and an additional one for workers. These are available on the CITB website.**

CDM 2015 introduced significant changes.

☑ It applies to both domestic and commercial clients.

☑ The role of CDM co-ordinator has been removed and the role of principal designer has been introduced.

☑ It requires all duty holders to have sufficient knowledge, training, experience and organisational capabilities to overcome the health and safety risks involved in the project.

☑ It provides improved clarity on the relationship between the principal designer and principal contractor.

☑ A construction phase plan is now required for all projects regardless of whether or not they are notifiable.

☑ It provides improved reference to worker engagement and consultation.

For further information refer to the Construction (Design and Management) Regulations chapter in Section A of GE 700 *Construction site safety*.

CITB has produced a short video which explains the basics of CDM 2015.

www. **A free app called CDM Wizard has been produced by CITB to assist duty holders in complying with the regulations and compiling construction phase plans for smaller projects.**

CDM Wizard app

When the regulations apply

Every construction project, no matter how small, is subject to the requirements of CDM 2015. If a project is notifiable, there is a requirement for the client to notify details of the project to the enforcing authority and for the principal designer to ensure a health and safety file is created and passed to the client on completion of the project.

The regulations are structured to ensure the following.

☑ There is a co-ordinated approach to health and safety on site, particularly where there are several contractors on site at any one time.

☑ Adequate time and resources are committed at a sufficiently early stage to draw health and safety into the design and planning phases.

☑ There is adequate co-operation and communication between everyone on site who has responsibility for health and safety.

☑ Everyone on site has the necessary skills, knowledge, training and experience to do their job.

☑ Health and safety issues are considered at the design and planning stage for the whole life cycle of a new structure, which include the items below.

– Site preparation.	– Everyday use.
– Construction.	– Cleaning.
– Maintenance.	– Demolition.
– Alteration or extension.	

Construction work means carrying out any building, civil engineering or engineering construction work that includes construction, alteration, conversion, fitting out, commissioning, renovating, assembly of prefabricated elements, [or] installation of mechanical, electrical or telecommunication services. (For a full definition refer to the regulations.)

Notification by the client

The regulations require that details of notifiable projects are sent at the earliest opportunity to the relevant **enforcing authority**. This could be the HSE, the Office of Rail and Road (ORR) or the Office for Nuclear Regulation (ONR). The easiest way to do this is on an electronic F10 notification form.

A blank F10 form can be downloaded from the CDM section of the HSE website.

If the client is a domestic client the duty to notify can be carried out by the contractor or principal contractor (where appointed), or principal designer, when it has been agreed that the principal designer will fulfil the client's duties.

A
02

Domestic clients are clients for whom construction work is not connected with a business, for example a householder who engages a contractor to carry out work on their private house or the home of a family member, providing the house is not used in connection with a business. However, where a job is carried out on a domestic property as part of, for example, a property development project or on behalf of a body (such as a housing association), the work is not for a domestic client but for a commercial client.

The F10 includes details of (for example) the following.

☑ Address of the project.

☑ Planned start date.

☑ Project description.

☑ Maximum number of people on site.

☑ Planned number of contractors.

Projects are notifiable if the construction work on a construction site is scheduled to:

☑ last longer than 30 working days and have more than 20 workers working simultaneously at any point on a project; or

☑ exceed 500 person days.

Holidays and weekends do not count if construction work is not scheduled to be carried out at those times.

The F10 is a 'living' document which may need updating throughout the project.

The CDM Regulations promote teamwork, co-operation and co-ordination

Overview of the regulations

The following parts of the regulations apply to all projects, from concept to completion.

☑ Part 1: Introduction.

☑ Part 2: Client duties.

☑ Part 3: Health and safety duties and roles.

☑ Part 4: General requirements for all construction sites.

☑ Part 5: General.

☑ Schedule 1: Particulars to be notified under Regulation 6.

☑ Schedule 2: Welfare facilities *(refer to Chapter B08 Health and welfare).*

☑ Schedule 3: Work involving particular risks.

- ☑ **Parts 1, 2, 3 and 5 of the CDM Regulations cover the whole construction project, from concept to completion.**

- ☑ **Part 4 relates to the type of works that may be carried out on the construction site.**

Duty holders

Under the regulations, the following have specific legal duties.

- ☑ Clients (domestic and commercial).

- ☑ Principal designer.

- ☑ Designers.

- ☑ Principal contractor.

- ☑ Contractors.

Whilst duties are not placed specifically on **workers** by these regulations, duties are placed on every person to work safely, which includes workers.

Client duties

The client's duties under CDM are summarised as follows.

- ☑ Make arrangements for managing a project, including allocating sufficient time and resources.

- ☑ Ensure arrangements are maintained throughout the project.

- ☑ Appoint a designer and contractor or, where the work is likely to involve more than one contractor, a principal designer and principal contractor.

- ☑ Provide pre-construction information to every designer or contractor.

- ☑ Ensure a construction phase plan is created before the construction phase begins.

- ☑ Ensure the principal designer prepares and reviews a health and safety file, as required.

- ☑ Take reasonable steps to ensure the principal designer and principal contractor comply with their duties.

- ☑ Make sure suitable welfare facilities are provided.

Where there is more than one client, one of them can be elected in writing to be the 'client' under the CDM Regulations.

Domestic client duties

A domestic client has the same duties as a commercial client. However, they can transfer the client's duty to notify the enforcing authority and the client's general duties to:

- ☑ the contractor on a single contractor project

- ☑ the principal contractor on a project where there is more than one contractor

- ☑ the principal designer where the domestic client chooses to enter into a written agreement for them to carry out their duties.

Principal designer duties

The principal designer is the designer appointed by the client where projects involve more than one contractor. They can be an individual or an organisation. Their role and duties are summarised on the following page.

- ☑ Plan, manage, monitor and co-ordinate health and safety in the pre-construction phase of a project.

- ☑ Ensure designers carry out their duties, including the duty to identify, eliminate or control foreseeable risks, taking into account the general principles of prevention.

- ☑ Co-ordinate health and safety aspects of design work and co-operate with others involved with the project.

- ☑ Facilitate good communication between the client, designers and contractors.

- ☑ Liaise with the principal contractor about ongoing design.

- ☑ Help the client to identify, collect and pass on pre-construction information.

- ☑ Prepare and update the health and safety file.

- ☑ Hand over the health and safety file to the principal contractor if appointment finishes before the end of the project.

A principal designer's aim is not only to secure the health and safety of those involved in building the structure and those who during its life will use and maintain it, but also those who will remove or demolish it.

Designer duties

Designers are in a unique position, at an early stage of a project, to reduce the potential risks to health and safety that could arise during the construction phase. Building health and safety into the design element remains an important part of the regulations.

- ☑ Eliminate hazards and reduce risks that may arise during construction or maintenance once the building is built.

- ☑ Provide information about the remaining risks to the principal designer.

- ☑ Check that the client is aware of their duties.

- ☑ Take into account the principles of prevention and any pre-construction information, to eliminate, so far as is reasonably practicable, foreseeable risks to the health or safety of any person:
  - carrying out or liable to be affected by construction work
  - maintaining or cleaning a structure
  - using a structure designed as a workplace.

- ☑ Provide any information needed for the health and safety file.

- ☑ When designs are prepared or modified outside Great Britain, ensure designer duties are complied with.

- ☑ *Design* includes drawings, design details, specifications, bills of quantity and calculations prepared for the purpose of design.

- ☑ *Designers* include architects, consulting engineers, quantity surveyors, interior designers and contractors and may include tradespeople on smaller domestic projects.

- ☑ The HSE has produced CDM red, amber and green (RAG) lists. These are practical aids for designers on what to eliminate or avoid and what to encourage. An example is shown on page 40.

Principal contractor duties

The principal contractor is the organisation or person that co-ordinates the work of the construction phase of a project involving more than one contractor so that it is carried out in a safe and healthy way. Their role and duties can be summarised as follows.

- ☑ Plan, manage and monitor the construction phase in liaison with contractors.

- ☑ Ensure anyone they appoint has the necessary skills, knowledge, training and experience, or organisational capability.

- ☑ Prepare, develop and implement a construction phase plan and site rules.

- ☑ Provide contractors with the relevant parts of the construction phase plan.

- ☑ Make sure suitable welfare facilities are provided from the start and are maintained throughout the construction phase.

- ☑ Ensure that all workers have site inductions and any further information and training needed to carry out the work.

- ☑ Consult with the workers.

- ☑ Liaise with the principal designer regarding ongoing design.

- ☑ Secure the site and prevent unauthorised access.

- ☑ Ensure construction work is carried out, so far as reasonably practicable, without risk to health or safety.

- ☑ Co-ordinate the implementation of relevant legal requirements to ensure workers, including the self-employed, are protected.

- ☑ Apply the principles of prevention.

- ☑ Liaise with the principal designer for the duration of the project and ensure that information is provided for the health and safety file.

 A principal contractor has the same role, regardless of whether they are working for a domestic or a commercial client. However, they may assume some of the client duties when working for a domestic client (refer to page 29).

Contractor duties

A contractor is anyone who directly employs or engages construction workers or manages construction. The duties of a contractor apply if the workers under their control are employees, self-employed or agency workers. If there is more than one contractor on site, the contractor must comply with the directions given by the principal contractor and relevant parts of the construction phase plan. **Where there is only one contractor then the contractor must draw up the construction phase plan.**

Their role and duties can be summarised as follows.

- ☑ Plan, manage and monitor construction work and that of their workers.

- ☑ Make the client aware of their duties.

- ☑ Appoint workers who have the necessary skills, knowledge, training and experience or those that are in the process of obtaining them.

- ☑ Assess the training needs of workers.

- ☑ Provide information and instructions to their workers.

- ☑ Provide appropriate supervision – taking into account the workers' education, physical ability, literacy and attitude.

- ☑ Prevent unauthorised access to site.

A
02

A 02

- ☑ Comply with the specific requirements in Part 4 of the regulations.

- ☑ Ensure there are adequate welfare facilities for their workers.

- ☑ Co-operate with the principal contractor in planning and managing work, including reasonable directions and site rules.

- ☑ Provide any information needed for the health and safety file.

- ☑ Inform the principal contractor of problems with the construction phase plan.

- ☑ Inform the principal contractor of reportable accidents, diseases and dangerous occurrences.

- ☑ Provide a site induction if one is not supplied by the principal contractor.

Duties of all those involved

Everyone involved with a construction project has a responsibility to look after themselves and others. Every person involved in a project who is working under the control of another person shall report to that person anything they are aware of that is likely to endanger the health or safety of themselves or others.

This includes the following.

- ☑ Making sure those appointed have the right skills, knowledge, training and experience.

- ☑ Co-operating with others and co-ordinating work so as to ensure the health and safety of construction workers and others who may be affected by the work.

- ☑ Reporting obvious risks.

- ☑ Taking account of and applying the general principles of prevention when carrying out duties.

Consultation with the workforce

There is a requirement to consult and engage with workers in good time on health and safety matters in accordance with the **Safety Representatives and Safety Committee Regulations** and the **Health and Safety (Consultation with Employees) Regulations**. The CDM Regulations also make it very clear that the principal contractor should consult and engage with the workers.

The workforce may have first-hand experience of actually carrying out the job and may therefore have valid and valuable knowledge and experience about the risks involved.

Gaining willing and effective worker participation and feedback will be achieved when the workforce:

- ☑ has sufficient opportunity to be consulted and are involved in decisions about health and safety

- ☑ feels sufficiently confident that managers and supervisors will listen to ideas and concerns and, if required, will act upon them

- ☑ has sufficient knowledge to recognise when something is not safe

- ☑ are given the opportunity to provide effective feedback.

Ample opportunity must be given for all members of the workforce to consult with management on any concerns regarding health and safety that they might have.

The principal contractor must:

- ☑ engage with workers, to co-operate effectively and promote measures to ensure the health, safety and welfare of the workers

- ☑ check these measures are, and remain, effective

- ☑ consult workers on matters that may affect health, safety and welfare on site

- ☑ ensure workers can inspect and take copies of any information which relates to the planning and management of the project, or which may affect their health, safety and welfare.

 For further information refer to Chapter A05 Leadership and worker engagement.

Feedback boards provide opportunities for consultation

Appointing the right organisations and people

Throughout the regulations, the need to employ individuals with the necessary **skills, knowledge, attitude, training and experience** is emphasised. If they are an organisation they must have the appropriate organisational capability.

Employing individuals or organisations with these attributes is key in reducing accidents and the incidence of occupational ill health that can arise out of construction activities. Appointments should be made on the basis that the person is assessed as being capable (or that they will be capable) of performing the role. In order to help them to be capable of performing their appointed role, the contractor will need to provide them with adequate resources in the form of sufficient information, instruction, training and supervision, and physical resources (such as plant, equipment, machinery, materials and people).

 Competence is accepted as being a blend of skills, knowledge, attitude, training and experience (SKATE).

However, it must be remembered that skills cannot come before training and knowledge, and that training, knowledge, understanding and experience are all steps on the way to developing skills.

Co-operation and co-ordination

The regulations require that all duty holders communicate and co-operate with each other and that they co-ordinate their work activities to enable the project to proceed without risks to health or safety.

Co-ordination of work activities should be an integral part of planning any project to ensure that, for example, the timing of any activity does not clash with any other so that nobody is put at risk.

An example of co-operation would be one contractor allowing the workers of another contractor to use a scaffold to carry out work that would otherwise have been done using a ladder. (It should be noted that the configuration of the scaffold must be suitable for the second workforce. The use of scaffolds should be under the management of the principal contractor.)

A
02

Project documents

There is a legal duty to compile the following project documents for all projects. The content of the project documentation will vary depending on the size and nature of the project, but must be proportionate to the risks involved.

The project documentation should consist of:

- ☑ pre-construction information
- ☑ the construction phase plan
- ☑ the health and safety file.

An example of what might be found in the project documentation is described on the following pages.

Pre-construction information

 Pre-construction information is information about the project which is in the client's possession or is easily obtainable.

Information gathered at the start of the project is unlikely to be sufficient; therefore it must be added to as the design process progresses to reflect new health and safety risks and how they should be managed.

It is the duty of the client to prepare the pre-construction information. This information must be provided to every designer or contractor appointed or being considered for appointment. The principal designer should help the client carry out this duty.

Pre-construction information must:

- ☑ be relevant to the project
- ☑ have an appropriate level of detail
- ☑ be proportionate, given the health or safety risks involved.

Pre-construction information must include the following information.

- ☑ **Project.**
  - Key dates.
  - The client's brief (the brief produced by the client for the duty holders).

- ☑ **Planning and management of the project.**
  - Resources and time allocated to each stage of the project.
  - Co-operation and co-ordination requirements between duty holders.
  - Provision of welfare facilities.
  - Site security arrangements.

- ☑ **Health and safety hazards of the site and how they will be addressed.**
  - Design considerations and suggested work methods.
  - Arrangements for ongoing design changes and co-ordination.
  - Information about significant risks identified during design.
  - Information about on-site risks (such as asbestos, hazardous waste and underground services).
  - Any relevant information from an existing health and safety file.

Construction phase plan

The aim of the construction phase plan is to record the arrangements for managing health and safety risks associated with the construction phase.

It is the responsibility of the contractor (if there is only one contractor) or principal contractor (if there is more than one contractor) to prepare the construction phase plan and provide contractors with relevant parts of the plan (where applicable). A construction phase plan is a document that records:

☑ health and safety arrangements for the construction phase

☑ site rules

☑ specific control measures which fall within the categories set out in Schedule 3 of the regulations, for example working at height or where there is a risk drowning.

The construction phase plan must:

☑ be relevant to the project

☑ have sufficient level of detail to set out the arrangements clearly (for example the site rules)

☑ give details of any special arrangements needed to manage the construction phase

☑ be proportionate to the scale and complexity of the project.

The plan should **not** include documents such as generic risk assessments and detailed method statements but should include information of significant importance (such as the routes of underground services, the location of overhead lines, and so on).

The client must ensure that the construction phase plan is drawn up **before** the construction phase begins.

The principal designer must ensure that the designers provide information that will help contractors prepare the construction phase plan. For projects with more than one contractor, the designer(s) should liaise with the principal designer to ensure the information is provided.

The following list of topics should be considered when drawing up the plan.

☑ **Description of the project**, including key dates and members of the project team.

☑ **How the works will be managed**, including health and safety aims, site rules, site induction, welfare facilities, arrangements for co-operation and worker involvement.

☑ **Arrangements for controlling significant site risks, including:**

– falling from height

– risk of burial from earth falls

– being engulfed in swamp land

– working with chemical or biological substances

– working with ionising radiation

– working near high voltage power lines

– working on wells, underground earth works and tunnels

– work carried out by divers with a supply of air

– working in caissons with a compressed air atmosphere

– working in confined spaces

– working with explosives

– assembling or dismantling of heavy, prefabricated components.

**A
02**

Health and safety file

The health and safety file is only required for projects involving more than one contractor.

It should only include information likely to be needed to ensure health and safety during any future works (such as cleaning, refurbishment, maintenance or demolition).

It is the responsibility of the principal designer to ensure that a health and safety file is prepared, reviewed and amended as the project progresses. The principal contractor should pass information to the principal designer for inclusion in the file. If the client has an existing health and safety file they must pass this to the principal designer, as it may contain information that needs to be included in the pre-construction information. The health and safety file should be passed to the client when the project is complete and it can be kept electronically, on paper or film.

The following should be considered for inclusion within the health and safety file, if it could be relevant to health and safety during any future construction work.

☑ A brief description of the work carried out.

☑ Any hazards that have not been eliminated through design and construction processes.

☑ Important structural principles (such as bracing, sources of substantial stored energy and safe working loads for floors and roofs).

☑ Hazardous material used (such as lead paints and special coatings).

☑ Information regarding the removal or dismantling of installed plant and equipment.

☑ Health and safety information about equipment provided for cleaning or maintaining the structure.

☑ The nature, location or dismantling of significant services (such as fire-fighting services, gas supply and underground cables).

☑ Information about, and as-built drawings of, the building.

The file does not need to include things that will be of no help when planning future construction work, maintenance or demolition.

Health and safety on construction sites

Part 4 of the regulations outlines the requirements for the management of health, safety and welfare on site. The following information is a summary of the duties of the principal contractor, contractors and the self-employed, with regard to health and safety on site.

Regulation number and title	Details of duties and requirements
16. Application of Regulations 17 to 35.	This regulation states that everybody carrying out construction work must comply.
17. Safe places of work.	Every place of work must be safe to access, egress and to work at.
18. Good order and site security.	Sites must be tidy, secure (to prevent unauthorised access), have appropriate signs and have no projecting sharp objects.
19. Stability of structures.	Buildings and structures must not be allowed to become unstable during work and any supports provided must be adequate for the job.
20. Demolition or dismantling.	These activities must be carried out so as to prevent any danger and there must be a written plan (for example, method statement) in place before work starts.
21. Explosives.	Explosives must be stored, transported and used safely.
22. Excavations.	Work in excavations must be properly planned. They must not be allowed to collapse or have materials falling or slipping into them. No-one should become trapped because of inadequate shoring. Excavations must be inspected and reports written as appropriate. Work in an excavation must not start where an inspection has revealed that it is not safe to do so.
23. Cofferdams and caissons.	Cofferdams and caissons must be suitably designed, constructed, maintained and inspected. Work in cofferdams or caissons must not start where an inspection has revealed that it is not safe to do so.
24. Reports of inspections.	The duty to carry out inspections refers to Regulations 22 and 23 and requires inspections to be made at the start of every shift and after any event likely to affect the safety of the excavation, cofferdam or caisson. A written record of an inspection must be made at intervals not exceeding seven days.

A 02

Regulation number and title	Details of duties and requirements
25. Energy distribution installations.	Energy distribution systems (power cables, pressure hoses or pipes and so on) above, on and below ground, must be protected against being damaged or causing injury or damage. Work must not take place where there is a risk of damage to, or accidental disturbance of, energy distribution systems, unless suitable control measures have been taken.
26. Prevention of drowning.	Where there is risk of a person drowning because of falling into water or other liquid, suitable measures must be put in place to prevent falls and, where a risk remains, a rescue plan must be in place. Where workers are transported over water to and from their place of work, suitable steps must be taken to ensure this is carried out safely.
27. Traffic routes.	Traffic routes must be organised to protect people from injury from vehicles, preferably by physical segregation, and be suitable for the vehicles and persons using them. Traffic routes must be properly maintained, suitably signed and regularly inspected. Where it is unsafe for pedestrians to use gates intended for use by vehicles, separate pedestrian gates must be provided and kept free of obstruction.
28. Vehicles.	Arrangements must be made to prevent unintended movement of any vehicle. They must be used safely, not overloaded, and prevented from falling into any excavation. No-one must be allowed to ride on any vehicle unless it is designed to carry passenger(s) and it is safe to do so. No-one must remain on any vehicle that is being loaded unless a safe place is provided and maintained on the vehicle.
29. Prevention of risk from fire, flooding and asphyxiation.	Steps must be taken to avoid the risk of fire, explosion, flooding and asphyxiation from any substance.
30. Emergency procedures.	A plan must be in place for the safe evacuation of all people on site in situations where there is a foreseeable risk of an emergency. Everyone on site must be made aware of the emergency plan and it must be practised at suitable intervals.
31. Emergency routes and exits.	Adequate means of evacuation (emergency escape routes) to a safe place must be established. Routes must be kept clear of obstruction and be adequately signed.

Regulation number and title	Details of duties and requirements
32. Fire detection and fire-fighting.	Suitable fire-fighting equipment, fire detection equipment and alarms must be provided at suitable locations and must be examined and tested at suitable intervals. Manual fire-fighting equipment (such as hand-held extinguishers) must be easily accessible and indicated by appropriate signs. An appropriate number of on-site staff must be trained in the use of fire-fighting equipment.
33. Fresh air.	Places of work must have adequate fresh or purified air available. Where fresh or purified air is provided by plant, it must be equipped with suitable audible or visible warnings to indicate any inadequacy in the supply or machine failure.
34. Temperature and weather protection.	Steps must be taken to ensure that indoor temperatures are reasonable. Outdoor workplaces must be arranged to provide adequate protection against adverse weather, taking into account usage and any protective clothing or equipment provided.
35. Lighting.	Every place of work, its access and egress routes and any traffic route must be adequately lit, preferably by natural light. Where lighting is by artificial means, a back-up system must be in place where failure of the primary system would result in risks to health or safety. Artificial light must not adversely affect the perception of any health and safety sign.

A
02

The HSE has produced CDM red, amber and green (RAG) lists. These are practical aids for designers on what to eliminate or avoid and what to encourage. An example is shown below.

A
02

CDM RAG lists

Red lists
Hazardous procedures, products and processes that should be eliminated from the project where possible.

- Lack of adequate pre-construction information (such as asbestos surveys, details of geology, obstructions, services and ground contamination).
- Hand scabbling of concrete (such as stop ends).
- Demolition by hand-held breakers of the top sections of concrete piles (pile cropping techniques are available).
- Specification of fragile roof lights and roofing assemblies.
- Processes giving rise to large quantities of dust (such as dry cutting and blasting).

Amber lists
Products, processes and procedures to be eliminated or reduced as far as possible and only specified or allowed if unavoidable. Including amber items would always lead to the provision of information to the principal contractor.

- Specification of heavy building blocks (those weighing > 20 kgs).
- Chasing out concrete, brick or blockwork walls or floors for the installation of services.
- Specification of heavy lintels (the use of slim metal or hollow concrete lintels are better alternatives).
- Specification of solvent-based paints and thinners, or isocyanates, particularly for use in confined areas.
- Specification of blockwork walls > 3.5 m high using retarded mortar mixes.

Green lists
Products, processes and procedures to be positively encouraged.

- Adequate access for construction vehicles to minimise reversing requirements (one-way systems and turning radii).

- Specification of concrete products with pre-cast fixings to avoid drilling.

- Specification of half board sizes for plasterboard sheets to make handling easier.

- Early installation of permanent means of access, and prefabricated staircases with handrails.

- Off-site fabrication and prefabricated elements to minimise on-site hazards.

- Encourage the use of engineering controls to minimise the use of personal protective equipment.

A
02

A
02

03

Health and safety management systems

A
03

What your employer should do for you
1. Provide a written safety policy which is signed and dated (if there are five or more employees). The policy needs to have a review date and it must be in date.
2. Identify the roles and responsibilities of everybody concerned.
3. Implement a set of health and safety standards to be achieved, and a means of measuring performance and compliance.
4. Set procedures and controls which must be followed.
5. Have a procedure in place for reporting and investigating accidents, incidents and near misses.
6. Arrange for systems and practices to be monitored, audited and reviewed.
7. Have a procedure in place for identifying training needs and providing the training.
8. Put measures in place to ensure effective two-way consultation and communication on matters of health and safety. Seek and listen to the views of the workforce and take account of their ideas, skills and other capabilities before making health and safety decisions.
9. Put arrangements in place to ensure effective co-operation between everyone who is or will be involved in a project. Ensure workers are co-operating effectively on all health and safety matters.
10. Provide site inductions and other training that meets the needs of workers whose first language is not English, if required.
11. Display the official health and safety law poster or give each employee a copy of the official leaflet or card.

What you should do as a supervisor

Checklist	Yes	No	N/A
1. Read, understand and comply with the company health and safety policy.			
2. Check that the policy has been signed and dated.			
3. Check that the policy has a review date and is in date.			
4. Ensure that the company has identified your roles and responsibilities and those of everyone you supervise.			
5. Know and understand your responsibilities as a supervisor.			
6. Assist with ensuring that health and safety standards are achieved as far as possible.			
7. Follow company procedures and ensure specific site procedures are drafted, published and implemented.			
8. Ensure you monitor work activities and your workers follow the required safe systems of work. Correct any deficiencies and report any shortfalls to senior management.			
9. Contribute to audits and reviews carried out by the company or the competent person.			
10. Advise the company on the training needs of yourself and your workers and provide training if asked.			
11. Help to ensure an effective two-way consultation and communication on matters of health and safety. Seek and listen to the views of the workforce and take account of their ideas, skills and other capabilities before making health and safety decisions.			
12. Comply with arrangements to ensure effective co-operation between everyone who is or will be involved in a project. Ensure your workers are co-operating effectively on all health and safety matters.			
13. Report accidents, incidents and near misses and co-operate with investigations.			
14. Ensure site inductions and other training provides for the needs of workers whose first language is not English, as and when appropriate.			
15. Explain the official health and safety law poster or a copy of the official leaflet or card to your workforce.			

A
03

Introduction

This chapter introduces and explains the HSE's recognised model for managing health and safety – **HSG65**. This approach consists of the following key stages.

☑ **Plan.** To implement the policy, an effective health and safety management system will need to be established and maintained.

☑ **Do.** Delivery depends on an effective management system to ensure, so far as is reasonably practicable, the health and safety of employees and other people affected by work activities.

☑ **Check.** Monitor and report on health and safety arrangements and the performance of the health and safety policy.

☑ **Act.** Health and safety management systems will need to be reviewed, to ensure they are effective in managing risk and protecting people.

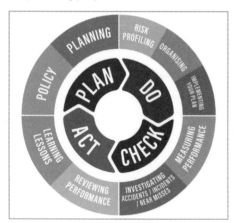

HSG65

Organisations have a legal duty to put in place suitable arrangements to manage health and safety. The HSG65 model will assist employers to put the right measures in place to manage the real risks to health and safety in their organisations. It can help to achieve a balance between the systems and behavioural aspects of management. It also treats health and safety management as an integral part of good management generally, rather than as a standalone system.

The HSG65 model provides sufficient detail and guidance to produce a company-specific health and safety management system. It explains how to decide what information to include, what controls and arrangements to put in place, how to carry out checks and how to measure and review performance.

 For a free guidance document for leaders, owners and line managers on safety management systems, *Managing for health and safety* (HSG65), visit the HSE's website.

Competent person

Health and safety law requires that every employer has access to competent health and safety advice, which in practical terms means that the employer must:

☑ be competent to manage relevant health and safety issues themselves, and/or

☑ have an employee who is, or

☑ bring in external expertise.

Competence can be described as a combination of the following.

Skills	The ability to perform a specific task to a desired standard, time after time.
Knowledge	Understanding how to do the job, to the extent it can be explained to others.
Attitude	Having the right approach and behaviour.
Training	Gaining knowledge, instruction and information.
Experience	Gained over a period of time in the workplace (not just theoretical).

This can be referred to as SKATE. (Physical attributes and mental attitudes can also affect someone's competence.)

- ☑ **A principal contractor** will have to satisfy the client and the principal designer that they are competent as an organisation to carry out their legal duties. This will include taking into account the competence of their employees, contractors and self-employed persons who will be carrying out the work.

- ☑ **A contractor working for a principal contractor** will have to satisfy the principal contractor that they themselves, their employees and any other people they bring onto site (such as sub-contractors) are competent to do the work they have been contracted to do.

- ☑ **Contractors** have to satisfy themselves of their own competence, that of their employees and any other people they bring onto site (such as sub-contractors).

 The HSE provides guidance for employers on managing contractors. For further information visit their website.

Plan (Setting standards)

Nobody can develop or implement plans, or set standards, until they are sufficiently competent in health and safety to know what the law requires to be done and how to interpret those requirements into safe and healthy working practices.

The aim of any health and safety management system must be to prevent injuries, occupational disease and near misses from occurring and to improve health and safety engagement and worker consultation. In doing this, employers must:

- ☑ commit themselves to proactively managing the health and safety aspects of their work activities

- ☑ actively involve employees in the health and safety decision making process and maintain their interest

- ☑ recognise areas of health and safety weakness

- ☑ select appropriate actions to overcome these weaknesses

- ☑ ensure that sufficient resources (time, competent people and money) are in place to implement the actions

☑ implement the actions and make sure they are complied with

☑ monitor the results to establish if improvements can be made

☑ review, at least annually, or as a result of an incident or a worker bringing something to the employer's attention

☑ investigate when things go wrong to prevent them happening again.

Ultimately, the effectiveness of the plans will depend upon the assessment and control of the risks to health and safety, which arise out of the employer's work activities. As expanded upon later, the Management of Health and Safety at Work Regulations place a legal requirement on employers and the self-employed to carry out suitable and sufficient assessments on the risks to the health and safety of employees and other people who may be at risk. *(Further details of assessment programmes may be found later in this chapter.)*

Risk assessments must be reviewed periodically to ensure they are still valid and be amended, if necessary.

Setting the policy

The basic principles of a health and safety management policy mean that a company must have the following.

☑ A **health and safety policy statement** specific to their business, with a statement setting out the company's intentions and commitment to managing health and safety.

☑ An **organisational structure** that shows the responsibility tree (some larger companies may have one on each site).

☑ The **arrangements** that explain the duties of each position on the responsibility tree.

In many companies there is also an **environmental policy** *(refer to Chapter E28 Environmental management).*

 Health, safety and the environment must be proactively managed, in the same way that a good supervisor and manager will manage people, quality and productivity.

The starting point for all health and safety must be a clear policy statement. This will inform employees of the company's intentions towards the health, safety and welfare of the workforce and the standards to which they aspire.

Managing health and safety at work is a **legal requirement** and must always be an integral part of any business activity.

 For an example of the self-improving cycle of Plan, Do, Check, Act, which can be used as a template health and safety management system, visit the HSE website.

Safety policy (policy, organisation and arrangements)

Every employer with five or more employees must have a written health and safety policy. The policy should be specific to their business, with a statement setting out their general policy for protecting the health and safety of their employees at work. It should include details of the organisation (the who) and arrangements for putting the policy into practice (the how).

 Even if someone is self-employed or employs fewer than five people the law still requires them to have a policy (even if it is not written down).

Employers must ensure the policy is clearly displayed or give a copy of it to each employee and ensure that it is fully understood.

Employers with fewer than five employees must formulate how they are going to proactively manage health and safety as an integral part of their work activities.

A policy should describe the following in full.

- ☑ The known and foreseeable risk (as in the organisation's risk profile).
- ☑ How the company is going to set up and maintain a safe working environment.
- ☑ What health and safety responsibilities already exist.
- ☑ Who is responsible and for what.
- ☑ The arrangements for developing safe systems of work.
- ☑ Arrangements for reviewing and updating the policy as necessary.

The policy should be signed and dated by the person with ultimate responsibility for health and safety (for example, the managing director). It should be periodically reviewed and updated as necessary, then re-signed and dated.

A copy of a company's health and safety policy is often requested when companies are tendering for work and to get onto approved supply chain lists.

Do (Delivering)

Does everybody know what their specific responsibilities and roles are with regard to maintaining safe places of work?

Who is responsible for the following roles?

- ☑ Developing and implementing safe systems of work.
- ☑ Issuing instructions on how work is to be carried out safely.
- ☑ Supervising or managing day-to-day health and safety issues.
- ☑ Making sure that everyone is competent to do what is required of them.
- ☑ Developing risk assessments and (if necessary) method statements.
- ☑ Carrying out periodic health and safety inspections.
- ☑ Dealing with maintenance matters.
- ☑ Measuring health and safety performance and reviewing or updating procedures as necessary.

The Management of Health and Safety at Work Regulations and the Construction (Design and Management) Regulations (CDM) specify that any employer, contractor (or principal contractor) who appoints anyone else to carry out work is responsible for checking the appointee's resources and competence, and ensuring that they have developed and adhere to safe systems of work.

Furthermore, under the requirements of the CDM Regulations, contractors who do not have or cannot obtain the necessary competencies are required to exclude themselves (refuse the commission).

Training

The Health and Safety at Work etc. Act 1974 requires that employers provide all necessary information, instruction, supervision and training to enable their workforce to carry out their tasks safely and without risks to their health.

Questions that should be asked.

☑ **Is there provision for training now, and for the future?**

☑ **Who is going to identify the gaps between the skills needed and those held to establish the training needs of individuals and be responsible for ensuring that it is carried out?**

Training may take many forms in addition to conventional training room sessions. Some of these are:

☑ site inductions

☑ toolbox talks

☑ safety leaflets, books and information on posters

☑ explaining the company's health and safety policy and procedures

☑ on-the-job training and instruction on particular plant, tools or equipment

☑ explaining risk assessments or method statements.

Procedures should be in place to:

☑ track what training has been received by whom

☑ provide assessment and feedback to confirm that the training was appropriate and has been understood and, if not, make arrangements for additional training.

Everyone needs to be involved to ensure a safe site

Communication

What are the arrangements for the following?

☑ Receiving and distributing information.

☑ Effectively communicating with workers whose first language is not English.

☑ Delegating health and safety duties.

☑ Enabling anyone to report suspected or actual failings in health and safety management to someone in authority.

☑ Reporting and recording accidents.

☑ Reporting dangerous occurrences or near misses.

Refer to Chapter A05 Leadership and worker engagement for further guidance on communicating with workers who have limited or no understanding of English.

The system of communication on larger sites, with perhaps many companies on site and several tiers of sub-contractor, must allow for the health and safety concerns of individuals to be considered by someone with the authority to rectify the situation. It is possible that the person on the tools and their supervisor are more aware of an unsafe situation developing at the workplace. Employees must be given the opportunity to feed any health, safety or welfare concerns that they have directly to a site-based manager or supervisor who has the authority to take the appropriate action.

If you or your appointed contractor recognise a trade union and employ union members then the appointed contractor and you must be prepared to accept union safety representatives and their role in the site safety inspections and safety committee meetings.

Consultation with employees

An essential part of health and safety management is the two-way communication process between employers (or their representatives) and employees. There are legal duties on both parties with the intent that communication takes place in both directions.

Employers and their managers must talk to, and listen to, the people who actually do the work.

Where a trade union is recognised within organisations they may appoint safety representatives on behalf of their members. This is to create a situation where co-operation between the employer and the workforce is maximised.

The Safety Representatives and Safety Committees Regulations give certain functions to union appointed safety representatives. The prescribed functions include:

☑ the right to carry out workplace safety inspections

☑ the right to be involved in accident investigations

☑ taking part in safety committees

☑ setting up a safety committee, where two safety representatives make a request in writing.

Large sites may provide customised site safety guides

Where there is no union representation, the requirements of the **Health and Safety (Consultation with Employees) Regulations** apply. These place a legal duty on employers to engage in two-way communication with the workforce on matters of health and safety, either through direct contact or through the employees' elected representatives. As part of the consultation process, site management must display the official health and safety law poster in places where it can be read by all employees, or give each employee a copy of the official leaflet or card containing the same information.

A
03

For further information refer to Chapter A05 Leadership and worker engagement.

Check (Measuring performance)

There are several ways in which a company can monitor and report on health and safety arrangements and the performance of the health and safety policy. They include the following.

☑ The results of inspections, whether regular, random or unannounced, or specific.

☑ The results of health and safety audits.

☑ Benchmarking against previous audits.

☑ Evaluating the effectiveness of earlier risk assessments.

☑ The level of health and safety awareness among employees in the form of feedback from training courses and safety committee meetings.

☑ The investigation of worker feedback on near misses and dangerous occurrences.

☑ Gathering and evaluating information on the number of accidents and work-related ill health over a reference period, their effects and probable causes, and providing feedback.

Gathering information regularly makes performance measurement easier

Health and safety audits

Health and safety audits are a demonstration of the management's commitment to monitor and improve, where necessary, the effectiveness of the company's safety management system from the top down. Audits may identify problems that have arisen due to design issues, and may also identify good practices that should be shared and incorporated into a process of improvement.

Depending on the company's health and safety management system, audits and inspections could be carried out by a number of different people, for example a member of the management team, a director, a health and safety representative, a workforce representative or a sub-contractor could audit another contractor. The aim should always be to identify problem areas, implement improvements and increase the overall standard of safety awareness and performance.

It requires attention to the following.

- ☑ Work environment.
- ☑ Person carrying out the task.
- ☑ Task itself.
- ☑ Safety culture.
- ☑ Way in which each affects the others.

 CITB has developed the *Construction site health, safety and environment auditing system* (SA 03 CD).

The system is in two parts.

- ☑ Health, safety and environmental management systems audit, dealing with auditing the procedures and arrangements upon which the health and safety management system is based.
- ☑ Site operations audit covering the way in which company policies and procedures are put into practice on site.

Monitoring

Monitoring involves carrying out observations to measure and ensure compliance with a system or procedure and to correct, in real time, minor deviations from that system or procedure.

Employers are required to monitor performance and there are two types of monitoring used in auditing and inspecting.

- ☑ **Proactive monitoring** measures the current level of compliance with legislation and company procedures.
- ☑ **Reactive monitoring** investigates anything that has happened: accidents, incidents, near misses and ill health.

Health and safety inspections, including recording and reporting (proactive monitoring)

Health and safety inspections tend to be the site manager's or supervisor's view of the health and safety standards on site at any one time. Alternatively, or in addition, a company's health and safety adviser or director may carry out these inspections.

A health and safety inspection may examine the big picture or focus on only one feature; irrespective of who carries out the inspection, they must have the knowledge to enable them to detect unsafe situations and practices, and the authority to ensure they are rectified.

By comparison, health and safety monitoring inspections are normally a less formal style of audit; the results are not necessarily recorded and they may be more appropriate on some smaller sites. Remember, however, no record – no proof!

Both health and safety audits and inspections are carried out on a pre-notified or no-notice basis as suits the situation at the time. If too many are pre-notified or regularly scheduled, it may tend to create a false impression, as those on site may only improve their behaviour or practices in the short term.

The important thing is that, where shortcomings are found, remedial action is promptly taken and lessons learned to prevent recurrence.

Investigating accidents, incidents and ill health, including recording and reporting (reactive monitoring)

Accidents and illness resulting in serious injuries and fatalities, including health hazards, are too often a feature of work in the construction industry. The proactive management of health and safety should serve to keep such incidents and occupational ill health to a minimum.

An unsafe act creates an unsafe condition and may result in a near miss or fatal accident. It should not be forgotten that a near miss today could be a potential accident tomorrow. Supervisors have an important role to play in both proactive and reactive monitoring activities.

For further information on accident prevention, recording and reporting refer to Chapter A07 Accident prevention and reporting.

Act (Reviewing and learning lessons)

It is important that organisations review their health and safety performance. This allows the effectiveness of the leadership, management and competence to be assessed and the results should indicate whether the system is effective in managing risk and protecting people.

The lessons learnt from accident data and cases of ill health, plus the results of audits and monitoring, should be reviewed to see if control measures to prevent re-occurrence have been adopted and whether, as a result, performance has improved.

04

Risk assessments, method statements and permits to work

A 04

What your employer should do for you
1. Identify and assess workplaces and tasks and implement a suitable risk assessment and method statement process.
2. Provide suitable training for those carrying out risk assessments.
3. Ensure risk assessors have the necessary skills, knowledge, training, experience and qualifications (competence) to carry out suitable and sufficient risk assessments.
4. Arrange for training and, if required, put arrangements in place and nominate a person to be responsible.
5. Put arrangements in place to communicate the significant findings of risk assessments.
6. Appoint a person with the authority to decide upon and implement any control measures that are considered necessary.
7. Establish assessment review dates.
8. If employing young persons, complete risk assessments in respect of the young persons at work and assess their needs (for example, for training, supervision and safeguarding).
9. Complete risk assessments for new and expectant mothers where the nature of the work could put her, the foetus or the baby at risk.
10. Put procedures in place to ensure the safety of workers and ensure communication is effective (for example, for those whose first language is not English or who have reading or writing difficulties).

What you should do as a supervisor

Checklist	Yes	No	N/A
1. Assist assessors in preparing suitable and sufficient risk assessments and method statements.			
2. Ensure workplaces and adequate procedures are in place for your workforce and others who may be affected.			
3. Provide practical knowledge and experience to risk assessors to ensure risk assessments are suitable and sufficient.			
4. Ensure that the risk assessments and method statements are current and match the workplace situation.			
5. Check that the risk assessment and method statement match the tasks to be carried out.			
6. Communicate the findings of the risk assessments to your workforce and others who may be affected.			
7. Check that any control measures that are considered necessary are implemented.			
8. Take extra care of young persons and recognise their shortcomings due to immaturity and lack of experience.			
9. Identify if training is required, and report shortcomings to a person nominated to be responsible in the company.			
10. Ensure your workers whose first language is not English, or who have reading or writing difficulties, have a clear understanding of their work and the emergency measures in place on site.			
11. Implement the company policy for new and expectant mothers, where applicable.			

A
04

A
04

Introduction

This chapter explains the principles and process of risk assessment for controlling health and safety risks.

The principle of risk assessment is fundamental to the management of health and safety in the workplace. The Management of Health and Safety at Work Regulations (MHSWR) place a legal duty on **employers** to assess the risks that arise out of their work activities and that pose a risk to the health and safety of:

☑ their employees

☑ any other people who are not in their employment but who may be affected by their work activities.

The regulations place a similar duty on the **self-employed** to safeguard the health and safety of themselves and anyone else who may be affected by their work activities.

The regulations also require that arrangements are made for the effective planning, organisation, control, monitoring and review of the preventive and protective measures necessary to control the risks to health or safety, as identified by a risk assessment. If there are five or more employees, the significant findings of each assessment must be recorded.

The requirement for risk assessments also extends to a company's office premises, storage yards and so on, if they exist, plus the use of vehicles on company business.

In addition to the above requirement for general risk assessments, there is also a requirement in other sets of regulations for employers to carry out specific risk assessments in relation to specific threats to health or safety in the workplace, such as:

☑ the use of hazardous substances (COSHH)

☑ noise in the workplace

☑ hand-arm vibration syndrome

☑ manual handling activities

☑ the presence of asbestos

☑ exposure to lead.

However, this does not put an obligation on employers to carry out two risk assessments for the same hazard.

There is no legal definition of a *risk assessment* but, in practice, it can be described as a careful and structured examination of a work activity (or a group of associated work activities) to identify any feature of the work that could harm the health or safety of anyone and how, by the implementation of effective control measures, the risk of harm occurring may be eliminated or reduced to an acceptable level.

If a risk assessment is to be effective, it is essential that the person who carries it out is familiar with all aspects of the task being assessed.

 It is beneficial to involve the workers who are familiar with carrying out the type of work, in order to gain a better insight into any problem areas.

Risk assessments should focus on the known and reasonably foreseeable conditions and events, and should therefore concentrate on what could happen rather than what should happen.

Whilst risk assessments are primarily about reducing injuries, deaths and occupational ill health, the damage to plant and equipment, and the avoidance of environmental harm, should also be considered during the risk assessment process.

Some terms used in risk assessment

Anyone carrying out risk assessments must be familiar with the meaning of the following terms that are used in the process.

☑ **Hazard:** anything that has the potential to cause harm (ill health, injury or damage).

☑ **Risk:** the likelihood of an event occurring from a hazard, coupled with the severity of harm.

☑ **Likelihood:** the chance that an accident will occur (certain, likely, possible, unlikely or rare).

☑ **Severity:** the consequences of any incident that arises.

☑ **Danger:** a person is in danger when they are exposed to a risk.

☑ **Accident:** an event that results in injury or ill health.

☑ **Near miss:** (including dangerous occurrence) an event that, while not causing harm, has the potential to cause injury or ill health.

☑ **Competence:** having practical and theoretical knowledge, training and actual experience of the work activities involved.

Principles of risk assessment

Health and safety legislation is structured around a goal setting or risk-based approach to the management of health and safety hazards and risks in the workplace. Prescriptive control measures (such as the minimum height of scaffold guard-rails) only occur in a few instances.

The risk assessment cycle is shown below.

☑ **Identify the hazards** that arise out of the work activity being assessed.

☑ **Think about who might be harmed** by the hazards associated with the job.

☑ **Evaluate the risks** by considering what control measures are required to keep the people, identified as being at risk from harm, safe.

☑ **Record** the significant findings of the risk assessment.

☑ **Monitor and review** the risk assessment to ensure the control measures are implemented and are appropriate and effective.

Particular provision is made in the MHSWR for the protection of young persons (under 18 years of age) and women of childbearing age and expectant or new mothers, including those who are breastfeeding. However, when carrying out a risk assessment the assessor must also consider other vulnerable people.

The controls on what young people are allowed to do in the workplace are strict and specific. A full outline of the factors that must be considered when risk assessments have to take account of young people, or some female employees, is included later in this chapter.

Stages of risk assessment

1. Identify the hazards.

Some typical examples found on construction sites are listed below.

- ☑ An untidy site with lots of slipping and tripping hazards.

- ☑ The use of equipment with rotating blades (such as disc cutters).

- ☑ The use of power tools, creating dust or sparks.

- ☑ Work at height with the potential for falls (for example, roofing activities).

- ☑ Manual handling activities or working in cramped conditions.

- ☑ Confined spaces.

- ☑ The operation of construction plant near to people on foot.

- ☑ The presence of contaminated ground.

- ☑ The use of chemicals, solvents, paints and so on.

2. Think about who might be harmed and how.

Having established the hazards associated with the job, you will have to identify the individuals or groups of people who are at risk. Some examples are shown below.

- ☑ Yourself, vulnerable employees (particularly anyone young and inexperienced) and expectant or nursing mothers.

- ☑ Employees who need special consideration (for example, someone who is deaf or who is not fluent in English).

- ☑ Employees of other contractors.

- ☑ Visitors (such as delivery drivers, maintenance staff and clients).

- ☑ Members of the public or trespassers (particularly children).

- ☑ Anyone else who might be affected by your work (for example, neighbouring businesses).

3. Evaluate the risks and decide upon precautions.

Having identified the hazards, now consider what risk control measures are necessary to keep the people who have been identified as being at risk, from harm.

Even when control measures have been put in place there will usually be a risk that still remains – this is known as a residual risk. (For example, a site may have a one-way traffic system in place, but there will probably be points where pedestrians still have to cross or share a roadway with vehicular traffic.) Control measures must be specific to the workers undertaking the task. For example, a control measure stating 'Provide adequate edge protection' is not acceptable. A better description of the control measure would be 'A double handrail will be fixed along all exposed roof edges. Toe-boards will also be provided'.

If you choose to use the risk assessment tool included later in this chapter, you will have to exercise your judgment as to whether, in your opinion, the residual risk is **high**, **medium** or **low**.

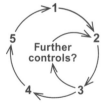

This part of the assessment is a loop. If, after identifying risk control measures, you think that the level of residual risk is still too high, it will be necessary to introduce further control measures (for example, the introduction of speed limits and designated crossing points). Again evaluate the level of residual risk and continue the process until it is considered to be acceptable. It is a case of asking yourself the following question.

 What have I done to control the risks and what more do I need to do?

Using a remote controlled trench compactor eliminates the risk of a person entering the excavation

4. Record your findings and implement them.

Health and safety law requires that all employers carry out risk assessments for their work although, legally, only employers with five or more employees need to record the significant findings of their risk assessments. Risk assessments may be recorded electronically, providing that they can be easily retrieved for reference if required.

 All risk assessments should be recorded.

The law does not specify how a risk should be measured although three common conventions have evolved over time.

☑ **A qualitative risk assessment,** which outlines the hazards present and the risk control measures necessary. No attempt is made to quantify the level of residual risk.

☑ **A semi-quantitative risk assessment,** which outlines the hazards present and the risk control measures necessary, and in which residual risk is quantified by categorising it as 'high', 'medium' or 'low' to enable corrective actions to be prioritised.

☑ **A quantitative risk assessment,** which assigns numerical scores rather than a grade to the likelihood and severity of the risk.

 Irrespective of how a risk assessment is laid out, it is considered good practice for it to identify the:

☑ **person who will manage the residual risks**

☑ **date(s) by which any essential actions must be taken, in the interests of health or safety.**

5. Monitor, review and revise if necessary.

Risk assessments should be reviewed from time to time to ensure the control measures are still appropriate and effective. The assessment must be reviewed and the risks re-evaluated if there is a change to any aspect of the way the job has to be carried out, that might affect health and safety, such as in the examples below.

☑ Having to use a different item of equipment part way through the job.

☑ The arrival of a new operative who is inexperienced.

☑ Unexpected deteriorating weather conditions.

☑ The late arrival of materials.

A 04

Suitable and sufficient – summary

Employer duties

The regulations require that all risk assessments are suitable and sufficient. For a risk assessment to comply with this requirement, it must:

- ☑ establish the risks that are inherent in the workplace, or arising from the work activity

- ☑ be appropriate, given the nature of the workplace and the work, and such that it remains valid for a reasonable period of time

- ☑ be proportionate to the level of risk and the nature of the work

- ☑ identify and prioritise the control measures required to protect the health and safety of the employees and others who may be affected.

Supervisor duties

- ☑ Receive, if necessary question, and accept the risk assessments.

- ☑ Check the suitability of the assessments when compared with the workplace and the work to be carried out (carry out a point of work risk assessment).

- ☑ Question anything that does not seem to be right. **If in doubt ask!**

Establishing control measures

When establishing appropriate control measures, consideration should be given to the following techniques.

- ☑ **Combat risks at source** (for example, use a safe product rather than rely on personal protective equipment (PPE)).

- ☑ **Take advantage of technical progress** and adopt new, safer methods of working (for example, use a modern trestle system, complete with guard-rails and toe-boards, rather than scaffold boards supported on improvised hop ups).

- ☑ **Replace the dangerous with the non-dangerous or less dangerous** (for example, prohibit the use of all 230 V power tools, allowing only battery-powered or 110 V tools).

- ☑ **Adopt collective measures that protect the greatest number of individuals**, collective before individual, passive before active (for example, safety nets protect everyone working above them, whereas a safety harness only protects the wearer, and even then the protection provided is dependent on the wearer wearing the harness properly and hooking it onto a suitable anchor point).

- ☑ **Give appropriate information**, instruction and training to employees and others – assess the need for training.

- ☑ **Provide PPE:** always the very last resort.

What do you do after your risk assessment as an employer?

- ☑ Put into effect the measures that you have decided will adequately control the risks.

- ☑ Communicate the findings of your risk assessments, particularly details of the hazards identified and what control measures are in place, to anyone who needs to know (for example, the principal contractor, your employees, sub-contractors and so on).

It is important that the findings of risk assessments are communicated to anyone whose health and/or safety is likely to be affected by the job. Do not just store them away.

What do you do after you receive a risk assessment as a supervisor?

☑ Speak to the site manager on a regular basis about the work ahead, and what is happening that could affect your working area.

☑ Check that the risk control measures to be put in place are right for the work situation.

☑ Seek clarification of uncertainties and make your manager aware of any findings of a point of work risk assessment so that control measures are corrected.

☑ Before briefing your workers, ensure the risk assessments and method statements are correct.

☑ Explain the risk assessments and method statements to your workers, ensure understanding (by asking questions) and record the names of those briefed (and when).

 Do not rely on generic risk assessments. As a supervisor it is your responsibility to make sure that your workplace is safe.

Young persons

A young person is classified in law as anyone who is not yet 18. A risk assessment for a work activity in which a young person will be involved must take account of the following.

☑ Their inexperience, lack of awareness and immaturity.

☑ The layout of the workplace (for example, will young people be expected to work at height or in excavations).

☑ The nature, degree and duration of exposure to physical, biological or chemical agents (noise and vibration are physical agents).

☑ The type of equipment that the young person would be expected to operate and how the work is organised and supervised.

☑ The amount of health and safety training that the young person has received.

☑ The level of supervision required.

☑ Possible exposure to extremes of heat, cold, noise, vibration, toxic chemicals, and so on.

 In practical terms, the main implications of a young person being on site are restrictions in what they are allowed to do and, initially at least, a higher level of supervision.

These points are not intended to discourage the employment of young persons; they only highlight the factors that must be taken into consideration when planning the work that they are going to do.

Any risk assessments carried out at work for young people under the age of 18 (for example work-placement trainees) must be shared with their parents or guardians.

A 04

Special arrangements must be in place for young persons on site

New and expectant mothers

Special consideration must be given within risk assessments to any employee who is pregnant, has given birth within the past six months or who is breastfeeding, where the nature of the work could put her, the foetus or the baby at risk.

The assessment may identify the need to alter the work environment, work pattern, work activity, working hours, and provide additional temporary facilities or support.

Any employee who is pregnant, has given birth within the past six months or who is breastfeeding must notify her employer in writing of this fact within a reasonable length of time. Until the employer receives further notification, they are not required to take any further action.

Point of work risk assessment

An employer's risk assessment has generally not been prepared **on the day at the workplace** so supervisors must ensure that they are correct before briefing their workforce. A simple point of work risk assessment could be used.

Remember the STAR principle	☑ Stop
	☑ Think
	☑ Act
	☑ Review

☑ Before you start work **stop** and **think** about where you are and what you are going to do.

☑ If it's safe to proceed you can start, or else make it safe (**act**).

☑ When you have finished **review** what you have done.

If anything was learned from the job, report back to your employer (lessons good or bad for improvement in the future).

 Think before you act – has the situation changed? If in doubt, stop and ask.

Risk assessment tools

Qualitative risk assessment

The HSE has produced a simple template that does not use ratings but instead uses the headings listed in the example on page 67. Some people prefer this method as it follows logical risk assessment steps. It can also be easier for the workforce to understand.

Semi-quantitative risk assessment

The risk of something going wrong is considered in terms of **likelihood** (probability) and **severity** (consequences).

The **likelihood** of a hazard actually causing harm or an accident happening is rated as being **high, medium** or **low** in accordance with the following.

High	It will happen regularly, or it could be a usual or a common occurrence.
Medium	It is less regular, but is still recognised as being likely to happen.
Low	Something that is theoretically foreseeable but has never happened or it has not happened for a long time; it is known to be infrequent and is not likely to happen.

The severity of the event, should it happen, can then be categorised as follows.

High	The result could be a fatal accident or multiple injuries, major property damage or a substantial loss resulting in pollution or having a major environmental impact.
Medium	It would probably cause serious injuries, or persons would be off work for over seven days due to their injuries, or substantial property damage or loss resulting in pollution or having some environmental impact.
Low	There would be minor injuries to persons or some slight damage to property with minor losses.

Calculating the risk rating

1. Likelihood and severity are mapped on a matrix, as shown below.

Likelihood	High			
	Medium			
	Low			
		Low	Medium	High
		Severity		

2. As an example, for an activity where likelihood is assessed as **high** and severity is assessed as **medium**, the overall risk rating is plotted, as shown below.

Likelihood	High		X	
	Medium			
	Low			
		Low	Medium	High
		Severity		

3. The combined likelihood/severity risk rating is then graded by taking the highest of the two individual ratings, as shown below.

Likelihood	High	High	High	High
	Medium	Medium	Medium	High
	Low	Low	Medium	High
		Low	Medium	High
		Severity		

Risk assessments, method statements and permits to work

- ☑ A combined risk rating of **high** should be totally unacceptable and the work should not be undertaken until the risk has been reduced.

- ☑ When there is a combined risk rating of **medium**, action must be taken and work stopped, if necessary, to reduce the risk level.

- ☑ If the combined risk rating is **low**, it is acceptable to start the work as long as everything reasonably practicable has been done in order to reduce the risk. The risk assessment must be reviewed at regular intervals.

Using this information, decisions can now be made on whether it is sufficiently safe to continue with an activity, or whether further control measures are necessary.

Consider this example

Roof trusses have to be installed on a two-storey house. One of the obvious hazards is a fall from height. If a ladder is to be used to access the top of the walls with no further protective measures taken, the likelihood of a fall back to the ground during the installation of the trusses could be assessed as **high**. Similarly, the severity of a fall from height, particularly someone falling from eaves height onto the floor below, could also be assessed as **high**.

If instead, a scaffold platform were erected around the house at eaves height and airbags installed below, across the full span of the house, both the likelihood of a fall occurring, and the severity of any fall that did occur (onto the scaffold platform or onto the airbags), could be assessed as **low**.

By revising the work method, a **high/high** situation, which gave a combined risk rating of **high**, has been reduced to **low/low**, which gives a combined risk rating of **low**.

An alternative work method, by which the whole roof-truss assembly is manufactured at ground level and craned into place, would be a better option as it would serve to reduce the risks of working at height.

(A suggested format for laying out risk assessments can be found on the next two pages.)

 For an interactive risk assessment form visit the GE 700 companion website.

 For further information on controlling risks within the workplace visit the HSE website.

Qualitative risk assessment (Example)

What are the hazards?	Who might be harmed and how?	What are you already doing?	What further action(s) is/are necessary?	Action by who?	Action by when?
Heavy vehicle movement around the site.	General public, site operatives, other site visitors: ■ pedestrians being struck by delivery vehicle ■ lorry getting bogged down and becoming unstable.	Segregation of on-site vehicle and pedestrian routes. Vehicle to reverse only with the aid of a vehicle marshaller. Site roads made up to a satisfactory standard; safe access to public highway. Everyone else kept out of the area during unloading.	Ongoing site inductions to include warning about keeping clear of vehicle unloading activities.	Site manager.	Before date of each delivery.
Mechanical lifting operations – unloading.	Delivery vehicle driver, others in the area: ■ contact with suspended load ■ falling or toppling load ■ lorry unstable during lifting.	Drivers must report to office on arrival for induction and checking of competence card – lorry loaders. Materials lay-down area ready for heavy, stacked materials. Other people kept out of the area.	Qualified slinger made available if required by vehicle driver.	Site manager.	Before each delivery is unloaded.
Mud deposited on public roads.	General public – road users: ■ slippery road surfaces.	Vehicle wheel wash installed; mandatory use when site is muddy.	Road sweeper is available if needed; mandatory use when site is muddy.	Site manager.	Immediately before vehicles leave site.

A
04

Semi-quantitative risk assessment (Example)

Work activity	Working near to excavations.
Persons at risk	Operatives carrying out the tasks, vehicle drivers, other contractors and site visitors.

Hazard	Fall of people or plant into the excavation.		
Risk control measures	Safe ladder access into and out of excavation. Install fencing around excavation. Install lighting. Install warning signs. People and vehicles not involved in activity excluded from the area. Stop blocks installed to keep site vehicles at a safe distance. Construction plant tipping into the excavation controlled by a trained vehicle marshaller and only carried out when the excavation is unoccupied.	*Owners of the risks*	*Date by which any actions must be taken*

Risk rating	High	Medium	Low	Combined risk rating
Likelihood			X	Medium
Severity		X		

Method statements

A method statement is a document that describes in a logical sequence exactly how a work activity is to be carried out in a manner that is safe and without risk to health.

Method statements enable the principal (or main) contractor to examine the proposed working methods of all contractors and sub-contractors and to establish where tasks that are to take place at the same time may conflict with the interests of health and safety.

Well written method statements provide an ideal means of communicating vital health and safety information to those who will be doing the work, usually by the method statement being explained to them by the supervisor.

 It is important for the supervisor to check that the workers have understood the method statement (for example by asking simple questions about it).

To a large extent, the way in which any task will be undertaken, and therefore how it is detailed in the method statement, will reflect the findings of the risk assessment(s) for the task.

The control measures selected for controlling hazards and risks will influence the method of carrying out the task. The person writing the method statement should refer to the risk assessment(s) for the task.

For routine and repetitive activities (work that is carried out many times where the hazards and risk are broadly the same), a previous method statement may be applied again, provided it has been reviewed at point of work (by the supervisor) to ensure that it is still relevant for the task and the workplace. This is referred to as a **generic method statement.**

Where the work is more complicated or the ground or the weather conditions require it, a specific method statement will have to be produced. For new work (work that has not been done before) a new risk assessment and method statement is required before the task is undertaken.

Permit to work

A permit to work is a formal, dated and time-limited certificate signed by a properly authorised and competent person.

Whilst there is no requirement in law to use a permit to work system, they are often used to regulate how potentially high risk activities are to be carried out in a healthy and safe manner. As such, they are supported by the risk assessment from which they are derived.

Permits to work are often, but not exclusively, required where the work:

- ☑ involves entry into a confined space
- ☑ depends upon the isolation of high-voltage electrical equipment
- ☑ involves the disturbance of any system carrying a fluid or gas under pressure
- ☑ involves hot works.

Receipt of a permit is acknowledged by the signature of the person in charge of the work, who will retain a copy; another copy will be retained by the person issuing the permit to work.

Other signatures on the permit will certify that any control measures necessary for the job to start have been implemented (for example, locking-out an electrical supply or checking the atmosphere in a confined space).

A
04

A permit will indicate the time and date at which it expires. If the work is not completed at that time, depending upon the circumstances:

☑ it is usually necessary to make everything safe, for everyone to leave the work area before the permit expires and for the permit to be cancelled

☑ it may be safe, with approval from the issuing authority, to extend the expiry time and for the work area to be reoccupied.

When the work is completed, or the expiry time has passed, the person in charge of the work must close and return their copy of the permit to the authorised issuing authority. The permit can then be cancelled.

A
04

05

Leadership and worker engagement

A 05

What your employer should do for you

1.	Consult with and involve all workers, provide training and match activities to capability.
2.	Attend to health and safety matters as a part of good management.
3.	Understand that a reputation can be lost by poor industrial relations.
4.	Recognise that accident rates are lower where workers are involved in planning safe systems of work.
5.	Undertake training in communication skills and understand the importance of feedback.
6.	Appreciate that responding in an agreed timeframe is important.
7.	Understand that people's behaviour influences safety in the workplace.
8.	Involve the workforce in decision making, encourage suggestions and provide feedback.
9.	Encourage the workforce to be actively involved in enhancing safety and management systems.
10.	Design workplaces for the work activity.
11.	Provide information in a way or form that is easily understood by anyone receiving it.
12.	Train staff in the recognition of workers with little or poor understanding of English.
13.	Provide opportunities for face-to-face discussions.
14.	Recognise workers who have reading, writing or hearing difficulties, or visual impairment.
15.	Ensure that workers get the right information at the right time.
16.	Provide supervisory staff with visual tools to aid safety-critical communication for those who have poor or no spoken understanding of English.

What you should do as a supervisor

Checklist	Yes	No	N/A
1. Pay attention to health and safety matters as a part of good management.			
2. Ensure that workplaces are designed for the work activity.			
3. Appreciate that people's behaviour influences safety in the workplace.			
4. Involve workers when planning safe systems of work.			
5. Assist in consultation with and involving workers, provide training and match activities to capability.			
6. Encourage the workforce to become involved in health and safety decision making, support suggestions and give feedback.			
7. Provide support to enable the workforce to be actively involved in enhancing safety and management systems.			
8. Ensure that the workforce get the right information at the right time.			
9. Explain information in a way or form that is easily understood by anyone receiving it.			
10. Recognise the difficulties faced by workers with little or poor understanding of English.			
11. Participate in communication skills and training, and understand the importance of feedback.			
12. Appreciate that workers who have reading, writing or hearing difficulties, or visual impairment, need help.			
13. Use visual tools to aid safety-critical communication for those who have poor or no understanding of spoken English and those with poor literacy skills in English.			
14. Encourage opportunities for face-to-face discussions.			
15. Ensure that responses are given within an agreed time.			
16. Be aware that a reputation can be lost by poor industrial relations.			

A
05

Introduction

An essential part of health and safety management is the **two-way** communication process between employers (or their representatives) and employees (or their representatives). There are legal duties on both parties with the intent that communication takes place in both directions.

Employers and their representatives (managers, supervisors, and so on) must talk to, and listen to, the people who work for and with them.

Talking to, listening to and involving employees helps to:

☑ make the workplace healthier and safer

☑ raise standards

☑ improve motivation and productivity.

Good preparation helps to gain the commitment of the employees (or their representatives), so that they feel involved and enthusiastic about tackling health and safety together.

For further information refer to the leadership and worker engagement chapter in Section A of GE 700 *Construction site safety*.

Helping to look after your business

Good health and safety management and a successful business are complementary. Employers should already have in place ways of cutting down losses and reducing waste. Properly applied, these controls should also help manage health and safety. You will want to do this so people are both healthy and safe.

If the company loses important people through inadequate relationships and poor health and safety performance, the business will be put at risk. The key to good management is getting the workforce to recognise that managing health and safety is important too and a top priority of management.

Helping to look after your reputation

Society and workers expect companies to comply with health and safety legislation. Failure to do so can bring penalties of imprisonment or unlimited fines, as well as adverse publicity which will:

☒ put customers off doing business with your company

☒ prejudice the company's position on any pre-qualification or preferential supplier lists

☒ spread a bad reputation more quickly through the industry than a good performance.

Looking after your people

When staff are well protected, involved and well trained they add value to the business because they:

☑ are better motivated

☑ take less sickness absence

☑ show greater loyalty.

To help in involving the workforce management must:

☑ set a good example

☑ inform, instruct, train and supervise them

☑ listen to their concerns

☑ encourage them to suggest solutions to problems

☑ provide feedback on how any concerns raised will be dealt with

☑ treat them with respect.

When raising a health and safety concern, it is essential that workers can raise it with someone on site who has the authority to appropriately take the issue forward.

The person raising the issue should be given assurance that their concern will be investigated and that feedback will be provided on the outcome.

The best way to protect the business, reputation and the workforce (and others) is to involve them.

☑ Talk to each other about issues.

☑ Listen to their concerns.

☑ Seek and share views and information.

☑ Discuss issues in good time.

☑ Consider what employees say before decisions are made.

☑ Make a secure commitment to any decision made.

Communication

The HSE's 'Fit3' campaign (Fit for work, fit for life, fit for tomorrow) resulted in the following findings.

☑ Accident rates are lower where employees have a say in health and safety matters.

☑ Employee involvement creates a more positive health and safety culture.

☑ Stronger employee involvement makes for better control of common workplace risks.

☑ Employers can learn about risks through consultation.

☑ Employers with health and safety committees have fewer work-related injuries.

Understanding how we communicate
It is estimated that verbal communication only makes up around 10% of communication as a whole. Other aspects include such areas as sincerity, honesty, eye contact, body language, facial expression and timing – not forgetting that a picture tells 1,000 stories (that is, it is not so much what we say but how we say and present it).

 Management must lead by example.

Assertive communication
The most effective and healthiest form of communication is to use an assertive (confident) style. It is how we naturally express ourselves when our self-esteem is intact, giving us the confidence to communicate without games and manipulation. The style of communication will generally depend on your past experiences and lessons learnt to get the most effective results.

Consulting the workforce
Management should consult the workforce about the following.

☑ Any changes that may have an effect on the workforce's health, safety and welfare.

☑ Arrangements for getting competent people to help the company meet its legal and moral health and safety obligations.

☑ Provide information on the likely risks in the workplace and the precautions that are or will need to be taken.

A
05

- ☑ The best way for information to be shared (consider language, literacy and learning disabilities).

- ☑ Planning of health and safety training.

- ☑ Health and safety consequences of introducing new technology.

Management should not limit the scope of consultation to a pre-set list of persons because there will be times when employees (and others) who are not on the list will need to be involved.

Good practice

- ☑ Commit to early involvement as a matter of routine.

- ☑ Involve employees in addressing work-related health issues, such as:
  - stress in the workplace
  - musculoskeletal disorders
  - sickness or injury.

- ☑ Provide feedback to explain the decisions and responses to issues.

- ☑ Agree to respond to issues within a certain timeframe.

- ☑ Solve problems jointly with employees participating as equals to resolve issues.

- ☑ Have a plan in place in case of inability to engage the workforce for reasons beyond your immediate control.

Consultation does not always result in agreement but an organisation should be able to resolve differences of opinion by being open, explaining the reasons behind decisions and following agreed procedures for resolving problems.

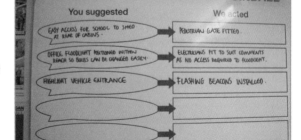

A 'you suggested – we acted' board helps workers see that concerns are being listened to and acted upon

Benefits of worker involvement

Aside from meeting their legal duty to consult, workplaces where employees are involved in taking decisions about health and safety are safer and healthier. Employees influence health and safety through their own actions. They are often the best people to understand the risks in their workplace. Engaging the workforce has proven to have major benefits in the workplace for all involved.

Talking, listening and co-operating with each other can help:

- ☑ comply with legal requirements
- ☑ reduce accidents and ill health, plus their related costs to the business
- ☑ develop a positive culture where risks are managed sensibly
- ☑ identify joint solutions to problems
- ☑ bring about improvements in overall efficiency, quality and productivity
- ☑ meet customer demands and maintain credibility.

 A healthy and safe workforce is a harder working and happier workforce.

The HSE has a free leadership and worker involvement toolkit aimed at reducing harm by learning from the best in the construction industry. The toolkit has been developed by the construction industry to help employers, managers, supervisors and workers learn how to make health and safety improvements in their businesses.

 The *Leadership and worker involvement toolkit* is available on the HSE website.

Achieving safety awareness within a company

The employer's role is to ensure that everyone, regardless of their level, is competent to do what is required of them and empower them to stop work and challenge any situation that they believe to be unsafe.

Your role, as supervisor, is to provide clear direction to those under your control and to support managers in their objective of achieving a level of health and safety awareness that reduces incidents and accidents.

Everyone contributes to a safe workplace

Adequate information, instruction and training must be provided in the following situations.

- ☑ For work on a new site.
- ☑ When new people start on site.

- ☑ When new equipment is introduced.
- ☑ If a new phase of the job or major activity starts.
- ☑ When new safety procedures are required, because of changes to work practices or routines.
- ☑ At any other appropriate times (for example, daily briefings).

Proactively manage day-to-day health and safety matters on site in the following ways.

- ☑ Ensure the company health and safety policy is adhered to.
- ☑ Ensure that there are well-defined roles and responsibilities.
- ☑ Monitor the day-to-day standards of health and safety on site.
- ☑ Ensure that adequate training, information, instruction and supervision are provided.
- ☑ Provide a means for employees to voice any concerns they have on health and safety issues.
- ☑ Acknowledge your own limitations and seek access to specialist health and safety advice where necessary.

Introduce safe systems of working by:

- ☑ carrying out risk assessments, and implementing procedures required to control the problems identified by those assessments
- ☑ implementing adequate written procedures of work activities and other relevant systems (for example, method statements and permits to work where appropriate).

Introduce regular inspection schedules to include:

- ☑ audit inspections
- ☑ improvement plans.

Ensure that sound maintenance arrangements are carried out:

- ☑ using competent staff
- ☑ at appropriate intervals
- ☑ in the correct environment
- ☑ with adequate facilities being provided.

Develop and initiate plans for responding to the following.

- ☑ Site evacuation in the event of an emergency situation.
- ☑ Serious accidents or occurrences that require investigating or reporting.
- ☑ Trespassers or anyone causing damage on site.

Engage with and consult the workforce on health and safety issues.

- ☑ Involve them in the decision-making process on risk reduction.
- ☑ Listen to their concerns.
- ☑ Take positive action to reduce risks where their observations are valid.
- ☑ Provide feedback on how their concerns have been dealt with.

If health and safety matters are to be taken seriously by the workforce, management must make a visible commitment to health and safety and lead by example.

Attention to health and safety issues must be seen as an integral part of the job and not just as a bolt on. Operatives should become accustomed to doing any kind of work with consideration to the health and safety of anyone who could be harmed, including themselves.

SLAM technique

The SLAM (Stop…Look…Assess…Manage) technique reminds workers to stop work if they think that their health and safety is at risk.

Encouraging workers to use the SLAM technique

By using the SLAM technique, workers will value the importance of health and safety and so create a healthy and safe site. By remembering SLAM, workers are more likely to stop work if a task appears unsafe or risky to their health, or stop their colleagues behaving in an unsafe or unhealthy way.

How to use the SLAM technique

The four stages of SLAM are shown below.

1. **Stop** the task and think. Look at each step and ask the following questions.

   ☑ Is this a new task?

   ☑ Has the task changed?

   ☑ When was the last time this task was carried out?

   ☑ Is everyone competent to do this task?

   ☑ If not, is there a need for training?

2. **Look** before, during and after completion of the task.

   ☑ Inspect the work area for potential hazards (such as unsecured ladders or untidiness).

   ☑ Identify the hazards for each step of the task.

   ☑ Evaluate what to do about any hazards identified.

3. **Assess** if workers are equipped to perform that task safely. Check that everyone has the correct:

   ☑ training

   ☑ knowledge

   ☑ skills

   ☑ resources.

   Ask what is needed to perform the task safely.

   ☑ Help? (Workers should be encouraged to ask for help.)

   ☑ More training? (Workers should not perform the task until they have been trained.)

4. **Manage** by taking appropriate action to eliminate or minimise any hazards on site by:

   ☑ ensuring the proper equipment is used and is well maintained

   ☑ thinking about the task just completed and asking:
   - what went well?
   - what did not go well?
   - did anything unexpected happen?
   - how can we be better prepared and plan for this in future?
   - what must we add into the plan?

What next?

☑ Share this information with workers and management.

☑ Use this information to encourage safe working practices.

☑ Use safety briefings and toolbox talks to teach the workforce and encourage them to use SLAM techniques.

A
05

For further information on health and safety in the construction industry visit the HSE website.

There are other processes available, such as the STAR principle. *(Refer to Chapter A04 Risk assessments, method statements and permits to work)*; others include SUSA, STOP, MAD, SAFE and Take 2, Take 5 or Take 10.

Behavioural safety

Behavioural safety attempts to determine why people act the way they do in relation to work activities. It is based on a process of observation and feedback, and aims to identify, in advance, any difficulties in completing tasks safely.

It is proactive, trying to identify and deal with potential problems rather than reacting to past accidents and mistakes.

Whilst the term *behavioural safety* is used throughout this section, the principles apply equally to preventing occupational health problems by influencing the behaviour of individuals and groups.

***Behavioural safety* is a combination of organisational, job and individual factors which influence behaviour at work in a way that can positively affect health and safety. To put it another way, the 'human factors'.**

Using behavioural safety

Historically, improvements in health, safety and environmental performance have been achieved through improvements in engineering technology, that is non-human ways, and enhancing safety management systems. In many ways, this methodology has reached its peak performance and the related improvements in health and safety performance have begun to level off.

Future performance gains will be achieved by taking more account of the way people interact with aspects of the workplace; and through integrating and understanding the human element of risk management.

We all have our own perception of risk and safety based on our individual experiences and it is not easy to make direct comparisons between different views and opinions. Despite this, most people have a genuine desire to work safely through adopting good practice; after all, no-one goes to work planning on or intending to have an accident.

☑ **The following HSE publications give clear guidance on managing safety and human factors:**

    – ***Reducing error and influencing behaviour* (HSG48)**

    – ***Managing for health and safety* (HSG65).**

☑ **For further information refer to the CITB Achieving Behavioural Change (ABC) course.**

For further information refer to the behavioural safety chapter in Section A of GE 700 *Construction site safety*.

The human factors

The organisation

Organisational factors, like workplace layouts, have the greatest influence on behaviour yet they are often overlooked during the design of work and investigation of accidents and incidents. There is a need to establish a positive health and safety culture.

The job

Tasks should be designed in accordance with ergonomic principles to take into account limitations and strengths in human performance (such as physical restrictions – matching the person to the task).

The individual

People bring personal attitudes, skills, habits and personalities to the job. These can be strengths or weaknesses depending on the task and the individual concerned. Generally, personalities and aptitude cannot be changed but skills and attitudes may be changed and enhanced.

Individuals are far more likely to respond positively to behavioural safety if they feel involved in the decision-making process; this is often referred to as worker or employee engagement. Workers and employees should be:

☑ asked for their views on how they feel about the way that health and safety risks are being managed

☑ empowered to stop work if they feel that working conditions are not safe and encouraged to report the incident to someone in authority at site level

☑ provided with feedback on their suggestions, including how, if necessary, the issue is to be taken forward.

Why are workers tempted to carry out tasks using clearly unsafe practices or in plainly unsafe conditions?

Beliefs, expectations, attitude and behaviour

We all have our own beliefs (attitudes) that underlie how we think and define the way we act. If managers and supervisors are not committed or don't believe that health and safety is a priority, a powerful negative message will be sent to employees. Low expectations and poor leadership from management can create negative attitudes from employees, resulting in poor methods of working that lead to poor health and safety performance. For example, if workers believe management wants them to take risks they may well do so, but if they believe that management wants them to work and be safe they are more likely to follow the safe systems and demonstrate good behaviours and co-operation.

Unsafe working at height

**A
05**

The challenge

Implementing a behavioural approach has always presented a challenge to industry because of the mind-set, culture and mistrust of a constantly changing workforce. Past attempts at behavioural safety may not have been properly planned, may have been poorly explained and managed, or been reactive or fragmented. Ingrained and learned behaviours cannot and will not be changed overnight but they can be changed.

It is increasingly being recognised that integrating a systematic, proactive process within the organisation's arrangements can add significantly more value by addressing behavioural aspects of health and safety at the same time as optimising efficiency and productivity.

Furthermore, the HSE makes it clear that human factors must be taken fully into account when managing risk.

Significant improvements can be made to performance through an open communication and reporting process based on what is happening and encouraging near-miss reporting. This will enable the better assessment of risk and the need for bridges to be built, if trust is to be enhanced. The workforce must be encouraged to participate if issues are to be resolved and solutions found.

The solution

A simple, fully integrated process that stimulates discussions on everything that is going on, whether or not they are related to health and safety, is progressed through an action plan that may include toolbox talks, weekly briefings, training and personal coaching. Once people see that positive discussions lead to positive gains for all, without the difficult and generally unpopular observation process, greater and more productive workforce involvement will occur.

Research has shown that when employers engage workers in discussions about health and safety, there is a reduction in the number of accidents.

Leading by example

The behaviour of supervisors and managers can directly affect the behaviour of operatives. The effect of failing to intervene in an unsafe situation or to challenge an unsafe act, is to condone that activity, practice or behaviour. This in turn sends a message to the operatives that the activity concerned is permitted and confuses site teams. Therefore, intervention by managers and supervisors is critical in every case.

Communication

'Actions speak louder than words'. For trust to be built, an individual's behaviour and body language must reinforce what is being said – 'walk the talk, not just talk the talk', as some people say.

Communication is at the heart of all that we do, both at work and in our own time. It is vital to give the person receiving information the time and space to be able to think and formulate a response. In communication, it is the quality, not the quantity, that matters.

One method of enhancing any safe system of work is through frequent and open discussions.

The Health and Safety (Consultation with Employees) Regulations require employers to consult with their employees and make available such information, within the employer's knowledge, as is necessary to enable the employees to participate fully and effectively in the consultation process.

Managing change

Planning for the human side of change will make plans more likely to succeed. No single behavioural safety process fits into every company but some prescriptive processes may be a necessary step towards achieving open communication between the employer and the workforce.

Changes always create issues for people (for example, there may be new leaders, changed roles and the need to develop new skills and capabilities). Employees may be uncertain and resistant because they do not see the need for change or feel that they will be disadvantaged by it.

Benefits

Greater attention to improved working practices will bring about many benefits, including the following.

- ☑ Reducing the potential for accidents.
- ☑ Creating a better system of work.
- ☑ Improved performance and a greater awareness of issues and solutions.
- ☑ Reducing stress.
- ☑ Improving profitability.

Case studies

There is an undeniable link between behavioural safety (getting people to do what you want them to do) and actively engaging them in the decision-making process with regard to reducing site risks.

 For examples of how engaging with the workforce has brought about tangible benefits visit the HSE website.

Communication with non-English speaking workers

Good communication is essential for the management of health and safety on construction sites. The number of workers whose first language is not English has increased on UK sites over recent years. Some of these workers have excellent skills in spoken and written English, but there are others for whom understanding English is a problem. This can be a barrier to effective communication of health and safety information.

Several pieces of health and safety legislation, including the Health and Safety at Work etc. Act 1974, require that employers pass comprehensible information, instruction and training to their employees. In the context of foreign workers, the word *comprehensible* can be taken to mean **provided in a format that can be understood** by the worker. Therefore if you employ non-English speaking workers on your site and fail to engage with them because of language barriers, not only are you likely to put them in danger, you will also be in breach of health and safety legislation.

 One option for improving communication is for training materials to be represented in a pictorial form (images).

The effectiveness of images to overcome language barriers has been confirmed through research, which resulted in the development of a bank of images for this purpose.

A
05

CITB has developed a handy-sized, ring-bound book titled *Safety critical communication – Toolbox talks* (GT 701). Examples are available on the GE 706 companion website.

The images can be used to support site induction, toolbox talks and other training. They can also be used during spot checks to indicate the understanding of relevant issues. Furthermore, copies of the relevant images can be overlaid on site plans to indicate the location of welfare and first-aid facilities, fire-fighting equipment, the assembly point and so on.

06

Statutory inspections, checks and monitoring

A 06

What your employer should do for you

1. Provide plant and equipment with current examination and test certificates.

2. Ensure that examinations of plant are carried out in line with statutory requirements.

3. Provide formats for recording inspections and examinations and keep records.

4. Establish and maintain a system for marking unsuitable plant and equipment and putting it out of possible use (quarantine).

5. Implement and maintain a system of daily inspections and weekly recorded inspections. Remember, no records – no proof!

6. Provide and record toolbox talks and monitor their effectiveness.

7. Arrange for training of the workforce in the daily pre-use inspections of plant and equipment.

8. Allocate responsibilities to the workforce for monitoring and control of activities.

What you should do as a supervisor

Checklist	Yes	No	N/A
1. Ensure authorised operators are trained and competent in the daily and pre-use inspections of plant and equipment.			
2. Make plant available for examination in line with statutory requirements.			
3. Check that plant and equipment have current examination and test certificates.			
4. Use forms for recording inspections and examinations and keeping records.			
5. Arrange to mark unsuitable plant and equipment and put it out of possible use (quarantine).			
6. Carry out daily inspections and weekly recorded inspections. Remember, no records – no proof!			
7. Accept responsibility for monitoring and control of activities of the workforce.			
8. Ensure your workers carry out daily and weekly checks and inspections.			
9. Present and record toolbox talks and report on their effectiveness.			

A
06

Introduction

This chapter gives an outline of some of the requirements for the completion and use of various statutory and non-statutory forms, notices, signs and registers used within the building and construction industry, and the keeping of some records and other details.

Also included is some guidance on the types of daily and weekly inspection activities that should be carried out and the records that must be kept.

Record keeping

Record keeping is important as it is the means used to ensure that inspections and examinations are carried out as required by legislation and/or company policy.

Some inspections are required by legislation and others by the employer as they are good practice and seen as proactive measures, vital in helping to prevent accidents.

Records are generally split into two categories.

☑ Proactive: for example, records of inspections of scaffolding and excavations.

☑ Reactive: for example, accident investigations.

Records of toolbox talks are also important as this demonstrates that training (usually site-based) is being provided.

Daily site briefings are often a good way of reviewing what has happened previously and looking at what has to be done and the associated hazards. This can be extended to point of work risk assessments.

For further information refer to Chapter A04 Risk assessments, method statements and permits to work, Chapter A05 Leadership and worker engagement.

Daily user and visual checks

Daily user and pre-use visual checks form a vital part of good site management and reduce the risk of plant and equipment breakdown or failure, as in the following examples.

☑ Engine or motor seizure due to lack of lubrication.

☑ A low pressure tyre being damaged or causing a vehicle to overturn.

☑ Missing scaffold edge protection, increasing the likelihood of falling materials.

☑ Damaged power plugs, sockets and leads.

Scaffold inspection in progress – note inspection tags in place

Construction plant and equipment are exposed to harsh environments and as such they require effective maintenance regimes to avoid developing defects.

A programme of pre-use visual checks, regular inspections and servicing schedules should be established in accordance with the manufacturer's instructions or recommendations and the risks associated with the use of each vehicle or item of plant and equipment.

Plant hire companies must provide information with all plant and equipment they supply to enable it to be used and maintained safely. Such equipment should only be used and operated by trained and competent persons. In many cases operatives should be formally appointed in writing and procedures put in place to prevent unauthorised and incompetent persons from using the equipment.

Contractual arrangements between user and hirer should set out who is responsible for maintenance and inspection during the hire period and these should be made clear to all parties, including competent and authorised operatives.

Plant and vehicles should have a maintenance log to help manage and record maintenance operations. Employers should establish procedures designed to encourage supervisors and competent operators to report defects or problems, and ensure that problems with plant and vehicles are rectified. Planned inspection and maintenance must follow manufacturer's instructions.

Inspections and examinations

The table on the following page sets out the recommended daily user checks, weekly inspections, statutory inspections and examinations. This table is only to be used as a guide. A competent health and safety adviser will confirm the frequency of checks required.

For further information refer to the inspections and audits and statutory forms, notices and registers chapter in Section A of GE 700 *Construction site safety.*

A
06

Statutory inspections, checks and monitoring

| Work activity plant item | Pre-use daily | Statutory or recommended | | | | | Form for statutory examination or report to comply with |
		Weekly record	Monthly record	Three monthly record	Six monthly record	12 monthly record	
Excavations, cofferdams and caissons	✓ Inspect	✓ Inspect					Construction (Design and Management) Regulations
Plant and equipment (not electrical or for lifting)	✓ Inspect	✓ Inspect			✓ Examine	✓ Examine	Provision and Use of Work Equipment Regulations
Plant and equipment (electrical) including fixed RCDs	✓ Inspect	✓ Inspect		✓ Examine			Construction (Design and Management) Regulations, and HSG107
Cranes and plant for lifting people, MEWPs, harness, lifting accessories and safety nets	✓ Inspect	✓ Inspect			✓ Examine	✓ Examine	Provision and Use of Work Equipment Regulations, Lifting Operations and Lifting Equipment Regulations
Cranes and plant used for lifting	✓ Inspect	✓ Inspect				✓ Examine	Lifting Operations and Lifting Equipment Regulations
Work at height, all scaffolds, working platforms, mobile towers, ladders and steps, etc.	✓ Inspect	✓ Inspect			✓ Examine		Work at Height Regulations, Provision and Use of Work Equipment Regulations, Construction (Design and Management) Regulations
Fire-fighting appliances			✓ Inspect			✓ Examine	Construction (Design and Management) Regulations, Regulatory Reform (Fire Safety) Order
Site offices electrical equipment and installation		✓ Inspect				✓ Examine	Construction (Design and Management) Regulations, Workplace Health, Safety and Welfare Regulations

Note: this table is to be used only as a guide. A competent health and safety adviser should confirm the frequency of the checks required.

07

Accident prevention and reporting

A 07

What your employer should do for you
1. Report and keep records of work-related accidents, reportable injuries, industrial diseases and dangerous occurrences.
2. Investigate all accidents and incidents and take corrective actions as identified.
3. Understand the definitions of specified injury and over three and seven-day injuries and inform employees.
4. Understand the term *dangerous occurrence* and train employees in recognising and understanding the importance of reporting.
5. Understand the meaning of work-related illness and occupational diseases, what they are and how they must be treated and reported.
6. Define the term *near miss* and ensure others understand it. Set up a regime for reporting, investigating and recording all near miss events or occurrences.

What you should do as a supervisor

Checklist	Yes	No	N/A
1. Understand the accident reporting procedure.			
2. Be aware of and understand the definitions of specified injury and over three and seven-day injuries.			
3. Understand the term *dangerous occurrence* and, if one occurs, know what actions to take.			
4. Have an understanding of the types of work-related illness and occupational diseases that must be reported.			
5. Encourage workers to report all accidents and incidents.			
6. Encourage near miss reporting.			
7. Ensure accidents, incidents and near misses are recorded, reported if required and investigated.			

A
07

Introduction

> An *accident* is an unplanned, unwanted, unscheduled event or occurrence which may result in injury to persons or damage to property.

It is noteworthy that:

- ☑ the injured person may not be an employee
- ☑ the property may not have been yours
- ☑ many accidents are easily preventable with forethought and monitoring.

Year after year, the same types of accident and incident are repeated whilst carrying out construction activities. In many cases, simple precautionary measures would have prevented injuries and ill health.

Accidents and incidents

The following points highlight common types of accident and incident, along with some potential risks to consider.

- ☑ **Working at height.** Have risk assessments been carried out and has the work been properly planned? Is the work supervised and is it being carried out by competent and adequately resourced people?

- ☑ **Slips, trips and falls.** Is the site generally, and all emergency access and escape routes in particular, kept free from debris, materials and other tripping and slipping hazards?

- ☑ **Site plant operations.** Are all plant operators trained and authorised, and have effective measures been taken to segregate, so far as is reasonably practicable, operating plant and people on foot?

- ☑ **Manual handling.** Have manual handing activities been identified and assessed and are work activities organised to minimise the need for manual handling?

- ☑ **Hazardous substances**. Are hazardous substances properly stored, have they been properly assessed and has a COSHH inventory been produced? Has the risk of leaks, spills or escapes been considered? Have measures been taken to limit access to the store and the substances and have measures been put in place to eliminate or reduce exposure?

How bad is the accident situation in the industry?

For many years the construction industry has had a disproportionately high number of fatalities and non-fatal accidents, given the percentage of the total working population in the UK and the percentage of the population that work in the construction industry. Official accident statistics may not tell the whole story, especially as anecdotal evidence suggests that as many as 40% of reportable accidents are not reported. Failure to report a specified injury, an over seven-day injury or a designated dangerous occurrence is a criminal offence.

What causes accidents to happen at work?

There is no easy answer to this question but the following are some common causes to be aware of.

- ☑ Poor communication. *'I wasn't told how to do the job', 'I thought they knew that, after all, it's common sense.'*

- ☑ Lack of safety awareness. *'I didn't realise that ... I didn't know ... I didn't think ...'*

- ☑ Lack of concentration. *'I've done this job so often I let my mind wander just for a second. I didn't think.'*

☑ A lack of training, information or instruction. *'I didn't know. The foreman just told me to get on with it.'*

☑ Unfamiliarity. *'But it's similar to other tools I've used so I never thought it would happen.'*

☑ Incorrect plant and equipment. *'It was only a simple job so it wasn't worth setting up the right equipment. It should have only taken a moment.'*

☑ Poor decision making. *'I needed a quick job done, so I suppose I cut a corner. I didn't know ... I didn't think.'*

☑ Poor attitudes. *'Who needs instructions on a job like this? It's common sense.'*

☑ Accidents only happen to others. *'In all my years of experience, I've never had an accident yet.'*

The Health and Safety Executive (HSE) has attributed many accidents to poor, or a total lack of, management, supervision or training. Whilst it may be the first reaction to blame the operative for the types of accident described, they are usually caused by a combination of circumstances and events. A competent employer, manager or supervisor should detect that a situation is becoming unsafe and intervene as necessary.

A 07

Unsafe conditions

Something with the potential to cause harm

Near misses

An incident that nearly resulted in an injury, damage or loss

Accidents

An accident that caused an injury, damage or loss

A
07

Employers, managers and supervisors have a responsibility for ensuring that operatives receive adequate instruction, training and supervision, and follow the specified safe system of working. Different groups may require differing levels of supervision.

 A near miss is an incident that caused no harm but had the potential to cause injury or ill health, financial or other loss or damage. Management must encourage the workforce to report near misses so that lessons can be learnt and any recurrence of the situation can be prevented.

Cost of accidents

To the injured party	To employers
Life or death	Criminal prosecution or civil action
Pain and suffering	Damaged equipment
Disability	Lost working time
Worry and stress	Lost business and damaged reputation
Financial loss, family conflict and dependence on others	Worry and stress
Reduced job expectations	Insurance costs

Accident prevention

 Prevention is better than cure.

Putting these words into practice requires the following.

☑ An understanding of what can go wrong.

☑ Carrying out risk assessments and implementing the control measures identified.

☑ Developing safe systems of work.

☑ Ensuring that equipment and the working environment are safe.

☑ The correct attitude by everyone concerned (employers, supervisors and managers must engage with the workforce).

☑ A robust system enabling anyone to report hazardous situations and be certain that they will be put right.

☑ Learning from past incidents.

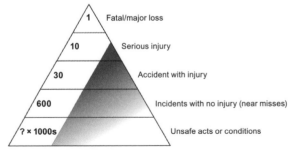

Bird's accident ratio triangle

This illustration shows the theoretical relationship between accidents with differing levels of severity. In theory, for every fatal accident there will be a greater number of specified injuries, even more over seven-day accidents and so on. The theory is that if the number of minor and recordable over three-day accidents can be significantly reduced, then the base and height of the triangle will be reduced. For example, if there are fewer near misses and minor incidents, then there are fewer opportunities for a major or fatal incident.

Accident reporting

Failure to report an accident is a criminal offence and any lack of company evidence of an incident having occurred, or of the circumstances at the time, will make it harder for a company to defend itself if an injured person claims for compensation at a later date, or if a company is facing prosecution.

Inspectors from the HSE have the right to investigate any incident occurring on a construction site. If there are trade union-appointed safety representatives on site, they can assist in the investigation, but they also have the right to carry out their own investigation.

Accident book

Employers are required under the Social Security (Claims and Payments) Regulations to keep an accident book readily available, into which details must be entered of every accident causing personal injury to any employee. Wherever possible, each entry should be made by the injured employee. Where this is not possible, entries may be made by anyone acting on their behalf.

Making an entry in the accident book does not meet or replace the employer's obligation to report specific accidents and dangerous occurrences to the HSE under RIDDOR.

Employers may use an official Accident Book BL510 or may develop an in-house method of recording accidents (paper or electronic), providing it enables the recording and retrieval of all the relevant details.

Under the Data Protection Act, accident details are confidential between the employer and injured person once a record has been completed. It is therefore essential that irrespective of what method of accident recording is used, no-one making a subsequent entry can see previous accident records. This is achieved if using Accident Book BL510, as it has perforated pages, which can be detached and stored in privacy.

All accident books or other forms of accident record must be kept for three years from the date of the last entry. Health surveillance records must be kept for 40 years.

The above arrangements may provide essential information in compensation claims and other actions. They do not, in any way, relieve the employer of the responsibility to provide the HSE or Local Authority with any information the law may require.

All near miss incidents and accidents should be investigated to ensure that any lessons that can be learned are learned, and that any control measures that can be implemented are implemented, to ensure the event does not happen again.

The Reporting of Injuries, Diseases and Dangerous Occurrences Regulations (RIDDOR)

The Reporting of Injuries, Diseases and Dangerous Occurrences Regulations (RIDDOR) place a legal duty on the responsible person to report certain events to the appropriate enforcing authority, either the HSE or the Local Authority (environmental health officer).

Accident prevention and reporting

☑ The responsible person will be the employer (or their representative) in the case of an injury or other event affecting an employee, or the person in control of the site where the affected person is self-employed or a member of the public.

☑ The enforcing authority will usually be the HSE.

The responsible person must report any of the following events that happen in connection with work.

☑ Fatalities.

☑ Specified injuries.

☑ Any injury that results in an employee not being able to either come to work or carry out their normal work for more than seven days.

☑ An injury to a member of the public that results in the injured person being taken to hospital directly from the scene of the accident.

☑ Specified occupational diseases.

☑ Certain dangerous occurrences.

Trainees are not specifically mentioned within these regulations, but other regulations require that non-employed trainees be regarded as employees for all health and safety purposes.

Specified injuries

Injuries and serious conditions that are classified as specified injuries for the purposes of RIDDOR include the following (as defined by the HSE).

☑ A fracture, other than to fingers, thumbs and toes.

☑ Any amputation.

☑ An injury likely to lead to permanent loss of sight or reduction of sight in one or both eyes.

☑ Crush injury to the head or torso causing damage to the brain or internal organs.

☑ Any burn injury, including scalding covering more than 10% of the body, or damaging the eyes, respiratory system or other vital organs.

☑ Scalpings (separation of skin from the head) which require hospital treatment.

☑ Unconsciousness caused by head injury or asphyxia.

☑ Any other injury arising from working in an enclosed space that leads to hypothermia, heat-induced illness or requires resuscitation or admittance to hospital for more than 24 hours.

If an employer becomes aware of the death of an employee that:

☑ resulted from a previous reportable accident, and

☑ occurred within one year of the original accident

the employer must report the death to the enforcing authority within ten days of becoming aware of it, on an approved form (Form F2508) even though the original injury had been previously reported.

Reportable dangerous occurrences

Dangerous occurrences are certain, specified events, but not all such events require reporting.

Examples of dangerous occurrences that are likely to occur in the building and construction industry and that are reportable under RIDDOR are shown below.

- ☑ Collapse, overturning or failure of any load-bearing part of any lifting equipment, such as a winch, lift, hoist, crane, derrick, mobile-powered access platform, access cradle, window cleaning cradle, excavator, piling rig, forklift truck or lorry loader (for example, Hiab).

- ☑ Failure of any closed vessel.

- ☑ The accidental release of any substance that could cause injury to any person.

- ☑ Plant or equipment coming into contact with overhead power lines.

- ☑ Electrical incident causing fire or explosion.

- ☑ Collapse or partial collapse of any scaffold over 5 m in height or fall of any cradle and so on.

- ☑ Collapse of 5 tonnes or more of any building or structure, or any false work, or any wall or floor in any workplace.

- ☑ Accident or incident which results or could have resulted in release of any biological agents likely to cause severe human infection or illness.

- ☑ Any unintentional explosion.

- ☑ The failure of equipment involved with pipeline works which could cause personal injury to any person, or which results in the pipeline being shut down for more than 24 hours.

- ☑ Malfunction of any breathing apparatus whilst in use or when being tested before use.

There are a total of 27 categories of dangerous occurrences that are relevant to most workplaces. For a full, detailed list refer to the HSE online guidance.

A matrix guide to reporting accidents and incidents can be found in Chapter B09 First aid and emergency procedures.

'Over three-day' accidents

The employer or their representative must keep a record of any accident if the worker is incapacitated (for example, unable to do their normal work) **for more than three consecutive days**, under the requirements of the Social Security (Claims and Payments) Regulations.

It is not reportable to the HSE until the injured person has been off work or incapacitated for seven days after the accident. However, it is advisable that such incidents are appropriately and adequately investigated.

'Over seven-day' accidents

The responsible person (the employer, their representative or the person in charge of the premises or site) must report within 15 days, on the approved form (F2508), any workplace accident resulting in an injury that prevents a person from coming to work, or carrying out their normal type of work, for more than seven consecutive days.

In calculating the over seven-day (and the over three-day) period:

- ☑ the day that the accident occurred is not counted

- ☑ any rest days (for example weekends and bank holidays) that the injured person would have not been able to come to work had they been working days, are counted.

e.g. If an employee is injured on a Thursday and is still off work because of the same injury on the following Friday, the accident becomes reportable.

Reporting deaths, specified injuries and dangerous occurrences

The procedure for reporting deaths, specified injuries, dangerous occurrences and specified work-related illnesses should be set out in detail in company safety policies and associated documentation. Procedures should be clearly explained to employees.

The main requirements of the regulations are summarised on the following pages.

- ☑ Where an accident or dangerous occurrence has to be reported under RIDDOR, that report should be submitted online, via the HSE website.

- ☑ A telephone service remains for reporting fatal and specified injuries only.

- ☑ Form F2508 can be completed online, via the HSE website.

All incidents can be reported online. A telephone service is also available for reporting the following.

- ☑ The death of any person as a result of an accident at work.

- ☑ An accident to any person at work resulting in a specified injury or serious conditions specified in the regulations.

All fatal accidents must be reported to HM Coroner via the local police. Police officers have a statutory duty to investigate fatalities in conjunction with the HSE. The police investigation takes precedence in the event of a fatality. *(Also refer to the earlier Corporate manslaughter section.)*

Exceptions

In general, reports are not required for deaths and injuries that result from:

- ☑ road traffic accidents, unless the accident involved:
  - the loading or unloading of a vehicle
  - work alongside the road (such as construction or maintenance work)
  - the escape of a substance being conveyed by the vehicle
  - train accidents.

Reporting occupational diseases

The occurrence of certain occupational diseases, if resulting from particular work activities or if the work activity is likely to aggravate or make the condition worse, must be reported to the enforcing authorities by the quickest possible means. The form used for reporting occupational disease is F2508A.

The methods available for reporting occupational disease are the same as for reporting accidents and dangerous occurrences.

Listed below are the occupational diseases (with possible sources) that are more common to the construction industry.

- ☑ Hand-arm vibration syndrome (using hand-held vibrating tools).

- ☑ Carpal tunnel syndrome (similar to above).

- ☑ Severe cramp of the hand or forearm (a possible indication of hand-arm vibration syndrome or carpal tunnel syndrome).

- ☑ Tendonitis or tenosynovitis of the hand or forearm.

- ☑ Silicosis (from stone-cutting or working with masonry).

- ☑ Occupational dermatitis (through contact with any one of many types of substance that irritate the skin).

- ☑ Occupational asthma (breathing in the fumes of any one of the many substances that irritate the respiratory tract (airways)).

- ☑ Any occupational cancer (such as asbestosis from refurbishment or demolition).

- ☑ Any disease attributed to an occupational exposure to a biological agent.

- ☑ Illness resulting from exposure to a biological agent, such as legionellosis (from working on air conditioning systems) or leptospirosis (contracted while working in places likely to be infested with rats or other small mammals).

Keeping records

Company records of events that are reported under RIDDOR must be kept. No precise method is prescribed, but a photocopy of the approved form is acceptable, as are computer files and the transcript of reports made by telephone.

An in-house accident form is acceptable as long as it provides for the recording of the same details as on the approved form.

The minimum particulars that must be kept are the:

- ☑ date and time of the accident or dangerous occurrence

- ☑ injured person's full name and occupation

- ☑ nature of injury.

In the event of an accident to a non-employee the following minimum details are required.

- ☑ The injured person's full name and status (for example, passenger, customer, visitor or bystander).

- ☑ The nature of the injury.

- ☑ The place where the accident or dangerous occurrence.

- ☑ A brief description of the circumstances of the accident or dangerous occurrence.

- ☑ The date on which the event was reported to the enforcing authority.

- ☑ The method by which the event was reported.

A
07

Post-accident investigation

Following an accident, you should attend to the need of any injured person first, ensure the area is made safe and then try to establish the events leading up to the accident.

- ☑ Note anything that appears significant, including making sketches, taking photographs and so on.

- ☑ Establish exactly what processes were being carried out.

- ☑ Find out whether a method statement and/or permit to work was in force and, if so, whether they were being complied with.

- ☑ Check whether the safe system of work, as determined by the risk assessment, was being followed.

- ☑ Find out who was operating any equipment that was involved in the accident and whether they were competent and authorised to do so.

- ☑ Find out if the injured person was authorised to be doing what they were doing or to be where they were.

In many cases it will be necessary at some stage to:

- ☑ interview the injured person (if possible)

- ☑ interview the person in charge of the process or project

- ☑ identify and interview witnesses.

It is most important to carry out an investigation into any accident as soon as possible after it has happened, whilst events are still clear in the minds of the injured person(s) and any witnesses.

For further information refer to the accident prevention and control chapter in Section A of GE 700 *Construction site safety*.

08

Health and welfare

B
08

What your employer should do for you

1. Provide health information and protective measures to people working in environments that can cause work-related (occupational) ill health.

2. Ensure controls are in place to protect people from radiation (for example, ultraviolet light, infrared sources from lasers and welding).

3. Monitor and implement, if appropriate, the need for health surveillance for potentially hazardous work activities. Arrange for provision of health surveillance as required.

4. Ensure adequate personal protective equipment (PPE) and washing facilities with good housekeeping controls are in place to minimise the risk of ill health and diseases such as leptospirosis (Weil's disease).

5. Provide drying and/or changing rooms with secure lockers and, where necessary, separate facilities for men and women.

6. Provide washing facilities (including showers if necessary), which are equipped with hot (or warm) and cold water, soap and towels or a means of drying.

7. Provide toilet facilities that are suitably ventilated and lit.

8. Provide a supply of fresh drinking water, complete with suitable cups (unless from a water fountain or similar).

9. Ensure that there is a means of preparing and warming food.

10. Make arrangements to enable food to be eaten in reasonable comfort (an adequate number of tables and chairs with backs).

11. Provide a means of boiling water.

12. Ensure that the welfare facilities are clean, kept in good order and properly maintained.

13. Ensure that there are rest areas (including facilities for a pregnant woman or a nursing mother to rest lying down), as appropriate.

14. Implement a drug and alcohol policy, including prescription drugs awareness and a monitoring process for the workforce.

What you should do as a supervisor

Checklist	Yes	No	N/A
1. Ensure that health information and protective measures are provided and explained to people working in environments that can cause ill health.			
2. Assist in ensuring that controls are in place to protect people from radiation (for example, ultraviolet light, infrared sources from lasers and welding).			
3. Recognise and report on situations where you think that there is a need for health surveillance for potentially hazardous work activities.			
4. Check to ensure adequate PPE and washing facilities with good housekeeping controls are in place to minimise the risk of ill health and diseases such as leptospirosis (Weil's disease) and provide information to people affected.			
5. Check that drinking water is available and cups (where appropriate) are available.			
6. Inspect the area for preparing food to ensure its suitability and report defects to your manager.			
7. Ensure that food can be eaten in reasonable comfort (an adequate number of tables and chairs with backs).			
8. Check that the means of boiling water is safe (for example, that a kettle or boiler is tested and certified as safe).			
9. Arrange for welfare facilities to be clean, kept in good order and properly maintained.			
10. Check washing facilities, which are equipped with hot (or warm) and cold water, soap and towels or a means of drying, are known to the workers and report any defects.			
11. Ensure toilet facilities are in good working order and kept clean.			
12. Check that drying and/or changing rooms are kept clean, tidy and free from rubbish.			
13. Ensure that rest areas are properly maintained and waste is removed regularly.			
14. Report instances where the implementation of a drug and alcohol policy may be necessary, including monitoring people on prescription drugs.			

B
08

Introduction

Occupational ill health is the term used with regard to health issues that arise out of work activities. This chapter covers the most common occupational health topics associated with construction industry activities and gives details of welfare facilities that should be provided. Even employers that attempt to ensure the safety of their employees often overlook the threats to employees' occupational health.

☑ Stress accounts for around 35% of work-related ill health cases.

☑ Around 1.2 million working days are lost every year as a result of ill health.

☑ Ill health in the construction industry costs society around £400 million each year.

A reason for this might be that, in some cases, an occupational ill health problem may not be so obvious as the result of an accident (for example, a broken bone). Therefore, the potential seriousness of the situation may not be immediately apparent.

❗ Some forms of occupational ill health may take many months or years to develop.

Examples of occupational health issues are listed below.

☑ Dermatitis.

☑ Vibration.

☑ Noise.

☑ Construction industry related cancers from exposure to diesel exhaust fumes, asbestos and silica.

☑ Dust (for example asbestos, lead and silicosis).

☑ Manual handling, including repetitive movement.

☑ Stress and mental health.

There are more people off work as a result of occupational health issues at any one time than there are as a result of accidents.

For further information refer to:

☑ **Chapter B13 Dust and fumes (Respiratory hazards)**

☑ **Chapter B14 Noise and vibration**

☑ **Chapter B15 Manual handling.**

Occupational dermatitis

Bricklayers, masons, and painters and decorators represent trades that are most at risk of occupational dermatitis in the construction industry. It is a serious skin condition that is caused by irritants contained in many industrial materials. It cannot be passed on from the sufferer to other people. There are two general types, as outlined on the following page.

B 08

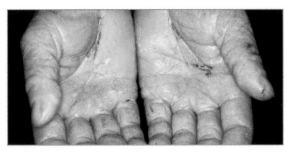

Dermatitis showing crusting and thickening of skin

Irritant contact dermatitis

This is usually caused by the skin coming into contact with an irritant substance, which is usually a chemical or dust. Anyone may be affected. The amount of time exposed, together with the strength of the irritant substance, will affect the seriousness of the complaint. Most cases of dermatitis are of this type.

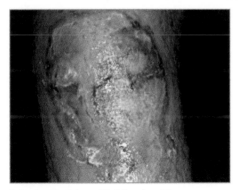

Irritant contact dermatitis 'pizza knee' from a cement burn

Allergic contact dermatitis (sensitising dermatitis)

Some people develop an allergic reaction to a specific substance. This reaction may follow after weeks, months or even years of use or exposure to a substance without any ill effects. However, once sensitive dermatitis has occurred, any future exposure to, or contact with, the substance will again produce an adverse reaction.

The skin's reaction to irritants varies from one individual to another. The reaction may be only a mild redness, or it can develop into swelling, blisters and septic ulcers that are both unsightly and painful.

Personal hygiene is particularly important when working with materials that may be irritants. Resistance to an irritant varies with the type of skin.

It is equally important that clothing is kept clean. Oil-stained and dirty overalls are a well known cause of skin problems around the groin.

B 08

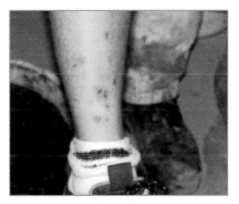

Allergic contact dermatitis of the leg

Controlling the risk

Employers should identify the:

- [✓] substances used by employees that have the potential to cause dermatitis
- [✓] individual employees who are at risk
- [✓] work activities that bring employees into contact with known irritant substances.

Control measures must be introduced to eliminate or minimise the chance of skin contact with the substance and therefore the risk of dermatitis.

Screening for the early signs of dermatitis can be carried out by simply conducting periodic hand and forearm checks of at-risk individuals by an employee who has been trained to recognise the symptoms. Where dermatitis is suspected, the sufferer must be advised to seek medical advice at the earliest opportunity.

For further information on dermatitis visit the HSE website.

Control measures

- [✓] Identify irritant substances.
- [✓] Substitute with a less harmful substance.
- [✓] Limit contact with harmful substances, for example:
  - dust extraction fitted to tools and machines
  - using the appropriate PPE (such as gloves).
- [✓] Frequent cleaning of protective equipment.
- [✓] Immediate washing of hands or other areas of affected skin.
- [✓] Use of reconditioning creams or barrier creams.
- [✓] Prompt reporting of skin irritation.
- [✓] Seeking medical advice.

Occupational dermatitis is a notifiable disease under the Reporting of Injuries, Diseases and Dangerous Occurrences Regulations (RIDDOR). If in any doubt, contact your local Health and Safety Executive (HSE) office or the HSE Employment Medical Advisory Service (EMAS).

For further information refer to Chapter B11 Hazardous substances and Chapter A07 Accident prevention and reporting.

Radiation

An increasing range of equipment that uses a radiation source as a means of measurement or detection is now being widely used in the construction industry.

Radiation sources that can give cause for concern include ultraviolet light and infrared sources, as well as lasers and some welding processes.

Exposure to radiation may lead to:

- [✓] burns (including sunburn)
- [✓] eye damage (cataracts and arc-eye)
- [✓] cancers (skin cancer and leukaemia).

B
08

Exposure may quickly reach danger levels in some cases. In others, the problems may develop over long periods.

Where a radiation source that has the potential to cause harm is being used, measures must be taken to keep those not involved in the operation out of the area.

If you notice or are working near to the warning sign shown here, seek advice from the person in charge on site.

Laser beams in operation

 For further information refer to the personal protective equipment chapter in Section B of GE 700 Construction site safety.

Sun safety

Even a tan that has been built up gradually can be harmful to health. A tan is a sign that the skin has potentially been damaged.

The damage is caused by the ultraviolet rays in sunlight. People whose jobs keep them outdoors for long periods of time (such as construction workers) may, if their skin is unprotected, get more sun on their skin than is healthy for them. They will then be at a greater risk of developing skin cancer.

 The HSE publication Keep your top on: Health risks from working in the sun (INDG147) provides more advice for outdoor workers.

Dangers

In the short term, excess exposure of unprotected skin to the sun causes sunburn, which can blister the skin and make it peel. Even a mild reddening of the skin is a sign of skin damage. In the long-term, too much sun will speed up the ageing of skin, making it leathery, mottled and wrinkled. However, the most serious issue is an increased chance of developing skin cancer.

Cases of skin cancer have more than quadrupled over the last 30 years and at least two young adults (aged 16 to 34) are now diagnosed with skin cancer every day in the UK.

This site provides information, including the daily UV level, and sun block cream for its workers

Risks

Some people are more at risk than others. People with pale skin are most at risk. Workers should take particular care if they have:

☑ fair or freckled skin that does not tan, or goes red or burns before it tans

☑ red or fair hair and light coloured eyes

☑ a large number of moles.

Prevention

- ☑ Wear close-woven fabrics (such as jeans) and long-sleeved shirts, which will help to protect you from UV rays.

- ☑ Try to work and take breaks in the shade.

- ☑ Wear a hanging flap on the back of your hard hat to protect your neck.

- ☑ Periodically check your skin for changes and damage.

 Some medicines and contact with some chemicals used at work (such as bitumen products) can make the skin more sensitive to sunlight.

Leptospirosis (Weil's disease)

Leptospirosis (Weil's disease) can be caught from coming into contact with the urine of rats, voles, mice and other small animals. It can be fatal if not diagnosed and treated quickly.

The disease is usually associated with working in sewers, on sewage plants, on old farm buildings and on sites close to rivers or canal banks, but can be caught anywhere that the small mammals that carry the disease exist (such as any wet site). A simple course of action is to discourage the presence of rats by making sure that food waste is properly disposed of.

 It is advisable that any workers who are particularly at risk of leptospirosis be issued with a risk card or neck-tag.

If a worker becomes ill, the doctor's attention can be drawn via the risk card to the possibility of leptospirosis, since the early symptoms of the disease are similar to, and may be mistaken for, influenza.

 For further information refer to the GT 700 *Toolbox talk*, B06 Weil's disease.

The common routes of entry into the body are:

- ☑ unprotected cuts and grazes on the skin

- ☑ swallowing water infected with the bacteria.

Anyone who has broken skin that could come into contact with anything that is contaminated should not be exposed to the risk. Preferably, someone else will be able to do the job or, as a minimum, cuts and grazes should be totally covered by a secure waterproof dressing.

The provision and use of adequate washing and, if necessary, showering facilities should further lessen the chance of anyone catching the disease.

A less serious, although still unpleasant form of leptospirosis can be caught from the urine of infected cattle. The routes of entry into the body are through the eyes, nose, mouth and broken skin. A safe system of work will help to prevent exposure, with PPE being used as a last resort. Construction work on farms and livestock markets (for example, where workers might get into the close proximity of cattle) presents the potential for those workers to catch this strain of leptospirosis.

Leptospirosis is a notifiable disease under RIDDOR. *(For more information refer to Chapter A07 Accident prevention and reporting.)* If in any doubt, contact your local HSE office.

B
08

Drugs and alcohol

The use of drugs or alcohol gives rise to the risk of poor performance and the possibility that an employee will compromise their own health and safety and that of other people, including members of the public.

Alcohol

The effects of alcohol in the body can remain for long periods. The speed at which alcohol is absorbed into your system (and how quickly your system gets rid of it) depends on factors such as your size, weight, age, when you last ate and any medication you are taking. It is impossible to know how long it will take to sober up after drinking. Eating, drinking coffee, sleeping and showering **do not** help you to sober up any faster. There are people at work that are never free of the effects of alcohol and, because of this, they are a constant source of danger to themselves and anyone working with them.

Too many people are killed and seriously injured on our roads in drink-driving crashes. Around one in six of all deaths on the roads involve drivers who are over the legal alcohol limit.

Alcohol affects sensory perception and reaction times.

From January 2016 the UK Chief medical officer and the National Health Service recommend a maximum weekly intake of 14 units for men or women. This is equivalent to five pints of average strength (5%) beer, lager or cider, six 175 ml glasses of average strength (12%) wine, or 14 single shots (25 ml) of 40% spirits.

More than 1 in 10 deaths of people in their 40s are caused by liver disease. Most are from alcoholic liver disease.

For further information on alcohol visit the Drinkaware website.

Psychoactive substances

Psychoactive substances or so called 'legal highs' (though illegal) are designed to produce similar effects to drugs such as cannabis, cocaine and ecstasy, whilst remaining chemically different enough not to be subject to control under the Misuse of Drugs Act. These substances are controlled by the new Psychoactive Substances Act, which was introduced in 2016. Five out of six deaths involving psychoactive substances are of males. Most deaths from psychoactive substances happen in people aged 20 to 29 and the average age for deaths involving a psychoactive substance is 28.

It is an offence to possess with intent to consume, produce, offer to supply, possess with intent to supply, import or export any substance for human consumption which is capable of producing a psychoactive effect under the Psychoactive Substances Act. Offences are punishable by a fine or seven years' imprisonment.

B
08

Illegal drugs

The maximum penalties for illegal drug possession, supply (dealing) and production depend on what type or class the drug is. Examples of maximum penalties are outlined in the table below.

Class	Examples of drugs	Possession	Supply and production
A	Crack cocaine, cocaine, ecstasy (MDMA), heroin, LSD, magic mushrooms, methadone, methamphetamine (crystal meth)	Up to seven years in prison, an unlimited fine or both	Up to life in prison, an unlimited fine or both
B	Amphetamines, barbiturates, cannabis, codeine, ketamine, methylphenidate (Ritalin), synthetic cannabinoids	Up to five years in prison, an unlimited fine or both	Up to 14 years in prison, an unlimited fine or both
C	Anabolic steroids, benzodiazepines (diazepam), gamma hydroxybutyrate (GHB), gamma-butyrolactone (GBL), piperazines (BZP)	Up to two years in prison, an unlimited fine or both (except anabolic steroids – it's not an offence to possess them for personal use)	Up to 14 years in prison, an unlimited fine or both

Prescription drugs

In addition to the dangers that can be caused on site by the use of psychoactive substances and illegal drugs, some prescribed drugs may have unwanted side effects. On every prescription there is a label giving details of the correct dosage to be taken and at what intervals. This dosage must be strictly adhered to, as taking more than directed may have adverse effects, particularly in the case of painkilling drugs and antihistamines.

Some direction labels may also give a warning, for example:

May cause drowsiness. If affected do not drive.

Do not operate machinery.

Do not take with alcohol.

Avoid alcoholic drinks while taking this medication.

Such warnings should not be ignored – they are there for the guidance and advice of the person for whom the drugs are prescribed and should be followed.

Over-the-counter medicines

Some over-the-counter medicines (such as cold and flu remedies) may have unwanted side effects that may lead to the person taking them being unfit for work on a construction site (for example, some hay fever medicines cause drowsiness and therefore loss of concentration).

Always read the instructions for the correct dosage and any information about the possible side effects.

B
08

Identifying alcohol and drug problems

Employers and managers should be aware of the various characteristics that may indicate a problem exists. These include the following.

- ☑ Absenteeism.
- ☑ Poor time-keeping.
- ☑ High accident levels.
- ☑ Poor work performance.
- ☑ Mood swings.
- ☑ Misconduct.
- ☑ Theft (to feed personal habits).
- ☑ Deterioration in appearance and personal hygiene standards.

Managers and supervisors should be trained in recognising and responding to the early stages of an alcohol or drug problem amongst the workforce.

An employee may come forward voluntarily and seek help. In other instances, the problem may be identified by a co-worker or supervisor. There is a need to ensure that employees who seek help will not be disadvantaged or punished. Confidentiality for employees undergoing any treatment or rehabilitation must be guaranteed.

Addressing alcohol and drugs at work

Consultation between a company and its employees, either directly or through their representatives, is essential if alcohol and drug problems are to be addressed effectively. Any such action must be supported by a drug and alcohol misuse policy, which all workers should have fully explained to them, either as part of their induction into the company or prior to any such policy being introduced.

For further information refer to the drugs and alcohol chapter in Section B of GE 700 *Construction site safety.*

Mental health and stress

One in four British adults will experience at least one diagnosable mental health problem in any one year. The most recent estimates suggest around 450 construction workers take their own lives every year. This is more than one a day, and more than in any other professional sector. 44% of employers are seeing a rise in reported problems, estimated to cost them around £26 billion.

Stress is defined as the adverse reaction people have to excessive pressures or other types of demands placed upon them. Stress is not an illness in itself, but it can lead to a reduced ability to perform at work and have an impact on the person's health and wellbeing. According to research, if not controlled, it can lead to common mental health problems (such as anxiety and depression) and also chronic physical health conditions (such as heart disease, back pain, headaches, gastrointestinal disturbances and alcohol and drug dependency).

Work-related stress and common mental health conditions are closely linked with similar signs and symptoms. For people with existing mental health conditions, work-related stress can trigger or worsen an existing mental health condition and so it can be difficult to separate the two.

It is therefore important to identify signs of a mental health condition as early as possible, so appropriate support and treatment (such as talking therapy, medication or other forms of support) can be accessed promptly. This may have an impact on organisations in a number of different areas, and notably in terms of managing their health, safety and wellbeing policies. Stress should be included in the risk assessment process as it is important to consider health as well as safety.

B
08

Six main causes of work-related stress have been identified and the HSE describes them as follows.

1. **Demands.** Issues that should be considered include work patterns, the workload and the working environment.

2. **Control.** How much control the individual has over the way they do their work and, in particular, the work patterns and the workload.

3. **Support.** Whether workers feel that adequate encouragement and resources are provided by the company, managers and colleagues, and whether there are systems that are easy to access for concerned individuals.

4. **Role.** Workers at all levels must understand their role and how they fit into the organisation, and have the skills, experience and support to deliver. There must not be any conflicting elements to the role.

5. **Change.** People (particularly vulnerable people) can be suspicious of the real motives behind organisational change which, whether large or small, must be well managed and effectively communicated.

6. **Relationships.** Workers at any level must not be subjected to unacceptable behaviours by anyone at work and conflicts must be effectively dealt with promptly and effectively. Bullying is a potentially significant factor for workplace relationships and can take many forms; what appears to be light-hearted banter to one person may be perceived as bullying by another. Personal and work-related bullying behaviours may both be evident within a workplace.

As a front line manager or supervisor you should be well placed to identify the early signs and symptoms of a mental health issue within your team. Examples may include, but not be limited to, the following.

- ☑ Erratic or changed behaviour.
- ☑ Poor work quality.
- ☑ Poor time keeping.
- ☑ Withdrawal from social contact.
- ☑ Increased absenteeism.
- ☑ Unusual shows of emotion.
- ☑ Changed appearance.
- ☑ Increased use of alcohol, drugs or smoking.
- ☑ Over performance – people pushing themselves to excess.

The earlier it is identified that an individual may be experiencing a mental health problem the better it will be for all involved. Early intervention is critical, with managers and supervisors playing a crucial role. Regular appraisal, work planning and informal chats will all assist in maintaining channels of communication, which will provide natural opportunities to discuss any issues an individual may have.

If someone feels that they are struggling to cope, they can be advised to do a number of things to help to address their challenges.

- ☑ Identify and tackle the underlying causes.
- ☑ Talk to someone they trust, with whom they can share issues and challenges.
- ☑ Speak to their line manager about modifying their role, task or the hours they work and any training and development required to support early resolution.
- ☑ Practise relaxation techniques, such as meditation or mindfulness, which research has shown to benefit people suffering from stress and depression.

B
08

☑ Improve their diet; avoid foods high in refined sugars and cut down, where appropriate, on alcohol, smoking and caffeine.

☑ Avoid regularly working long hours if possible.

☑ Take regular breaks at the workplace by moving and stretching.

☑ Take regular exercise.

☑ Take time off work for holidays.

☑ Seek additional support and guidance (such as from human resources or occupational health) if the workplace or other stresses are impacting their health.

☑ If signs and symptoms of stress are impacting their health, seek medical advice from their general practitioner.

☑ **Many other sources of help are available. For further information refer to organisations such as Mind, Time to Change and Bipolar UK.**

☑ **Training is available in how to help a person who may be developing a problem, experiencing a worsening mental health problem or in a mental health crisis. For further information refer to Mental Health First Aid UK.**

Health surveillance

The exposure of employees to some occupational health hazards will require that those employees are provided with appropriate health surveillance. The purpose is to detect the early signs of an occupational health problem so that appropriate measures can be put in place.

The extent of health surveillance will depend upon the nature of the potential health problem and how far it has progressed.

Employers are legally obliged to provide free-of-charge health surveillance as required. Employees are legally required to present themselves for health surveillance, if required.

☑ **At one end of the scale, a suitably trained person carrying out periodic skin checks of anyone exposed to an irritant is an example of simple health surveillance that can be carried out on site.**

☑ **An example at the other end of the scale is audiometry (hearing) checks carried out by a qualified technician using specialist equipment, at a hospital or health screening unit.**

Employers and managers should ensure that employees seek qualified medical advice if on-site health surveillance or discussion with the employee indicates that there could be an occupational health problem that needs medical attention.

Generally the need for health surveillance may result from exposure of employees to any of the following.

☑ Substances that have the potential to cause skin conditions, such as dermatitis.

☑ Levels of noise that have the potential to cause noise-induced hearing loss.

☑ Levels of hand-arm vibration that have the potential to result in occupational illnesses (such as vibration white finger).

☑ Levels of whole-body vibration resulting in back problems.

B
08

Medical surveillance.

There are some hazardous substances (such as asbestos, airborne crystalline silica dust and lead) and other agents where the law may require that the health surveillance programme includes statutory medical surveillance. This involves a medical examination. It can also involve tests by a doctor (who must have been appointed by the HSE), who has the appropriate training and experience.

B 08

Welfare facilities

The Construction (Design and Management) Regulations place a legal duty on:

- ☑ the principal contractor to provide suitable and sufficient welfare facilities for those who work on the site, so far as is reasonably practicable

- ☑ contractors to provide welfare facilities for their own employees or anyone working under their control on that site, so far as is reasonably practicable.

For projects with only one contractor, the contractor must provide suitable welfare facilities. For projects involving more than one contractor, co-ordination with the principal contractor is required.

General welfare requirements

The CDM Regulations require the following.

- ☑ Suitable and sufficient sanitary conveniences (toilets) must be provided or made available at readily accessible places.

- ☑ Suitable and sufficient washing facilities, including showers if required, must be provided or made available at readily accessible places.

- ☑ An adequate supply of drinking water, clearly marked with the appropriate sign, should be provided or made available at readily accessible places.

- ☑ Suitable facilities must be provided for the accommodation of clothing not worn at work and for clothing worn at work but not taken home (such facilities shall include provisions for drying clothing when it gets wet).

- ☑ Facilities must be provided to enable people to change clothing where a person has to wear special clothing for work and cannot change elsewhere (the facilities shall be separate for men and women, where necessary, for reasons of health and privacy).

- ☑ Suitable and sufficient facilities for rest (such as a site canteen) must be made available at readily accessible places, including:
  - sufficient tables and chairs (with backs)
  - where necessary, facilities for pregnant women and nursing mothers
  - a means for boiling water and suitable arrangements to ensure that meals can be prepared, heated and eaten.

Welfare facilities in general should be kept clean, adequately lit, ventilated as necessary and kept in a good state of repair.

Washing facilities must include the following.

- ☑ A supply of hot (or warm) and cold water, ideally from a running supply.

- ☑ Soap or other cleansers.

- ☑ Towels or another means of drying.

☑ Separate facilities for men and women, except where the facilities:

- are in a separate room that can be locked from the inside
- can only be used by one person at a time
- are only used for washing the hands, forearms and face.

No matter how basic or extensive the welfare facilities, they must be properly maintained, cleaned and well ventilated

Working at temporary worksites

So far as is reasonably practicable flushing toilets and running water must be provided for employees who are working at temporary places of work.

Portable toilet facilities are available from hire companies, ranging from those that require plumbing in, to self-contained units that come with their own generator and water supply. If this is not possible, consider alternatives (such as chemical toilets and water containers), as water must be provided. Retrofitting of hand washing facilities to vehicles or the use of mobile welfare facilities is also possible.

Use of public toilets and washing facilities should be a last resort and not used just because they are the cheaper option. This would not be acceptable where the provision of better facilities would be seen to be reasonably practicable.

Food safety

The Food Safety Act and the Food Safety (General Food Hygiene) Regulations apply to all workplaces, including building or construction sites, where food or drink is supplied, provided or sold for the benefit of employees and others working on site. They do not apply to sites where employees or other people only consume their own food and drink.

These regulations set out basic hygiene principles. They focus on how to identify and control food safety risks at each stage of the process of preparing and selling food.

The person in control of supplying food for the consumption of others must:

☑ identify food safety hazards

☑ know which steps in the activities are critical for food safety

☑ make sure food is supplied, prepared, stored and sold in a hygienic way

☑ ensure safety controls are in place, maintained and reviewed.

The location, design and construction of the premises must aim to avoid the contamination of food and/or the harbouring of pests and vermin. It must be kept clean and in good repair.

Surfaces in contact with food must be easy to clean and, where necessary, disinfected. This will require the use of smooth, washable, non-toxic materials.

B 08

Adequate provision must be made for cleaning foodstuffs, and the cleaning and (where necessary) disinfection of utensils and equipment. All possible steps must be taken to avoid the risk of contamination of food or ingredients.

Food handlers must maintain a high degree of personal cleanliness, work in a way that is clean and hygienic and wear clean and, where appropriate, protective over-clothes. Adequate changing facilities must be provided where necessary.

B
08

Food handlers must protect food and ingredients against any contamination that is likely to render them unfit for human consumption or create a health hazard.

Anyone whose work involves handling food should:

- ☑ observe good personal hygiene

- ☑ routinely wash their hands before handling foods

- ☑ never smoke in food handling areas

- ☑ report certain conditions and illnesses (for example, infected wounds, skin infections, diarrhoea or vomiting) to their manager or supervisor immediately, and stay off work if necessary.

Food handlers must receive adequate supervision, instruction and training in food hygiene. Each food business must decide what training or supervision their food handlers need by identifying the areas of work most likely to affect food hygiene.

09

First aid and emergency procedures

B
09

What your employer should do for you
1. Assess the need for the provision of sufficient qualified first aiders, emergency first aiders and appointed persons as required.
2. Provide and maintain sufficient and suitable first-aid facilities.
3. Assess and provide, where necessary, more extensive first-aid training and facilities where required.
4. Provide travelling first-aid kits for site vehicles and anyone who works in a remote location.
5. Arrange for initial or refresher first-aid training, as necessary, to maintain adequate cover within the company.
6. Put in place suitable arrangements to quickly locate and contact first aiders and emergency first aiders.
7. Provide adequate first-aid signs, clearly displayed.
8. Maintain and make available accident books that comply with the Data Protection Act, to ensure confidentiality once completed.

What you should do as a supervisor

Checklist	Yes	No	N/A
1. Identify and report if you consider that more extensive first-aid training and facilities are required.			
2. Ensure first-aid facilities and equipment are available, maintained and replenished when necessary.			
3. Ensure your workers know where to obtain first aid treatment.			
4. Ensure that travelling first-aid kits for site vehicles or remote locations are in place and checked and replenished when necessary.			
5. Inform your workers of the availability and location of first aiders or emergency first aiders and how to contact them.			
6. Check that you have provided and clearly identified an appointed person in the event of temporary absence of the first aider.			
7. Ensure workers' certification is current and report any training requirements.			
8. Maintain the display of adequate first-aid signs as appropriate.			
9. Understand how to complete the accident book, its confidentiality once completed, and the reporting and investigation procedure.			

B
09

B
09

Introduction

Construction projects must supply first-aid facilities and equipment in accordance with the Health and Safety (First Aid) Regulations.

The principles of first aid are as follows.

☑ Where a person requires assistance from a doctor or nurse, to preserve life and render other assistance until such help arrives.

☑ To treat minor injuries for which a doctor or nurse is not required.

The aims of first aid are to:

☑ preserve life

☑ prevent worsening

☑ promote recovery.

First aid needs assessment

The Health and Safety (First Aid) Regulations, together with the HSE guidance (L74), require employers and the self-employed to assess the need for both first-aid equipment and qualified staff, based upon an assessment of first aid needs.

The assessor should consider the following.

☑ The nature of the work carried out.

☑ The number of employees and how they may be dispersed.

☑ The remoteness of the site from any emergency services.

☑ The needs of travelling or lone workers.

☑ Whether any arrangements have been made for the sharing of first-aid facilities with other employers.

☑ The need for holiday and shift cover.

☑ The history of accidents in the organisation.

First-aid staff

HSE guidance (L74) will help employers and others understand the regulations and how to comply with them. It offers practical advice on what you need to do. The guidance includes details of an optional four-layer framework for first-aid provision. The layers are:

☑ appointed person (AP)

☑ emergency first aid at work (EFAW)

☑ first aid at work (FAW)

☑ additional training.

www. **For further information on L74 visit the HSE website.**

First aiders should be clearly identified

Based upon the findings of the assessment of first aid needs, the employer must:

☑ appoint a sufficient number of suitable and trained first aiders or emergency first aiders to render first aid to employees and others, and/or

☑ appoint persons who, in the absence of a trained first aider, will be capable of taking charge in an emergency, calling an ambulance and looking after first-aid equipment. They are not allowed to give first aid. Emergency first aiders undergo shorter training than first aiders and are more restricted in what they can do.

The HSE has published a guide for the number of first-aid personnel that should be available at all times *(refer to page 126).*

The figures are a guide only and do not allow for any special circumstances (such as high risk activities, shift cover or groups working in remote locations). Even those who are not trained in first aid but know how to carry out resuscitation may help to save a life.

The training of employees to become first aiders or emergency first aiders should only be carried out by organisations that have the necessary skills, qualifications and competence.

Certificates are valid for three years, after which time a re-certification course is required. Anyone whose certificate has expired must undertake a full course of training to be re-established as a first aider.

The HSE strongly recommends that first aiders and emergency first aiders undergo annual refresher training during their three-year certification period. Although not mandatory, this will help qualified people maintain their basic skills and keep up to date with changes to first-aid procedures.

First aiders have the potential to save lives.

First-aid equipment

Based upon the findings of the assessment of first aid needs, the employer must:

☑ provide and keep stocked suitable first-aid boxes and other appropriate equipment (such as eyewash stations and burns kits), as determined by the assessment, in places that can easily be accessed by all employees

☑ display notices giving the identity of first aiders and the location of first-aid equipment.

The minimum that would be expected on any site is a small, basic first-aid kit. On larger sites several kits may be necessary at dispersed locations and, depending on the results of the assessment, small, travelling first-aid kits may be required for those operatives who work alone or in remote locations. A travelling first-aid kit should be located and clearly identified in each company vehicle.

In situations where specific hazards exist, it will be necessary to consider providing more specialised training and first-aid equipment, such as resuscitation equipment, burns kits, trauma kits (for example following chainsaw injuries) and emergency showers.

B
09

Accidents and emergencies

Immediate action

If you are first on the scene where someone has suffered a serious accident you should ensure the following.

☑ Assess the situation to ensure there is no danger to yourself or others.

☑ If it is necessary and safe to do so, remove or isolate the source of danger, using other people to isolate the danger area, as far as is necessary.

☑ Only move the casualty if it is absolutely necessary.

☑ Stay with the casualty and send for qualified medical help; initially this may be a first aider.

☑ Confirm that someone has called the emergency services.

☑ Comfort the casualty, keep talking to them and keep them warm until help arrives.

☑ As far as possible, arrange for the area to be kept clear of other people (bystanders) unless they are helping.

The company health and safety policy (arrangements) must explain in detail the procedure to be followed by an employee who is the first on the scene at an accident.

 Only move a casualty to save a life or to prevent further injury.

After the casualty has been removed from the scene

Preserve any evidence as to why the accident occurred.

☑ Arrange for barriers to be erected and warning signs to be displayed if some hazards still exist.

☑ Report the accident to the HSE and police if appropriate.

☑ Investigate what happened and why.

☑ Learn from the event and amend procedures if necessary.

What your employer should do

☑ Communicate your company's first-aid arrangements to those who need to know.

☑ Be sure that they have taken in the information.

☑ Ensure that first-aid arrangements are updated as necessary, and are appropriate.

☑ Ensure that everyone knows what to do in an emergency.

What you, as supervisor, should do

☑ Communicate your company's first-aid arrangements to those who need to know.

☑ Be sure that they have taken in the information and know what to do.

☑ Check that the first-aid arrangements are in place and report any shortfalls.

 For further information refer to the first aid chapter in Section B of GE 700 *Construction site safety*.

Accident and incident reporting matrix

Type of incident	Enter in firm's records and investigate	Put in accident book	Send Form 2508 to enforcing authority*	Phone enforcing authority and send Form 2508*	Send Form 2508A to the enforcing authority*
Any incident or near miss	✓				
Every injury**	✓	✓			
Over three-days' time lost	✓	✓			
Over seven-days' time lost ***	✓	✓	✓		
Specified injury or fatality	✓	✓	✓	✓	
Dangerous occurrence	✓		✓		
Reportable occupational disease*	✓				✓

*   *Refer to the accident reporting section of this chapter for the different methods of submitting accident reports to the enforcing authority.*

** *Note employers and others with responsibilities under RIDDOR must still keep a record of all over three-day injuries. An accident book record will be enough.*

*** *Note the deadline by which the over seven-day injury must be reported is 15 days from the day of the accident.*

B
09

Suggested numbers of first-aid personnel to be available at all times people are at work

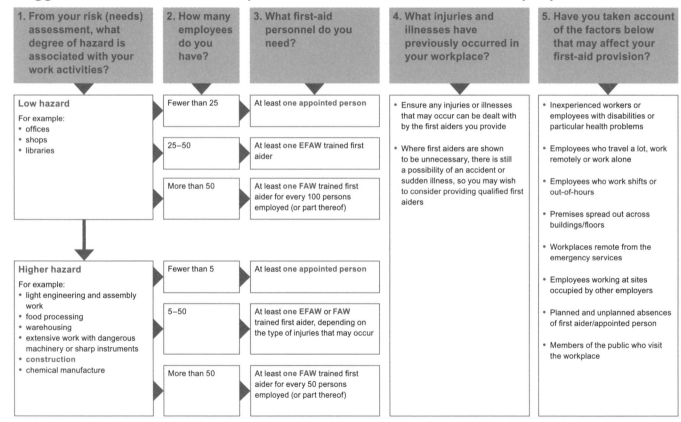

1. From your risk (needs) assessment, what degree of hazard is associated with your work activities?	2. How many employees do you have?	3. What first-aid personnel do you need?	4. What injuries and illnesses have previously occurred in your workplace?	5. Have you taken account of the factors below that may affect your first-aid provision?
Low hazard For example: • offices • shops • libraries	Fewer than 25	At least **one appointed person**	• Ensure any injuries or illnesses that may occur can be dealt with by the first aiders you provide • Where first aiders are shown to be unnecessary, there is still a possibility of an accident or sudden illness, so you may wish to consider providing qualified first aiders	• Inexperienced workers or employees with disabilities or particular health problems • Employees who travel a lot, work remotely or work alone • Employees who work shifts or out-of-hours • Premises spread out across buildings/floors • Workplaces remote from the emergency services • Employees working at sites occupied by other employers • Planned and unplanned absences of first aider/appointed person • Members of the public who visit the workplace
	25–50	At least **one EFAW** trained first aider		
	More than 50	At least **one FAW** trained first aider for every 100 persons employed (or part thereof)		
Higher hazard For example: • light engineering and assembly work • food processing • warehousing • extensive work with dangerous machinery or sharp instruments • **construction** • chemical manufacture	Fewer than 5	At least **one appointed person**		
	5–50	At least **one EFAW or FAW** trained first aider, depending on the type of injuries that may occur		
	More than 50	At least **one FAW** trained first aider for every 50 persons employed (or part thereof)		

Source: HSE First aid at work guidance on regulations Appendix 3 (L74)

10

Personal protective equipment

What your employer should do for you
1. Put avoidance and engineering controls in place to avoid the need for personal protective equipment (PPE) where possible.
2. Ensure a competent person assesses the need for PPE, engaging the assistance and advice of reputable suppliers if necessary.
3. Ensure everyone on site has been issued with the PPE that they need to carry out the jobs assigned to them.
4. Provide training and instruction in the proper use and care of PPE.
5. Ensure everyone on site knows how and where to obtain any extra PPE that they might need.
6. Provide facilities for everyone on site to obtain replacement PPE for that which is lost or defective.
7. Ensure that all PPE is obtained from a reputable supplier to avoid the accidental use of non-effective counterfeit items.

B
10

What you should do as a supervisor

Checklist	Yes	No	N/A
1. Check that avoidance and engineering controls are in place to reduce the need for personal protective equipment (PPE) where possible.			
2. Monitor the need for PPE, engaging the assistance and advice of reputable suppliers where necessary.			
3. Ensure everyone on site has been issued with the PPE that they require and it fits them correctly.			
4. Provide training and instruction in the proper use and care of PPE.			
5. Ensure everyone on site knows where and how PPE should be stored and how to obtain any extra PPE that they might need.			
6. Maintain a PPE issue log.			

B
10

Introduction

Personal protective equipment (PPE) is any item of equipment or clothing that is used or worn by a person to protect them from an identified risk to their health or safety. Two sub-groups of PPE are fall protective equipment (FPE) and respiratory protective equipment (RPE).

For simplicity, throughout this chapter, each reference to PPE will also include FPE and RPE unless indicated otherwise in the text.

Within the construction industry PPE is commonly thought of as equipment that is used to protect the head, ears, eyes, respiratory (breathing) system, skin, hands and feet.

However, it must be appreciated that PPE is also commonly used during construction activities to:

☑ prevent or arrest falls (for example, harnesses and lanyards)

☑ enable a person in distress to be rescued from a confined space (for example, a rescue harness)

☑ enable someone who has fallen into water to stay afloat and be rescued (for example, a lifejacket).

All PPE for use at work should be selected by a competent person who can ensure, in discussion with the supplier, that it meets the appropriate standards.

Duties of employers

Health and Safety at Work etc. Act 1974

The Health and Safety at Work etc. Act requires that employers, when providing anything in the interests of health or safety (for example, PPE), provide it free of charge.

Every self-employed person shall ensure that they supply themselves with suitable PPE, unless contract requirements stipulate otherwise.

Management of Health and Safety at Work Regulations

These regulations require that employers carry out suitable and sufficient risk assessments of the work they do, and then put in place measures to control those risks. A safe system of work should be developed in which the issue and use of PPE is permitted as a last resort control measure. This will necessitate a competent person identifying suitable and sufficient PPE, and management ensuring it is sourced, issued and used properly.

For further information refer to Chapter A04 Risk assessments, method statements and permits to work.

Control of Substances Hazardous to Health Regulations

The Control of Substances Hazardous to Health (COSHH) Regulations require that employers identify the hazardous properties of substances that are used at work or created by a work process. Control measures must be put in place to protect the health of anyone who would otherwise be affected by the hazardous properties of those substances. Using PPE as a control measure must only be considered after the implementation of other, more effective, control measures has been explored and found not to be practicable.

There are many substances that are used in the construction industry that have been identified as being potentially harmful if they are inhaled or come into contact with exposed skin. The fact that many construction workers suffer from occupational asthma and/or dermatitis, with numbers increasing annually, shows that the risks are not being properly controlled. In part this is the failure to adequately assess risks and provide alternative safe systems of work and also the failure to provide and/or wear PPE where it is necessary.

The importance of the correct PPE being provided and used, when risks cannot be controlled by other means, cannot be over emphasised

The following regulations require that appropriate PPE is supplied and worn where an assessment shows that there is a risk of exposure to the respective hazards.

☑ *Control of Asbestos Regulations (refer to Chapter B12).*

☑ *Control of Lead at Work Regulations (refer to Chapter B11).*

Personal Protective Equipment at Work Regulations

These regulations require the following of employers.

☑ Provide suitable and sufficient PPE for their employees and make sure that it is used properly.

☑ Make sure that items of PPE are compatible if more than one item of PPE is worn at the same time (for example, if wearing ear defenders it is possible that the headband would interfere with the correct fit of a safety helmet, or the use of safety glasses may interfere with the fit of ear defenders).

☑ Make an assessment of the most suitable PPE to protect against the identified risks.

☑ Make sure that PPE is properly maintained where this is necessary.

☑ Replace PPE that is damaged or lost.

☑ Provide employees with adequate information, instruction and training on:
   – the risks that the PPE will avoid or limit
   – why the PPE has to be worn and how it should be used
   – how to maintain the PPE in efficient working order and good repair.

☑ Provide suitable accommodation where necessary for PPE that is not in use.

B 10

Duties of employees

In the context of PPE, the Health and Safety at Work etc. Act 1974 requires that employees:

- ☑ look after their own health and safety and that of others, so far as matters are within their capabilities or control

- ☑ follow their employer's safe systems of work, including using anything provided for their health or safety as instructed.

 Employees must follow their employer's safe systems of work

The Personal Protective Equipment at Work Regulations place duties on employees to:

- ☑ use any PPE provided in accordance with the instruction and training provided

- ☑ report to the employer the loss of or defect in any PPE provided.

Risk management

After carrying out a risk assessment and establishing the hazards associated with a particular task, the employer must then implement measures to control the risks to health and safety. This may involve the identification and issue of appropriate PPE.

 PPE must only be selected as a means of controlling risk as a last resort.

All other methods of controlling the risks arising from the work activity must have been considered and found not to be reasonably practicable before the decision is taken to issue and rely upon PPE for protection.

It must be remembered that for PPE to be fully effective, the user must have received information, instruction and training in its use and how to care for and store it. The PPE must:

- ☑ have been designed to protect the user against the type of hazard that will be present

- ☑ be available at all times that it is needed

- ☑ fit the wearer properly and be compatible with other PPE worn at the same time

- ☑ be adjusted properly where necessary

- ☑ be worn/used during the period(s) of risk

- ☑ be treated with care and returned to its storage after use, where this is necessary

- ☑ be inspected and maintained as necessary

- ☑ be replaced if it becomes defective.

Failure of an item of PPE, or using the incorrect type of PPE, could expose an employee to the possibility of serious injury, ill health or even death.

Fall arrest systems are a type of PPE

Types of PPE

There is a vast range of PPE available to not only provide protection from numerous hazards but to ensure personal comfort as well. The range includes, for example:

☑ overalls and coveralls

☑ trousers and knee pads

☑ lifejackets

☑ high and low temperature clothing, and wet weather protection

☑ hard hat liners.

Eye protection
Eye protection is required by law when there is any possibility of eye injury due to, for example, grinding, welding, cutting, hammering or working with hazardous fluids. The risks include:

☑ impact by solids or flying particles

☑ ingress of liquid, dust or gas, splashes and mist

☑ splashes of hot metal

☑ exposure to harmful forms of light, including sunlight.

Depending upon the nature of the hazard some of the features of eye protection will be:

☑ chemical-resistant lenses or screen

☑ impact or heat-resistant lenses or screen

☑ lenses or screen that filter out harmful light (such as welding flash or laser light)

☑ an effective gas or liquid-proof seal around the face

☑ ventilated facepiece to stop the lenses misting.

Common types of eye protection worn during construction activities are safety spectacles (including light eye protection), safety goggles and face shields.

There should always be a type of eye protection available that will meet your particular needs. If there is any doubt about the best type, BS EN 166 or the supplier should be consulted.

 It should be noted that light eye protection (safety spectacles) may not be impact-rated and should therefore not be used for tasks that require impact protection (for example, operating grinders, cut-off saws and nail guns). They will also not protect against chemical risks or provide an effective gas or liquid seal.

B 10

Head protection

The requirement to wear suitable head protection on all building and construction sites is now covered by the PPE Regulations.

 Ensure that head protection is always worn by everyone on site, except when in designated safe areas (such as the site office or canteen).

Many makes of safety helmet are constructed to British Standards, and it is the duty of the employer to provide safety helmets that are suitable for the task and the wearer.

Employees must follow their employer's instructions and wear their safety helmets at all times when instructed to do so. They must report any damage or loss to their employer.

Safety helmets are designed to offer a pre-determined level of impact resistance when they are worn correctly.

 ☒ **The practice of wearing safety helmets back-to-front must not be tolerated.**

☒ **The wearing of hoods and/or beanie hats or other clothing under a hard hat must not be tolerated.**

 Proper hard hat liners designed to fit into the hat should be worn when required as these offer maximum protection in the event of an incident, where hoods and soft hats or caps do not.

It has been established that the solvents in some paint, adhesives and indelible markers can reduce the strength of the plastic from which helmets are manufactured. Employees must be prohibited from marking or otherwise decorating their safety helmets other than applying official stickers (such as 'First aider') or confirmation of site induction.

A safety helmet that has fallen from height onto a hard surface may have suffered damage that will affect its strength even though no cracks are visible. In such circumstances, a replacement helmet should be obtained.

Where the work involves leaning over exposed edges or similar, chinstraps must be fitted and worn, or other methods (such as screw ratchet headbands) must be used. Some safety helmets may have in-built features that enable compatible ear defenders or a face shield to be securely attached.

Under Section 11 of the Employment Act, construction workers who are practising members of the Sikh faith are exempt from wearing a safety helmet whilst wearing a turban. No other workers are covered by this exemption. Sikhs who are not wearing turbans are not exempt from the regulations and are required to wear the same head protection as other operatives.

In all cases the need for head protection must be because the risk of head injury cannot be controlled in other ways.

Hearing protection

 Refer to Chapter B14 Noise and vibration.

Hand protection

There are many types of glove available to protect the wearer against the different types of hazard that can be present in the workplace (such as cuts, abrasions, chemicals, heat, cold and other hazards).

Employers must provide the correct type of glove for the job as the wrong type will often offer no or little protection or could even make the matter worse.

Important points

☑ Assess the:
- task
- application (job task risks of wearing or not wearing gloves)
- wearer's needs
- suitability of gloves for the job, matching type and size.

☑ Once a decision has been made:
- record the assessment
- brief the workers.

Employers and supervisors need to understand that if gloves are not right for the job and create difficulty in use they are not likely to be worn. There may be situations in which gloves that provide the required level of hand protection do not allow the level of 'feel' to do the job and there may be the temptation to work without them or, if worn, they could even pose a hazard (such as entanglement) when using machinery.

Hand protection must be suitable for the job

Gloves will wear with use and it is important that a supply of replacement gloves is readily available or, inevitably, someone will end up working without wearing them. Even a small hole in a glove that is worn to protect the user against a hazardous liquid will make it ineffective.

It may be necessary to contact a PPE supplier or consult a PPE catalogue to investigate the types of glove that are available that will satisfy both the needs of the task and the worker. Modern materials enable the production of gloves that are both robust and permit a high level of feel or dexterity.

Foot protection

Accidents arising from manual handling activities are common causes of injury to the feet. Upward pointing sharp objects (such as nails sticking through pieces of wood) also have the potential to cause foot injuries.

B
10

Foot protection comes in many types and styles, from safety trainers, safety shoes and boots and safety wellington boots, to rigger boots.

☑ **Safety trainers** offer good grip on sloping or slippery surfaces and offer more comfort. They are more suitable to trades such as floor layers who repeatedly kneel and bend their feet.

☑ **Safety wellington boots or waders** are essential in preventing burns when operatives have to stand in wet concrete. The cement content, when mixed with water, becomes highly corrosive and will cause severe burns if it comes into contact with body tissue.

☑ **Rigger boots or safety boots**, as commonly worn by construction workers, provide the required level of protection with steel toecaps and a steel plate moulded into the mid-sole, protecting the wearer against dropped objects and penetration through the sole by sharp objects. Safety boots offer better ankle support than rigger boots.

The ankle support provided by some styles of safety boot is important in the prevention of injuries resulting from walking on uneven surfaces and some industries (for example, the rail industry) insist on this type of safety footwear.

Safety footwear can also be oil and slip resistant. Suppliers should be consulted if there is any doubt about the type of footwear that is available for specialist work activities.

Remember – workers may not want to wear footwear if it is uncomfortable or impractical, no matter how effective it is.

Harnesses

For information on fall protection PPE and the implications of apparently minor damage to fall arrest PPE, refer to Chapter D24 Working at height. For information on working over or near to water, refer to chapter F32

Hi-visibility clothing

Whether working on site or just visiting, site rules on most sites require all personnel to wear a high-visibility (hi-vis) jacket, waistcoat (vest) or overalls at all times.

Rail work requires specific hi-vis clothing

BS EN 20471:2013 specifies requirements for high visibility clothing which is capable of visually signalling the user's presence to operators of vehicles or other mechanised equipment during daylight conditions and under illumination of headlights in the dark. There are several classes of hi-vis clothing used and full specifications can be found in BS EN 20471.

B
10

The classes for roads and street works are shown in the table below.

Class	Description
1	Defines the lowest visibility level. Example: high-visibility trousers with two 5 cm reflective bands around each leg. These become Class 3 when worn with a Class 3 jacket.
2	Defines an intermediate visibility level. Example: vests with two 5 cm reflective bands around the body or one 5 cm band around the body and braces to both shoulders.
3	Defines the highest visibility level. Example: long-sleeved jacket with two 5 cm reflective bands around the body, arms and braces over both shoulders, and trousers with two 5 cm reflective bands around each leg.

Note: the colour of the background material should normally be fluorescent yellow and the reflective material should comply with BS EN 20471.

Supervisors and wearers must ensure the garment is in good condition, is properly fastened at the front and not modified (for example, cutting the bottom band off a hi-vis vest must not be allowed).

Respiratory protective equipment

It is not always reasonably practicable to completely eliminate respiratory hazards from the atmosphere. If no other control measure is reasonably practicable, or if after applying all other reasonably practicable measures there is a residual risk from exposure, suitable RPE must be provided for each worker exposed to the hazard.

There are many types of RPE available. Details of the types and typical uses can be obtained from the manufacturers.

The main types are listed below.

- ☑ Disposable half mask respirators.
- ☑ Reusable half mask respirators.
- ☑ Full face respirator masks.
- ☑ Powered respirators.
- ☑ Ventilated visor and ventilated helmet respirators.
- ☑ Self-contained breathing apparatus.
- ☑ Air-fed breathing apparatus.

 Nuisance dust masks (cup-shaped filters often held in place by a single strap with no BS EN markings) are not classed as PPE or RPE. They do not meet any current standards or legislative requirements and offer little or no protection to the wearer.

Selecting the wrong type of RPE could have serious, even fatal, consequences. RPE selection must be carried out by a competent person. The equipment must reduce exposure to a safe level and must also be suitable for the task, environment and wearer, to ensure the wearer can work freely and without additional risk caused by wearing the RPE.

B
10

137

Half mask respirator

☒ **Respirators must not be used in oxygen-deficient atmospheres.**

☑ **Breathing apparatus must be used where there is the possibility of reduced oxygen levels.**

Half mask respirators and filters are assigned one of three protection factor levels.

☑ FFP1 or P1 (protection factor of 4).

☑ FFP2 or P2 (protection factor of 10).

☑ FFP3 or P3 (protection factor of 20).

P1 or P2 masks are unlikely to provide sufficient protection against hazardous dusts, and should only be used for nuisance dusts.

Apart from correct selection, there are other important considerations in the use of RPE.

☑ **Face fit.** Users of RPE must undergo face-fit testing as part of the selection process, to ensure that they are using the type of facepiece that best fits the shape of their face. Many suppliers provide a face-fit service.

☑ **Facial hair.** The manufacturer's specifications for RPE are based on the user being clean shaven. Where the user has facial hair, the effectiveness will be reduced. Even light stubble can have an effect. This should be considered during selection and supervision. There are types of RPE available that can be worn with facial hair.

☑ **Training.** Workers need to be trained how to wear and look after their RPE. They should also be given information on the nature of risks from respiratory hazards for the site they are working on. This should be included in site induction training, as well as general and specific training.

☑ **Replacement.** Filters may become saturated and no longer provide sufficient protection. They must be replaced at appropriate intervals, depending on the level of use and level of contaminant in the air. There is no universal filter; different coloured filters are available for protecting against different hazards, such as dusts, gases or vapours.

☑ **Supervision.** It is essential for the employer and principal contractor to ensure that the correct RPE is being properly worn all the time it is needed. This requires effective supervision on site.

☑ **Storage.** Where equipment will be used across shifts, it will need to be properly stored, and not just left in a toolbox.

☑ **Hygiene.** Masks can become unhygienic quickly. Provision must be made for non-disposable equipment to be cleaned by the user.

Common RPE failings

☒ There is insufficient consideration given to the selection of RPE and, as a result, workers wear RPE that does not give them adequate protection.

☒ There is an assumption that workers know how to put on and use RPE, and so they do not receive adequate training.

☒ Disposable RPE is not replaced as often as it should be.

☒ There is inadequate supervision and enforcement of correct RPE use.

Selecting the correct PPE

How do I choose the correct PPE (size, fit and type)?

In asking this question, the employer must ensure that certain factors are taken into consideration.

☑ The task.

☑ The fit and individual.

☑ The reasons.

The task

Which risks to health and safety, that can only be controlled by the wearing or use of PPE, arise from this job?

The PPE selected must offer the level of protection required for the hazard(s) that have been identified and those hazards cannot be controlled by other more effective methods than PPE.
For example, will the task involve the following?

☑ Any process that could result in eye injuries?

☑ The use of substances that have the potential to create hazardous dust or fumes?

☑ The use of substances that could irritate or burn the skin?

☑ Creating airborne dust through cutting, grinding and so on?

☑ Creating fumes from hot-work processes?

☑ Working at height in circumstances where the wearing of a harness and lanyard is the only practical fall protection measure?

In addition to assessing PPE for the task employers must also assess any additional PPE requirements for the surrounding site conditions or from other risks (such as noise, dust, fumes, falling objects and so on).

B
10

PPE must be appropriate to site conditions

Manufacturers and suppliers have a statutory duty to provide information regarding the performance characteristics of the PPE products that they manufacture or sell. If necessary, they should be consulted.

 If you cannot prevent, you must protect.

The fit and individual

For some basic PPE (such as a pair of light eye protection spectacles), the exact fit may not be an issue. However, in selecting some PPE, achieving a satisfactory fit is essential.

☑ When a respirator is to be used, the effectiveness of the device is dependent upon the face fit, which in turn will require that the head-harness straps be adjusted to suit the wearer and facial features.

☑ Adjusting the head-harness of a safety helmet to suit the wearer will ensure that it is comfortable and secure.

☑ Gloves should be a close fit to protect from the hazards of chemical ingress, entanglement and to maximise dexterity. (Buying gloves in one size only should be avoided.)

☑ Adjusting the fit of a safety harness, which could have to take the shock loading of an arrested fall, is essential if the harness and the fall-arrest system are to be fully effective.

Where a satisfactory fit cannot be achieved the wearer is likely to suffer discomfort and, as a consequence, stop wearing the PPE or lose concentration. If PPE is required and a satisfactory fit cannot be achieved the wearer should take no part in the operation.

Co-operation between the employer, supervisor and employee is essential in the selection of comfortable and acceptable PPE.

Consideration must be given to the potential wearers' physical needs. If they wear glasses and have to wear a mask, goggles or safety glasses, they may require a special type. If they have a beard and have to wear respiratory equipment, can they obtain an airtight seal? These are crucial considerations.

 Protection is available for the hazard that you are about to work with. Find it and use it.

B 10

The reasons

As a supervisor you must ensure that employees understand 'why', 'what', 'who', 'how' and 'when' there is a need for PPE.

- ☑ **Why** is the PPE needed?
- ☑ **What** will be the implications of not wearing it? What harm can be done by not wearing or using the PPE correctly?
- ☑ **Who** is going to provide the PPE along with all necessary information, instruction, training and supervision?
- ☑ **How** is it fitted, worn or adjusted?
- ☑ **When** must it be worn?

Counterfeit PPE

Choose only products which are CE marked in accordance with the PPE Regulations and purchased from a reputable supplier. There has been a marked increase in cheap, counterfeit PPE, which offers little or no protection even though it looks like the real thing.

 Always buy your PPE from a reputable supplier.

 The CE (Conformité Européenne) mark shows conformity with the PPE Directive. While most items of PPE will comply with an EN (European Standard) it is possible for a CE mark to not have a standard if the manufacturer has a novel product.

Using PPE in practice

Construction industry workers will need to wear or use PPE on many occasions.

In circumstances when wearing or using PPE is necessary it must become second nature to those workers who are at risk. However, at present this is still often not the case.

- ☑ **Cases of occupational asthma and dermatitis show that PPE that protects the skin and respiratory system are obviously not being used where they should, or are not being used properly, indicating the problem is not being taken seriously either by employers, supervisors or employees.**
- ☑ **Deaths have occurred through falls, either because a harness and lanyard were not being worn or because they were worn but the free end of the lanyard was not clipped onto a suitable anchorage point.**

There is the temptation to ignore the need to wear PPE and the protection it gives because 'the job will only take a minute' …

… and that 'minute' may be all the time that the job needs to kill or injure someone.

Differing standards

The requirements for wearing PPE vary greatly in the construction industry. For example, many companies have mandatory requirements for wearing gloves (relevant to the task) and light eye protection (safety spectacles) as a recognition of a collective approach to help minimise injuries to their workforces' hands and eyes, with the ever present risk of dust due to the general environment.

B
10

141

Even if a site does not have a mandatory requirement (such as light eye protection), as a supervisor you should still be assessing the task being carried out and ensuring the appropriate PPE is worn when required.

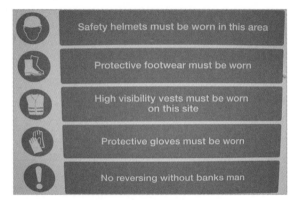

Different sites will have different requirements

Caring for PPE

The users of PPE are responsible for looking after it on a day-to-day basis. For simple items of PPE (such as safety spectacles), this might only involve keeping the lenses clean and free from scratches. For more complex PPE (for example, a safety harness) there will be a need for a:

☑ visual inspection before each use

☑ schedule of periodic, detailed and recorded examinations by someone who has been trained to do so.

The information supplied by the manufacturers of PPE should outline their recommendations on the need for inspections, maintenance and the general care of their products, including, where necessary, where there is a need for specialist knowledge and/or training.

 For further information refer to the personal protective equipment chapter in Section B of GE 700 *Construction site safety*.

Storage for work clothes and/or personal clothes may need to be provided

11

Hazardous substances

What your employer should do for you

1. Identify hazardous substances, produce a COSHH register and carry out suitable COSHH assessments.

2. Provide safety data sheets and a COSHH assessment for each product and make these available to workers likely to be exposed.

3. Take measures to prevent or control exposure to hazardous substances (for example, eliminate exposure, and provide ventilation and training for workers).

4. Monitor the effectiveness of control measures to ensure they are adequate.

5. Establish suitable incident, first aid and emergency control measures that include, where appropriate, provision of emergency spill kits in case of an incident and ensure they are in place.

6. Provide the correct personal protective equipment (PPE) and respiratory protective equipment (RPE) and provide training for operatives and supervisors on its use.

7. Provide training in the correct actions to take in the event of an emergency, especially the use of emergency spill kits, and exercise staff in spill control and reporting procedures.

8. Provide health surveillance where it is necessary.

B 11

What you should do as a supervisor

Checklist	Yes	No	N/A
1. Assist in maintaining an up to date COSHH register of all COSHH materials on site and ensure correct storage.			
2. Understand and review the contents of safety data sheets and COSHH assessments prior to work and explain the control measures to your workers.			
3. Use appropriate measures to prevent or control and monitor exposure to hazardous substances.			
4. Report any shortfall in the effectiveness of control measures to ensure they are adequate. Encourage your workers to report to you anything they feel might be wrong.			
5. Check that the hazard data sheet and COSHH register is readily available to the operatives likely to be exposed.			
6. Understand and communicate the correct incident and emergency control procedures. Make sure they are in place and that spill kits and other necessary equipment are readily available in case of incident or emergency.			
7. Issue the correct PPE and RPE and provide instruction, information or training in the correct use by the workers.			
8. Ensure health surveillance is provided for yourself and your workers where it is necessary.			

B
11

Introduction

Many substances that are used or are created as a by-product of a work activity have the potential to harm the health of the person(s) involved in the activity and others who are likely to be affected.

Employers must carry out a risk assessment to:

☑ identify the hazardous substances used in, or created by, a work process to which employees and others will be exposed

☑ establish the degree of risk to their health resulting from exposure

☑ devise safe systems of work that either eliminate exposure or control it to an acceptable level.

As with controlling any risk, the most effective course of action is to avoid using or creating the hazardous substance in the first instance. This chapter will outline the requirements of the:

☑ Control of Substances Hazardous to Health (COSHH) Regulations

☑ regulatory framework for management of chemicals – the Registration, Evaluation, Authorisation and Restriction of Chemicals Regulations (REACH).

Control of Substances Hazardous to Health Regulations

The Control of Substances Hazardous to Health (COSHH) Regulations are aimed at the protection of employees and others from the effects of working with any substances hazardous to health or that could cause harm to the environment. These substances are not limited to those that are obtained from suppliers, but also include some that are created by the work process.

The regulations do not cover exposure to asbestos, lead or radioactive substances, which have their own regulations. *(Lead is covered separately in this chapter and asbestos in Chapter B12.)*

The objective of the regulations is to prevent, as far as practicable, the exposure of employees and other persons to hazardous substances and, when this cannot be achieved, to control the level of exposure so that it is kept below that which may cause or prove to be harmful to health.

The objective is usually met by carrying out a (COSHH) risk assessment and implementing the necessary control measures identified in the assessment.

Many of the substances commonly used in construction activities have the potential to cause serious health problems if the risks are not evaluated and exposure not properly controlled.

 The Health and Safety Executive (HSE) publishes a guidance note *Workplace exposure limits* (EH40), which lists the range of substances where limits to exposure have been set and their exposure limits.

The workplace exposure limits (WEL) in EH40 are given for a wide range of substances and must be complied with if work is to be carried out safely and without risks to the health and safety of the workers.

Hazardous substances are commonly found on construction sites. They may be found as solids, liquids or in gaseous form, and may be dust or fibre, fumes, vapours, aerosols, sprays or mists. They may include the following.

- [✓] Cement, plaster, silica dust and the dust of some woods.

- [✓] Paint, thinners, bitumen and other sealants.

- [✓] Solvents, adhesives and acids.

- [✓] Vehicle fuels, hydraulic and other oils.

Operatives priming a slab, wearing PPE as identified in their risk assessment

Even natural materials can be harmful. For example, contact with some types of wood can cause dermatitis and asthma, wood dusts can cause asthma and nasal cancer, stone or concrete dust can cause lung disease (such as silicosis) and citrus oils can cause skin irritation.

B
11

Hazardous substances that may be created by a work process or are already on site include:

- [✓] contaminants in soil (brownfield sites)

- [✓] silica and other types of dust from cutting or cleaning operations

- [✓] fumes from hot-work processes (paint stripping)

- [✓] accumulations (piles) of bird droppings

- [✓] naturally occurring gases in confined spaces, such as methane or hydrogen sulphide

Hazardous substances may be:

- [✓] inhaled (breathed in)

- [✓] ingested (swallowed)

- [✓] absorbed through broken or unbroken skin

- [✓] injected (via a puncture of the skin).

Depending upon the nature of the substance, the effects may be instant or may only become apparent after several years. They can result in long-term or permanent illness and, in some cases, death.

Inhalation is the most common route of entry to the body, as some of the substances we breathe in contain particles that are invisible to the naked eye (for example, silica dust and diesel exhaust fumes).

Identifying hazardous substances

The packaging or container of a hazardous substance will carry one or more of the symbols below, in accordance with the Chemical Labelling and Packaging (CLP) Regulations. These symbols let us know that the chemicals being used might cause harm to people or the environment. In 2009 these new pictograms were introduced into UK legislation to comply with the internationally agreed (United Nations) globally harmonised standards (GHS). They are very similar to the old ones which should no longer be used.

Globally harmonised pictograms			
	Toxic (can be fatal) if swallowed or inhaled.		Hazardous to the environment and aquatic life.
	Contains gases under pressure. May explode if heated and can cause burns.		Oxidising gases, liquids and solids. May cause or intensify fire.
	Harmful skin, eye or respiratory irritation. May cause an allergic reaction, drowsiness or breathing difficulties.		Damage to organs and may cause serious longer-term health hazards (such as carcinogenicity and respiratory sensitisation).
	Flammable gases, liquids, solids and aerosols. Heating may cause a fire.		Corrosive and can cause severe skin damage or burns.
	Heating may cause an explosion.		**Further information on labelling and packaging can be found on the HSE website.**

B
11

The suppliers of hazardous substances have a legal duty to supply a safety data sheet for each product, which should be referred to when producing a COSHH assessment for the use of the product.

 Safety data sheets (SDS) are not COSHH assessments. They provide details and information to help employers carry out suitable assessments of how and where the product should be used.

Of course, hazardous substances that are created by a work process (such as dust from cutting slabs or fumes from hot works or welding) will not have a safety data sheet or health warning. However, if a substance is a potential risk to health, it and the risk it poses must be identified by the findings of a risk assessment, or in the case of asbestos and lead, the risk assessment will be undertaken following the relevant survey.

As in all risk assessments, the effort put into compiling it and the degree of control measures necessary need to be proportional to the degree of risk.

COSHH assessment

It is the responsibility of the employer to ensure that anyone who carries out any duties under the COSHH Regulations (including undertaking the assessment) has suitable knowledge, skills and experience to do so, and has received the necessary information, instruction and training, whether or not the assessor is an employee.

The majority of assessments for small building and construction work can be carried out without the need for the assistance of specialist outside consultants, provided the assessor is competent and:

☑ has access to the safety data sheets for the products concerned

☑ understands, in basic terms, what the COSHH Regulations require to be done

☑ is knowledgeable of the work process being assessed

☑ has the ability to systematically gather relevant information regarding exposures to hazardous substances and the subsequent risks to staff by:
  – observing working practices
  – obtaining information on substances used
  – asking questions in the workplace
  – making informed 'what if' judgements regarding possible divergences from standard working practices

☑ can specify the steps and control measures to be taken to comply with the COSHH Regulations

☑ can appreciate their own limitations; knowing when to call in specialists with certain skills (such as when there is a need to undertake air sampling)

☑ has the ability to make valid conclusions, to make a report and communicate findings regarding risks and precautions to the employer and employees.

The main requirements of the regulations are as follows.

Know what products and substances are in use

☑ Compile a list of the hazardous substances that are in use and what they are used for.

☑ Add to the list any hazardous substances that are created as a by-product of a work process.

B 11

Assess the health hazards that can be caused

- ☑ From manufacturer's information and other relevant sources, determine the level of risk to health, the degree of exposure and what action is needed to eliminate or control exposure.

- ☑ Carry out a COSHH risk assessment to establish how the hazardous substances might cause harm. Record the findings of the risk assessment and the control measures to be taken.

- ☑ Review the assessments regularly or whenever the exposure monitoring results indicate that it is necessary.

Eliminate or control the risk of exposure

- ☑ Avoid the use of a substance or material.

- ☑ Use a less hazardous substance.

- ☑ Have hazardous work carried out elsewhere (such as panels delivered ready cut or glued).

- ☑ Avoid hazardous working (for example, the scabbling of concrete).

- ☑ Design a work process that prevents exposure to, or the creation of, hazardous substances (this is not possible in many construction activities).

- ☑ Substitute or dilute the substance (designers and specifiers should look towards using less hazardous options).

- ☑ Use engineering controls, such as totally enclosing the process (often not feasible in the construction environment).

- ☑ Use dust or fume extraction (this may be a standalone extractor unit or built-in on some hand tools).

- ☑ Issue suitable personal protective equipment (PPE) including respiratory protective equipment (RPE) and make sure it is worn. This method of control should only be used after the use of all other risk control measures have been explored.

Before work starts, give information, instruction and training to employees

This should relate to the following.

- ☑ The nature and degree of known risks.

- ☑ The control measures adopted and how they will be put into operation.

- ☑ Reasons for, and the correct use of, PPE.

- ☑ Any exposure monitoring arrangements that are in use (for example to identify 'significant' exposure risks).

- ☑ The purpose of, and arrangements for, any health surveillance, if appropriate.

Issue personal protective equipment

Obtaining appropriate PPE for hazardous substances that can affect the skin might be as simple as identifying the correct type of gloves. However, where there is need for respiratory protection, selecting the correct type of RPE is critical.

A filtering face mask designed to only filter out dust will not protect the user against gases, fumes or vapours.

B
11

The need for employees to work in masks or respirators is always the last resort. If RPE is necessary, it must:

- ☑ adequately control exposure to the hazardous substance(s) identified
- ☑ be appropriate for the job
- ☑ suit the wearer (comfort and fit), achieved through a face-fit test
- ☑ be used correctly.

Before selecting RPE, proper thought must also be given to:

- ☑ the physical condition of the employee; breathing through some types of RPE for extended periods can require effort
- ☑ whether facial hair or glasses would make the equipment ineffective
- ☑ providing suitable training on the safe use and user maintenance of the RPE.

Carry out health surveillance

In many cases, health surveillance must be carried out by an occupational health practitioner and recorded. Employees must have access to medical records that apply to them.

Health surveillance has to be undertaken when an employee is exposed to:

- ☑ one of the substances, and is engaged in a process listed in Schedule 6 of the COSHH Regulations, to which reference should be made, although those listed are unlikely to apply to the construction industry
- ☑ a hazardous substance that is linked to an identifiable disease related to the exposure (for example, where exposure to a material or substance, such as wood dust, is known to cause asthma) and there are valid techniques for detecting indications of the disease (for example, lung function testing).

Monitor the effectiveness of any controls

Are the measures that are in place to control exposure effective?

Observation of the task and speaking to the people doing the job may provide the answer.

Ensuring control measures remain effective may require the regular testing of equipment (such as local exhaust ventilation), which must be kept in efficient working order.

Keep records

Monitoring arrangements and health surveillance must be recorded. Some COSHH records may need to be kept for 40 years, particularly health surveillance records.

In companies where there are union-appointed safety representatives, or representatives of employee safety, the above information should be available to them.

Produce accident, incident and emergency plans

- ☑ Identify and detail hazards.
- ☑ Make details available of specific hazards that are known to exist.
- ☑ Make appropriate first-aid provision.
- ☑ Develop warning and communication systems.

☑ Display emergency plans.

☑ Develop and practice safety drills (for example, site evacuations), as appropriate.

☑ Make relevant information available to the emergency services.

For further information refer to the control of substances hazardous to health chapter in Section B of GE 700 *Construction site safety*.

The HSE's COSHH Essentials web pages provide basic advice on what to do to control exposure to hazardous substances in the workplace. It provides straightforward advice via industry-specific direct advice sheets and generic control guidance sheets.

REACH Regulations

REACH is a European Union Regulation on chemicals and their safe use (EC 1907/2006). It deals with the Registration, Evaluation, Authorisation and restriction of CHemical substances.

REACH Regulations operate in conjunction with COSHH. The main aim of REACH is to provide a high level of protection for human health and the environment from the use of chemicals.

The basic requirements of REACH are to ensure that chemical manufacturers and importers provide better information on the hazards of chemicals and how they can be used safely by the supply chain, including on-site uses.

Control of Lead at Work Regulations

The COSHH Regulations do not apply in any situation where the Control of Lead at Work (CLAW) Regulations apply unless there is an additional substance (such as silica) where the COSHH Regulations apply. Then both CLAW and COSHH apply.

The CLAW Regulations apply to all work involving metallic or lead-containing materials (LCMs) such as removal of old lead paint and work producing lead dust, fumes or vapours. People who work with lead are most at risk of suffering ill health from exposure to it. However, other people who are working close by may also be exposed, depending upon the nature of the work being carried out and how well the risks of exposure are controlled. Families at home can also be indirectly affected (lead dust can be carried home on work clothing).

Lead is a cumulative poison that collects in the bone marrow and affects the body's capability to produce new blood cells. It affects the brain, central nervous and reproductive systems. It is usually taken into the body in the form of dust or fumes (breathed in), by ingestion (via the mouth) or absorbed (through the skin).

The CLAW Regulations, supported by the Construction (Design and Management) Regulations, require lead hazards to be identified. The regulations aim to give greater protection of health to people at work by reducing their exposure to lead and thus the concentrations of lead in their blood. Where lead concentrations prove to be too high, employers are required to remove employees from work with lead. This is called the **suspension level**. If employers cannot transfer employees to other work not involving exposure to lead, they must pay them suspension (level) pay under the Employment Rights Act.

Blood levels that are below the suspension levels are known as **action levels**. If these lower levels are breached, employers have a duty to investigate and remedy the cause.

Employers are also required to take positive steps to reduce the concentrations of lead in air to a level not exceeding the occupational exposure limits in the regulations. Women of child-bearing age and young people have lower blood-lead suspension levels than those applying to other workers.

Requirements of the regulations

The main requirements of the CLAW Regulations are shown below.

☑ Employers whose employees are to work with lead must carry out a suitable and sufficient assessment of the risk to the health of those employees arising from that work.

☑ Every employer shall ensure that the exposure of employees to lead is either prevented or, where this is not reasonably practicable, adequately controlled by means of appropriate control measures. Adequate control of exposure to lead covers all routes of possible exposure, including ingestion, inhalation, absorption and injection.

☑ Adequate steps must be taken to control ingestion. An employer must ensure that, as far as is reasonably practicable, employees do not eat, drink or smoke in any place which is, or is liable to become, contaminated by lead. Employees should be warned against doing so. Employers have additional duties under the CDM Regulations to provide suitable and sufficient rest facilities and facilities to eat meals, where food eaten in the workplace would otherwise be likely to become contaminated.

☑ All control measures which have been provided should perform as originally intended and be effective in protecting people from lead. Any defect in the equipment or failure to use and apply it properly, which could result in a loss of efficiency or effectiveness, thus reducing the level of protection, should be identified and rectified as soon as possible.

☑ Where employees are liable to receive significant exposure to lead, employers must establish monitoring by both air sampling and measuring the concentrations of lead in both blood and urine.

☑ Where exposure to lead is deemed to be significant, the employer should make sure that the employee is under medical surveillance by either a medical inspector (employment medical adviser) or a relevant doctor.

☑ Employers who undertake work liable to expose employees to lead shall provide such information, instruction and training as is suitable and sufficient so that affected employees know the risks to health and the precautions that should be taken.

Note: in addition to this, the Code of Practice that supports the legislation requires that an employer should issue a copy of the HSE's free leaflet entitled Lead and you *to all employees on their first employment on work with lead, and make copies available for issue at the request of any employees or their representative. Employers must additionally provide employees with written records of concentrations of lead in air to which they have been exposed, the results of the measurements of lead in their blood or urine, and an explanation of the significance of these results.*

☑ The employer, in an attempt to protect the health of employees from an accident, incident or emergency, must ensure that procedures, including the provision of first-aid facilities and safety drills, have been prepared and can be put into effect should such an occasion arise. The employer must also ensure that information on such emergency arrangements has been notified to accident and emergency services and that all such information is clearly displayed within the workplace.

For further information refer to the lead chapter in Section B of GE 700 *Construction site safety*.

Risk assessment

Employers must not carry out any work that may expose employees to lead unless a suitable and sufficient risk assessment has been carried out by a competent person. The purpose of the risk assessment is to enable the employer to:

- ☑ assess whether the exposure of employees to lead is likely to be significant
- ☑ identify the measures necessary to prevent or control exposure.

This includes other people who are not employees but who may be exposed as a result of the way the employer carries out the work concerned. The assessment must be reviewed as often as necessary and in other certain specified circumstances, and a record made of any significant findings if five or more people are employed. Such an assessment will allow the employer to make a decision on whether the work concerned is likely to result in an employee being significantly exposed to lead and to identify the measures needed to prevent or adequately control exposure.

Medical surveillance

Where employees are likely to have a 'significant' exposure to lead, as defined in the relevant regulations, the employer has a duty to arrange medical surveillance for the affected employees.

- ☑ Where any employee is liable to be exposed to a concentration of lead in the atmosphere exceeding half the occupational exposure limit for lead.
- ☑ Where there is a substantial risk of any employee ingesting lead.
- ☑ Where there is a risk of contact between the skin and lead alkyls or other substance containing lead which can be absorbed through the skin.

Medical surveillance to detect exposure to lead requires blood sampling and therefore the involvement of trained medical staff.

- ☑ **Find out more about how to protect yourself from lead by downloading the free HSE leaflet *Old lead paint* (Busy Builder series).**
- ☑ **For further information on medical surveillance for lead visit the HSE website.**

12

Asbestos

B 12

What your employer should do for you

1. Make sure that adequate, clear and accurate information about the location of asbestos on site is given to the workforce and others who may be affected.

2. Provide suitable training, relevant to the type of work being carried out. All workers whose tasks may foreseeably disturb the fabric of a building, or other item that may contain asbestos, must receive asbestos awareness training.

3. Develop suitable control measures to prevent exposure to asbestos and provide appropriate personal protective equipment (PPE), where required.

4. Arrange for health surveillance where legislation or policy requires it.

5. Provide supervision to make sure the control measures are being used properly.

6. Make arrangements for the safe disposal of asbestos waste.

What you should do as a supervisor

Checklist	Yes	No	N/A
1. Ensure workers are fully briefed on any asbestos refurbishment or demolition survey for remedial and refurbishment work prior to work starting.			
2. Ensure workers have received asbestos training relevant to the type of work they will be carrying out and ensure they know what to do if they suspect they have found asbestos containing materials on site.			
3. Ensure that all PPE provided is used, maintained and disposed of correctly, as required.			
4. Take account of other risks that might be present in addition to asbestos (such as working at height) and ensure the necessary precautions are in place to carry out the work safely.			
5. Make sure all workers know and comply with the arrangements for safe disposal of any asbestos waste.			

B
12

Introduction

Asbestos is a naturally occurring fibrous material and was widely used in the UK until it was banned in 1999. It was used as an insulator (to keep heat in and keep cold out), has good fire protection properties and protects against corrosion.

Because asbestos was often mixed with another material, it is hard to know if you are working with it or not. However, if work is being carried out in a building built before the year 2000, it is more than likely that some parts of the building will contain asbestos.

Asbestos may be found:

☑ in any structure built before 2000

☑ as a pure substance (for example, as fibrous lagging around pipework)

☑ as a constituent of a mixture of materials (for example, mixed with other substances in floor or ceiling tiles).

It has been suggested that asbestos has been used in over 3,000 products.

 If an unknown substance is encountered that could be or could contain asbestos, work must stop immediately and measures must be taken to keep the area clear of people.

The rule is that any unknown substance should be considered as asbestos until it is confirmed that it is not. The removal or disturbance of asbestos, or even taking samples of suspected asbestos for analysis, are specialist activities, which must be carried out by specialist contractors.

 Asbestos waste must carry a warning label. The label can also be used to identify and manage known in situ asbestos.

Asbestos-related diseases

Exposure to asbestos can cause asbestos-related lung cancer, asbestosis, mesothelioma and pleural thickening.

☑ **Asbestos-related lung cancer** is similar to lung cancer caused by smoking but it is caused by exposure to asbestos fibres.

☑ **Asbestosis** is scarring of the lung that occurs after heavy exposure to asbestos. It can cause progressive shortness of breath and in severe cases it can be fatal.

☑ **Mesothelioma** is a cancer of the thin, protective membrane (pleura) surrounding the lungs, heart and abdominal cavity, which is only caused by exposure to asbestos. It can take up to 50 years after exposure before symptoms develop. Mesothelioma is fatal in all cases, with death often occurring within months of diagnosis.

☑ **Pleural thickening** can occur after heavy exposure to asbestos. The lining of the lung thickens and swells, causing discomfort in the chest and shortness of breath.

Simon's Story:
Living with an asbestos related disease

Simon's Story

Locating asbestos

The identification of any substance thought to be or contain asbestos can only be established by laboratory analysis.

 Asbestos sample analysis is not expensive and results can be obtained relatively quickly.

There are three main types of asbestos.

- ☑ **Blue asbestos (crocidolite).** Has good insulation properties and was often used in lagging. It is highly carcinogenic.

- ☑ **Brown asbestos (amosite).** Good for insulation, particularly in Asbestos Insulation Board (AIB). It is also highly carcinogenic.

- ☑ **White asbestos (chrysotile).** The most common form of asbestos. It is commonly found in asbestos cement products. It is also a known carcinogen.

 Carcinogens are substances that can lead to cancer (cancer-causing agents).

Asbestos warning label

The colour of the asbestos that is discovered will often be misleading. The colour may have changed through ageing or by the application of heat, paint, or as a result of being encapsulated in other materials. Original building plans or specifications may help to confirm the presence of asbestos and give details about its type, but remember that asbestos could have been added to the building at a later date as a result of refurbishments or improvements.

The cancers and respiratory diseases that result from exposure to asbestos are notifiable under the Reporting of Injuries, Diseases and Dangerous Occurrences Regulations (RIDDOR). If in any doubt, talk to your employer.

Control of Asbestos Regulations

Asbestos was widely used as a building material in the UK until it was banned in 1999. Disturbance of the fabric of any building built before this date has the potential to expose those doing the work, and possibly other people, to asbestos.

If you are a contractor working on someone else's (non-domestic) premises, where asbestos is likely to be present, you must be given access to the asbestos register. This should outline the location and condition of the asbestos within the building. There is no legal requirement for privately owned domestic properties to have an asbestos register. However, there should be one for Local Authorities and housing association housing stock.

 Work being done for a Local Authority landlord, a housing association, or a private landlord is not classed as work for a domestic client under CDM 2015, as they are all engaged in a business venture.

 If you are organising or supervising the work and you have not been provided with the asbestos register, or a register does not exist, arrangements must be made for an asbestos survey to be carried out by a competent person or organisation. Do not start work until the survey has been completed and the results made known to you.

Employers have an obligation to assess the risks from asbestos in any workplace. If you are working in a domestic property, your employer should assess the risks from asbestos and ensure that the appropriate controls are in place.

Anyone who is at risk of exposure to asbestos as a result of the activities they perform (for example carpenters, electricians, data cable installers and general tradespeople) is required to have asbestos awareness training.

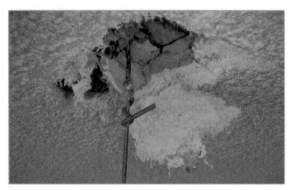

Damaged asbestos spray-applied acoustic ceiling material

 Under guidance outlined in the HSE publication *Asbestos: The survey guide* (HSG264), there are two types of survey.

☑ Asbestos management survey.

☑ Survey for refurbishment or demolition.

Where work is to be completed that will disturb the fabric of the building, a refurbishment or demolition survey must be carried out. This must be an intrusive (invasive) survey, which attempts to locate asbestos in likely hidden locations (such as voids in partition walls, roof spaces and underground ducts). The survey should reflect the extent of the works and cover all work locations.

The person who actually carries out the survey must:

- ☑ have sufficient knowledge, experience, qualifications and ability to carry out a survey and to recognise their limitations

- ☑ have sufficient knowledge of the specific tasks to be carried out and the risks involved

- ☑ be independent, impartial, and have integrity

- ☑ carry out the survey in accordance with HSG264.

 When selecting an asbestos surveyor your employer must take reasonable steps to ensure the surveyor's competency. A surveying company should be accredited to ISO 17020.

Asbestos soffit

Asbestos loft hatch

The employer or client must be specific when arranging a survey, to ensure there will be no limitations (caveats) to the surveyor's report that would leave uncertainty about the presence of asbestos in the area where work will be carried out. The survey must be appropriate for the work being performed. A management survey will **not** suffice for a demolition or refurbishment project.

The Control of Asbestos Regulations (CAR) direct the way in which asbestos must be handled, removed and disposed of.

The following points are a summary of the legislation.

- ☑ CAR prohibits most work with asbestos, except by holders of licences issued by the HSE. Certain non-licensed work must be **notified** to the relevant enforcing authority.

- ☑ Allows some work to be carried out by unlicensed contractors, providing certain time limitations are adhered to and/or if the work only involves certain materials that contain asbestos (such as an asbestos-cement sheet), providing the requirements of the CAR are complied with, and where notification has to be made to the HSE, certain records are kept.

- ☑ Requires that anyone in charge of premises effectively manages any asbestos that is situated in or on those premises.

- ☑ Prohibits the import, supply and use of asbestos.

- ☑ Stipulates the precautions necessary when asbestos is handled (such as the notification to the HSE of any asbestos identified and its intended removal or maintenance).

- ☑ Controls the way in which waste asbestos is managed.

 It is the contractor, not the client, who has the duty based upon risk to determine if works are licensed, notifiable non-licensed or non-licensed.

The requirements of the Control of Asbestos Regulations apply to both licensed and non-licensed asbestos work.

B 12

Asbestos

Under Regulation 4 there is a duty on anyone who has control of non-domestic premises, either through ownership, terms of occupancy or a maintenance or repair contract, to manage any asbestos that is in those premises.

 If a worker disturbs an unknown substance that could be asbestos or could contain asbestos, they must stop work immediately and warn others to keep out of the area and inform their supervisor or manager.

An employer whose employees carry out work with asbestos has the following obligations.

☑ Make a suitable and sufficient assessment as to whether asbestos is, or is liable to be, present in the premises, in particular, in the area where work is being carried out.

☑ Identify the type of asbestos or assume the material contains asbestos.

☑ Assess the nature and degree of exposure, and the steps to be taken to prevent or reduce it.

☑ Prepare a suitable written plan of work.

☑ Notify the enforcing authority in most circumstances.

☑ Provide adequate information, instruction and training for employees and others.

☑ Prevent or reduce asbestos exposure of employees to the lowest level reasonably practicable, by means other than the use of respiratory protective equipment (RPE).

☑ Ensure the proper use of RPE.

☑ Maintain RPE in a clean and efficient state, good order and repair, and make sure that exhaust ventilation and filtration equipment is regularly examined and tested.

☑ Provide adequate and suitable protective clothing and ensure that it is cleaned or disposed of appropriately.

☑ Ensure premises and plant involved in work with asbestos are kept clean.

☑ Prevent the spread of asbestos from the workplace.

☑ Designate, mark and limit entry to areas where exposure to asbestos exceeds, or is liable to exceed, the specified action level or control limit.

☑ Monitor the air where employees are exposed to asbestos and keep suitable records for a specific period.

☑ Ensure that any air monitoring carried out meets the required criteria.

☑ Ensure employees liable to be significantly exposed to asbestos receive regular medical surveillance by a medical employment adviser or appointed doctor.

☑ Provide washing and changing facilities that are adequate and suitable for employees exposed to asbestos. Provide storage for protective clothing and for personal clothing not worn during working hours.

☑ Regulate raw asbestos, asbestos waste storage and disposal, and ensure adequate packaging, sealing and marking in accordance with the regulations.

Training is mandatory for anyone liable to be exposed to asbestos fibres at work. This includes maintenance workers and others who many come into contact with, or disturb, material (such as satellite dish installers), as well as those involved in asbestos removal works.

Medical surveillance

Where an employee's exposure to asbestos is likely to exceed the asbestos-in-air action level, as defined in the Control of Asbestos Regulations, the employer has a duty to arrange medical surveillance for the affected employees.

 For further information on medical surveillance refer to the control of substances hazardous to health chapter in Section B of GE 700 *Construction site safety*.

Since April 2015, all workers, including self-employed persons, carrying out notifiable non-licensed work with asbestos must be under medical surveillance by a doctor. Workers who are already under medical surveillance for licensed work do not require another medical examination for notifiable non-licensed work. Medicals for notifiable non-licensed work are **not acceptable** for those doing licensed work.

The duty to manage asbestos in non-domestic premises (Regulation 4)

This is perhaps the most important regulation for the long-term protection of the health of employees and others. It states that any person who owns, occupies, manages or has responsibility for premises (or a part of it) that may contain asbestos has either:

☑ a legal duty to manage the risk from asbestos or asbestos containing materials, or

☑ a duty to co-operate with whoever has the duty to manage the risk.

 The HSE publication *A short guide to managing asbestos in premises* (INDG223) explains this duty to manage.

If you have any maintenance and/or repair responsibilities for non-domestic premises, either through a contract or a temporary agreement, or because you own or occupy the premises, then you have a duty. This duty will require you to manage the risk from asbestos in the following ways.

☑ Finding out if there is any asbestos or suspected asbestos containing materials (ACMs) in the premises, how much of it there is, where it is, and what condition it is in.

☑ Always presuming that it is asbestos or an ACM, unless you know or have strong evidence proving otherwise.

☑ Making and keeping an up to date record (an asbestos register) of the location and condition of all asbestos, ACMs or presumed ACMs in your premises.

☑ Assessing the risk that the materials pose to employees and others.

☑ Preventing any work on the premises that may disturb asbestos or ACMs until control measures to manage the risk have been put in place.

☑ Preparing a plan that sets out in detail how you are going to manage the risk from the material.

B
12

B
12

☑ Taking all of the steps that you need to take to put your plan into action.

☑ Reviewing and monitoring your plan and the arrangements that you made to put the plan in place.

☑ Providing information on the location and condition of the material to anyone who is liable to work on, or disturb it.

☑ Ensuring that anyone who has information on the whereabouts of asbestos in your premises is required to make this available to you as a duty holder. (Those who are not duty holders but control access to the premises have to co-operate with you in managing the asbestos.)

☑ Ensuring that any area from which asbestos has been removed has been thoroughly cleaned and certified as such before reoccupation.

For further information refer to the asbestos chapter in Section B of GE 700 *Construction site safety*.

☑ **For further information on *Asbestos essentials* and non-licensed work with asbestos visit the HSE website.**

☑ **The HSE has developed a web app aimed at helping to protect you and your workers from asbestos exposure.**

13

Dust and fumes
(Respiratory hazards)

B 13

What your employer should do for you
1. Make sure that respiratory hazards (such as dust, fumes and vapours) are either eliminated or minimised.
2. Provide systems and equipment to ensure that exposures to respiratory hazards are reduced to the lowest level possible.
3. Provide information and training on the hazards and controls (such as exhaust systems and wet cutting methods).
4. Issue workers with the appropriate respiratory protective equipment (RPE) required to protect their health, and train them how to use it properly.
5. Provide workers with face-fit testing, if they wear RPE, and health surveillance, if required.
6. Initiate a health surveillance programme, where required.

What you should do as a supervisor

Checklist	Yes	No	N/A
1. Make sure that respiratory hazards (such as dust, fumes and vapours) are either eliminated or minimised by the proper use of equipment (for example, dust extraction and dust suppression (wet cutting) equipment).			
2. Check that all the control measures planned for the work are in place and are working properly. In particular, make sure that dust suppression and extraction systems are working effectively.			
3. Ensure that workers have the correct RPE, they have had face-fit testing, where necessary, and they are trained to use it properly.			
4. Ensure that workers are wearing their RPE properly.			
5. Ensure that any reported defects or failings in control measures are dealt with immediately.			
6. Ensure, so far as is practicable, that workers attend health surveillance screening, when required.			

B
13

Introduction

Respiratory hazards are substances in the air (such as dusts, fumes, gases or vapours) that can be inhaled by workers and lead to a range of illnesses and diseases. The damage caused is mainly to the lungs and airways, and includes lung cancer and silicosis. However, some respiratory hazards can also result in disease in other parts of the body (such as the kidneys and liver).

B
13

☑ Each year many workers suffer with breathing or lung problems caused or made worse by work.

☑ The Health and Safety Executive (HSE) estimates that around 450 people every year are dying as a result of past exposure to silica dust, which causes lung cancer. Much of this exposure would result from activities such as cutting blocks, kerbs and so on.

☑ Some respiratory hazards can also cause sensitisation, which results in conditions such as asthma.

 At any one time there are far more people off work through occupational ill health than there are because of a work-related accident.

Conditions caused by respiratory hazards

When there is an accident on site, the injuries are usually immediate and obvious. The effects of exposure to most respiratory hazards are not immediate and may not be felt for years. Often they will lead to chronic, life-changing illnesses. However, some gases, fumes and vapours can have immediate toxic effects and cause unconsciousness and/or death.

Chronic respiratory disease can often result in employees being unable to work as hard or as efficiently as before, and sometimes they may never work again.

There are many diseases or conditions caused by substances that are or can be inhaled. Some conditions caused by respiratory hazards are described below.

Chronic obstructive pulmonary disease

Chronic obstructive pulmonary disease (COPD) is the name for a collection of lung diseases, including chronic bronchitis and emphysema. People with COPD have difficulties breathing, primarily due to the narrowing of their airways.

The following are typical symptoms of COPD.

☑ Increasing breathlessness when active.

☑ A persistent cough with phlegm.

☑ Frequent chest infections.

It is caused by the inhalation of substances that irritate the lungs and airways causing inflammation.

Silicosis

Silicosis is a significant problem within the construction industry. Respirable crystalline silica (RCS) is found in stone, rock, sand and clay, and so is contained in many construction products (such as concrete, blocks, bricks, ceramics, and so on). Common construction activities can produce RCS dust and many workers are exposed to it by breathing in silica particles.

 Silica is the biggest risk to construction workers after asbestos. Heavy and prolonged exposure to RCS can cause lung cancer and other serious respiratory diseases.

Exposure to RCS dust at low levels over a long period can cause silicosis, which causes fibrosis (hardening or scarring) of the lung tissue. Sufferers are likely to have severe shortness of breath and may find it difficult or impossible to walk even short distances or climb stairs. The effect continues to develop after exposure has stopped and it is irreversible. Sufferers usually become house- or bed-bound and often die prematurely due to heart failure.

Workers with silicosis are at an increased risk of tuberculosis, kidney disease and arthritis. Exposure to RCS dust may also cause COPD.

Occupational asthma

Occupational asthma is caused by exposure to respiratory sensitisers at work, which are inhaled into the lungs over a period of time. It can be a serious condition, leading to severe chronic asthma, if there is a prolonged exposure to respiratory sensitisers.

A worker with asthma may suffer an asthma attack when exposed to a range of irritants (such as smoke, dust and cold air). The attacks are not just or only brought on by the agent that caused the development of the condition.

Respiratory sensitisers can be chemicals, such as isocyanates (from spraying), wood dusts, colophony (from soldering) or some glues.

Cancer

Many forms of cancer (such as those listed) can be caused by breathing in substances at work.

☑ **Lung cancer.** Caused by many substances, but in construction, exposure to silica and asbestos are the major causes. Vehicle emissions, particularly from diesel engines, are also associated with the incidence of lung cancer.

☑ **Nasal cancer.** Caused by inhaling wood dusts over a long period of time. Hard wood dusts (such as teak) are particularly associated with nasal cancer.

☑ **Mesothelioma.** A cancer of the thin, protective membrane (pleura) surrounding the lungs, heart and abdominal cavity. It is only caused by exposure to asbestos. It can take up to 50 years after exposure before symptoms develop. Mesothelioma is fatal in all cases, with death often occurring within months of diagnosis.

☑ In addition, breathing in certain toxic substances (for example, solvent vapours and rubber fumes) is associated with various organ cancers (such as liver cancer and bladder cancer).

 Further information, including a short video about the devastating effects of asbestos, is available on the CITB website.

Acute toxic effects

Acute toxic effects are those effects that arise shortly after breathing in certain respiratory hazards. Some examples are below.

☑ **Carbon monoxide poisoning.** Breathing in carbon monoxide from combustion engines or some heaters can cause chemical asphyxiation. This is usually associated with the use of equipment in poorly ventilated environments. The effects depend on the concentration of the gas and can range from headaches to death.

☑ **Solvent fume intoxication.** Breathing fumes from solvent-based substances (such as certain adhesives) can cause intoxication. Symptoms can range from dizziness to coma and even death. Cases normally occur when substances are used with inadequate ventilation.

B 13

☑ **Hydrogen sulphide poisoning.** This gas is generated by rotting matter (such as sewage or animal waste). It can build up in sewers, vats and tanks and affect workers who enter. This is a knock-down toxin, which can cause unconsciousness or death with just a few breaths.

Biological hazards

Some biological agents can become suspended in dusts and aerosols, which can be inhaled and cause disease. The main biological respiratory hazards found in construction are shown below.

☑ **Legionellosis** or similar forms of pneumonia caused by inhaling small droplets of water containing legionella bacteria.

☑ **Psittacosis** and other related diseases caused by inhaling dust from pigeon and other bird droppings.

☑ **Aspergillosis** is a lung disease caused by breathing fungal dust from aspergillus fungi, which are often found in damp locations (for example, soil, decaying vegetation and organic matter, and basements in derelict buildings).

Types of respiratory hazard

Dust

The most common form of respiratory hazard encountered in the construction industry is dust. Dust is produced when solid materials are broken down into finer particles. The size of the dust particles has a major influence on the degree of risk posed by the dust.

Many dusts are too fine to be seen by the naked eye and are the cause of many serious health problems. Where dust exists in sufficient quantities, it may be considered hazardous even if the dust formed is from a non-hazardous substance and is clearly visible.

Mists and aerosols

Tiny liquid droplets are formed, for example, when spraying or using aerosols. They may be hazardous because of the substance from which they are formed, or they may carry bacteria and enable them to be deposited in the lungs, such as is the case with legionella bacteria.

Vapours

Vapours are the gaseous state of substances that are liquids or solids at room temperature. They usually form when substances evaporate. One example is the vapour from a tin of glue or solvent that has been left open. Solvent vapours can often be toxic if inhaled, causing dizziness, unconsciousness and death. They may also have chronic effects (such as causing liver damage or sensitisation). Harmful vapours are particularly hazardous in spaces with poor or restricted ventilation, enclosed spaces or confined spaces, where the vapours can quickly build up to dangerous concentrations, which may also be highly flammable or explosive.

Fumes

Fumes are microscopic particles of a solid, usually metal, that are created by hot processes (such as welding). A common illness caused by inhaling fumes is metal fume fever, which occurs when welders breathe in welding fumes, causing flu-like symptoms.

Gases

Gases are generally substances that are in gaseous form at room temperature and normally mix with the air that we breathe. Examples include carbon dioxide, carbon monoxide and hydrogen sulphide (H_2S). As well as having toxic qualities, gases may also be flammable or explosive (such as H_2S) or may be an asphyxiant (such as nitrogen).

Controlling respiratory hazards

The following simple steps are the main methods that can be taken to protect workers from respiratory hazards.

☑ **Avoid creating dust.** Choosing the right equipment or method of work can protect workers' lungs by potentially eliminating the risk altogether.

- Pre-order sized materials rather than cutting them on site.

- Use a block splitter rather than a disc cutter as this creates less dust and is quicker.

☑ **Stop the dust getting into the air.** If creating dust cannot be avoided then minimising the dust being released into the air should be the priority. This can be done in two ways.

- **Dampening down or wet cutting.** This is the cheapest and most effective way of minimising exposure. Water helps to form a slurry that prevents the majority of dust becoming airborne. Not only does it reduce what is breathed in, but it also has the benefit of less cleaning up afterwards. It is important to keep the flow constant while wet cutting or grinding and to dampen down before sweeping up.

- **Capturing the dust.** Some materials (such as wood) do not suit the use of water to suppress dust, so dust extraction should be considered. When purchasing or hiring tools, ensure that they have on-tool extraction wherever possible. It is far better if a vacuum is used to remove dust from work areas and tools rather than sweeping with a brush.

Circular saw incorporating vacuum collection

☑ **Wear respiratory protection.** Even the best control measures won't prevent dust generation completely, so suitable RPE must always be worn, even if you are wet cutting or using extraction.

 For information on RPE, refer to Chapter B10 Personal protective equipment.

Other possible control measures include the following.

☑ Follow substance manufacturer's guidance when using substances.

☑ Provision of information, instruction and training to employees.

☑ Effective supervision of employees, and the monitoring of work methods and practices.

**B
13**

☑ Avoid carrying out potentially hazardous work activities in confined spaces or areas with restricted or poor ventilation to lessen the chance of hazardous concentrations of dust, vapours or fumes building up.

☑ Correct disposal of waste materials and containers, as recommended by the manufacturers.

☑ Good housekeeping – keep the workplace clean (for example, by extracting dust using a vacuum cleaner, rather than stirring it up by sweeping).

Silica

Silica occurs as a natural component of many materials used in construction work. Crystalline silica is present in substantial quantities in sand, sandstone and granite, and often forms a significant proportion of clay, shale and slate. Products (such as concrete and mortar) also contain crystalline silica.

The health hazards of silica come from breathing in the dust. Work that can expose workers or members of the public to the dust includes working with stone, grit blasting, scabbling, cutting or drilling (such as kerbs and paving slabs) and demolition.

The use of power tools leads to high exposures if exhaust systems or wet cutting processes are not used and maintained.

For some work, exposure will depend upon how confined the working space is, and the presence or absence of ventilation. For example, tunnelling through dry, silica-bearing rock will always lead to high exposures for workers at or near the cutting face, unless precautions are taken.

Examples of materials containing silica and typical control measures are shown in the following table.

Materials containing silica	Sand, sandstone, granite, clay, shale and slate.
Common products containing silica	Concrete, mortar, bricks, blocks, ceramics, kerbs and paving slabs.
Common operations leading to silica exposure	Sweeping up, demolition and strip out. Drilling or breaking. Cutting (disc cutter, chasing machine or floor saw). Grinding, polishing, rubbing down, sanding and blasting.
Typical control measures for silica exposure	Manufacture off site or isolate process. Substitute process (for example, use block splitter rather than disc cutter). Use vacuum extraction systems on tools and equipment or local exhaust ventilation. Use water suppression. (Note that typically only 75% of particles are controlled). Use a vacuum system for cleaning up, and dampen down regularly, particularly when cleaning up.
Typical respiratory protective equipment	Half mask respirator or disposable face mask, rated P3 or FFP3. (Note that actual equipment selection must be based on assessment by a competent person.)

Carbon monoxide

Carbon monoxide (CO) is a respiratory hazard that is of particular importance to the construction industry. Carbon monoxide is a toxic gas formed by incomplete combustion and is colourless, odourless and tasteless.

Managing and controlling exposure to carbon monoxide is a vital challenge facing the industry as it can impact, sometimes lethally, on operatives working on site and also on any occupants of property where work is being undertaken.

At high levels CO poisoning can kill within minutes but long-term low-level exposure could result in a stroke, multiple mini-strokes, heart attack, memory loss, personality changes and eventual death.

Carbon monoxide is an issue in the construction industry in the following situations.

☑ Where site security workers and office staff use portable liquefied petroleum gas (LPG) heaters or LPG cookers and there is inadequate ventilation.

☑ Where combustion engine powered equipment, including generators, are used in enclosed or confined spaces, exposing workers and others to exhaust emissions containing carbon monoxide.

☑ Where refurbishment or other work is undertaken on existing buildings containing gas systems. Interference with gas equipment or flues can lead to construction workers or end users being exposed to carbon monoxide.

Carbon monoxide intoxication is often mistaken for other illnesses (such as a viral infection or chronic fatigue syndrome). Symptoms will increase with the concentration, so that low levels of intoxication may just cause headaches and tiredness. These symptoms will normally disappear when the person leaves the environment where the carbon monoxide is present.

Higher concentrations can cause the following symptoms.

☑ Pains in the chest or stomach.

☑ Erratic behaviour and decreased mental performance.

☑ Visual problems.

☑ Nausea.

☑ Breathlessness.

☑ Collapse and loss of consciousness.

Typically, the concentration of gas will build up in a poorly ventilated area, and so a victim will progress through some or all of the symptoms if they continue to be exposed. This can eventually lead to death, even when the injured person has been removed to fresh air and given oxygen therapy.

Carbon monoxide controls

Personal carbon monoxide alarm

In general, the controls that should be in place to prevent carbon monoxide poisoning should include the following.

☑ Ensuring gas heaters or similar equipment are only used in locations where there is suitable and sufficient ventilation. Siting of such equipment must be assessed and determined by a competent person.

Dust and fumes (Respiratory hazards)

- ☑ Where combustion engine powered equipment, including generators, are used in enclosed or confined spaces, these should only be used following a suitable and sufficient risk assessment, and there must be adequate ventilation.

- ☑ The use of carbon monoxide alarms, where necessary, to protect workers from the build-up of toxic gas concentrations.

- ☑ Training workers to ensure that they are aware of the risks from carbon monoxide, and in particular the early symptoms.

- ☑ Planning refurbishment works to ensure that any interference with gas systems, including flues, is undertaken by competent persons and systems are checked on completion of the refurbishment works, prior to re-activation of the gas system.

B
13

14

Noise and vibration

B
14

What your employer should do for you
1. Carry out assessments to monitor the exposure of workers to noise and vibration.
2. Control noise and vibration at source by selecting low noise and vibration work methods.
3. Have a policy for the purchase or use of equipment that emits low levels of noise and vibration. (Buy quiet/Buy smooth)
4. Put control measures in place to ensure that the limit values for exposure to noise and vibration are not exceeded.
5. Provide training and supervision to ensure that the noise and vibration controls are effective.
6. Provide hearing protection to workers exposed to high levels of noise that cannot be controlled by other means.
7. Where necessary, provide health surveillance to workers exposed to noise and vibration.

What you should do as a supervisor

Checklist	Yes	No	N/A
1. Ensure that noise and vibration assessments have been undertaken for workers.			
2. Ensure that you are aware of the significant noise and vibration sources on the site and that you understand the noise and vibration controls that have been put in place.			
3. Ensure that workers do not exceed the exposure limit value by using vibrating tools for excessive periods.			
4. Explain to workers why hearing protection is important and how to fit it properly.			
5. Ensure that hearing protection is available as required and is being worn properly.			
6. Check that hearing protection zones are in place, if necessary, and the signage is clear.			

B
14

Introduction

Exposure to noise and vibration, if not controlled or monitored, can cause irreversible damage. This chapter provides information on these subjects to help you comply with the law and good practice.

Noise

If protective measures are not taken, many construction activities create levels of noise that have the potential to cause permanent hearing damage.

In addition to the health implications for workers, noise is also a major source of nuisance to people neighbouring the site.

Noise may also cause the following issues.

- ☑ Stress.
- ☑ Loss of concentration.
- ☑ Fatigue and headaches.
- ☑ Masking of auditory warnings.
- ☑ The spoken word to not be heard, or to be misinterpreted, which could result in important safety messages not being understood or acted upon.

Plant, equipment and tools used in construction often emit high levels of noise, which may be continuous (such as the noise from a generator or compressor), intermittent (such as the stop-start noise from a hand-held hammer drill), or impact noise (such as high peaks of noise from impact equipment, for example pecker breakers).

Damage to hearing caused by noise is related to the **level** of noise at the ear, measured in decibels (dB), and the **duration** of the noise. These two measures combined are referred to as the **noise dose**.

Typical noise levels of some equipment used in the construction industry are shown below.

- ☑ Electrical hand tool 95 dB.
- ☑ Circular bench saw 107 dB.
- ☑ Hammer drill 102 dB.
- ☑ Rock drill 115 dB.

Noise legislation

The Control of Noise at Work Regulations 2005 place duties on employers to reduce workers' exposure to noise to as low as possible, and set a range of action values and limit values. These values are given as both daily dose and peak levels.

- ☑ **Daily dose (LEPd)** is the personal noise level over an eight hour period. It mathematically spreads all the noise received by a worker during the day over a standard eight hours. This allows noise exposures of different durations to be directly compared.

- ☑ **Peak level** is the energy in the highest single peak noise to which a worker is exposed during the day.

The action and limit values are as follows.

- ☑ **Lower exposure action level – 80 dB(A) daily dose or 135 dB(C) peak level.**

  At this level of exposure employers must ensure the following.

  - Risks to employees' hearing from noise are assessed and necessary measures are identified to comply with the Control of Noise at Work Regulations. (This may involve having a noise survey carried out and the marking up of hearing protection (noise) zones.)

  - Hearing protection is made available to anyone who requests it and it is maintained in good condition.

  - Employees are aware of the dangers of exposure to noise, what they must do to protect themselves, how and where hearing protectors can be obtained and their legal duties under these regulations.

☑ **Upper exposure action level – 85 dB(A) or 137 dB(C) peak level.**

At this level of exposure employers must ensure the following.

– Noise levels are reduced to as low as is reasonably practicable, other than by the provision of ear protectors.

– Areas of the site in which employees will be subjected to this level of noise are identified and signs are displayed in appropriate places to indicate hearing protection zones.

– Hearing protection is supplied and its use monitored to ensure that it is properly used by employees.

– Health surveillance is provided.

☑ **Exposure limit value – 87 dB(A) or 140 dB(C) peak level.**

The exposure limit value is the maximum level of noise to which anyone may be exposed, as measured at the ear (for example, inside ear defenders).

Hearing protection must be worn

In order to determine whether any worker on a construction site is being exposed at or above any of the action or limit values, the employer must undertake a noise assessment. This will require on site measurements.

Where the noise emission levels of items of equipment or activities are known, the HSE noise exposure calculator can be used to work out daily or weekly exposure levels, for comparison against the exposure limit and action values.

 An increase of three decibels is equal to the doubling of the noise level and would require an equivalent halving of the exposure time.

 For further information on the noise exposure calculator and ready reckoners visit the HSE website.

Noise control

Control of noise should follow this hierarchy.

Control at the source is the best option. Some of the available techniques are described below.

☑ **Buy quiet.** By specifying low noise equipment, noise can be effectively reduced at source. For example, effectively silenced generators can reduce much of the constant noise that often originates from construction sites.

The HSE has launched an initiative called *Buy quiet*. It aims to help manufacturers, importers, suppliers and users of work equipment to work together to reduce the risk of noise-induced hearing loss in the workplace.

 For further information on the *Buy quiet* initiative visit the HSE website.

☑ **Selection of work method.** Where possible, use work methods that are inherently quieter, or where the noise source is further away from the operative, as in the following examples.

– When cutting large holes in brickwork use a rotary diamond cutter rather than chain drilling with a tungsten drill bit, which requires hammer action.

B
14

- Use an excavator mounted pecker breaker rather than a hand-held breaker.
- Specify pre-fabricated components (such as factory-cut paving slabs) to avoid the need for on-site cutting (which also avoids hand-arm vibration and silica dust issues).

☑ **Maintain equipment.** Tools and equipment should be serviced and maintained in accordance with manufacturer's instructions and maintenance schedules.

Control of the sound path is the next best option; some of the available techniques are described below.

☑ **Siting or location.** Position equipment so that it is as far from the receivers as possible. This is particularly effective for control of environmental noise. Effective siting includes the following.

- Siting the source of noise as far from the work area or sensitive environmental receiver as possible.
- Orientating the plant to direct the noise away from the work area or sensitive environmental receiver.
- Placing site buildings, stores and so on between noise sources and the work area or sensitive environmental receivers. This is particularly effective if the buildings block the sight of the noise source, since people generally perceive a greater nuisance if they can see the noise source.

☑ **Use of barriers or enclosures.** A barrier placed correctly between a noise source and the receiver can reduce noise levels significantly (as in the following examples).

- Housing plant (such as generators) in soundproof enclosures.
- Siting spoil between noisy areas and sensitive receivers to create a noise bund.
- Using continuously boarded site hoarding that will act as a noise barrier.

☑ **Reducing the number of people in the sound path.** By the use of effective training and supervision, operatives should be encouraged not to stand near hazardous noise sources. It is common to see construction workers standing close to a colleague who is using a road breaker or other piece of high noise equipment, and whilst the worker using the equipment is wearing hearing protection, those around are not.

Control at the receiver is the last and least preferred option. This largely refers to the use of hearing protection to control the exposure of workers. In construction, it is often necessary to use hearing protection as part of the noise control strategy, as sufficient control may not be achieved using the control at source and control of path methods. This requires careful management in order to be successful.

Hearing protection

The management of hearing protection must include the following.

☑ Careful selection of hearing protection equipment.

☑ Training employees in the use and care of the equipment.

☑ Supervision to ensure the equipment is used properly.

There are many types of hearing protection available, but they broadly fall into two categories, namely earplugs and ear defenders (or earmuffs).

Earplugs take many forms (such as foam plugs, soft plastic valves and re-usable banded plugs). Although earplugs can be effective, there are a number of aspects that should be considered.

Foam in-ear earplugs

Banded semi-aural earplugs

☑ Foam earplugs need to be handled when fitted. Therefore, if workers have dirty hands these might not be suitable as dirt could be pushed into the ears, causing ear infections.

☑ Banded earplugs (or semi-aural plugs) can be fitted without touching, and so are better in dirty environments.

☑ Fitting is critical for in-ear earplugs. If not worn properly, their performance is drastically reduced. Workers should be trained to fit their earplugs correctly. Supervisors should be able to demonstrate to workers how to fit earplugs properly, and should ensure that they do so.

Foam in-ear earplugs worn incorrectly

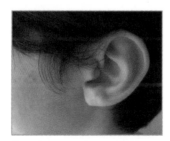

Foam in-ear earplugs worn correctly

Ear defenders cover the whole of the ear and make a seal against the head. They also come in a variety of forms, including overhead banded, helmet mounted, and those that contain radios and communication devices. Below are some important points regarding the use of ear defenders.

Helmet-mounted ear defenders

Ear defenders worn over long hair or with glasses reduces protection

B 14

☑ Ear defenders must be stored properly, to avoid them getting contaminated or damaged whilst not being worn.

☑ Ear defenders are very visible, so it is easy for supervisors to see if operatives are wearing them properly.

☑ They can become very sweaty, particularly in hot weather. If not regularly cleaned, they can become unhygienic. Users should also be provided with cleaning kits, and the ear defenders should be replaced when they become excessively dirty.

☑ The performance of ear defenders is reduced by wearing them with glasses or over long hair, and even large earrings can prevent a proper fit of the shell over the ear.

☑ Sometimes workers wear earphones under their ear defenders, so that they can listen to music. This practice is as dangerous, as it is distracting; the music may mask auditory warnings and reduce awareness of the environment. Such behaviour should be challenged and prohibited.

B 14

Vibration

The Control of Vibration at Work Regulations 2005 set requirements with which employers have to comply if their employees are exposed to harmful levels of hand-arm or whole-body vibration.

Hand-arm vibration

The most common form of vibration affecting those who work in construction is hand-arm or hand-transmitted vibration. This is vibration generated by hand tools and equipment, which is transmitted to and through the hands and can damage the circulation, nerves, soft tissues and bones in the hands and arms.

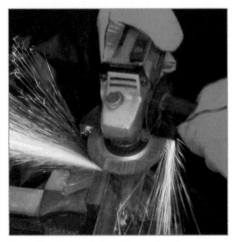

Examples of a tool that could cause hand-arm vibration if control measures are not implemented

The collection of conditions caused by excessive exposure to hand-arm vibration is known as hand-arm vibration syndrome (HAVS). The following are some of the rotating or percussive tools and equipment used in construction that can cause HAVS.

☑ Disc cutters.

☑ Needle guns.

☑ Hammer-action drills.

☑ Hand-held sanders.

☑ Poker vibrators.

☑ Scabblers.

☑ Plate compactors.

☑ Breakers.

The following factors can influence the incidence of HAVS.

☑ The frequency at which the tool vibrates.

☑ Duration of use (known as the trigger time).

☑ Rest periods between use of the tool.

☑ The sharpness and suitability of the cutting tool, disk, bit, and so on.

☑ The grip, push and other forces used to guide and apply the vibrating tools. The tighter the grip, the more vibration energy is transferred to the hands (vibration may increase as a tool becomes blunt and the user grips tighter and pushes harder).

☑ Hand temperature. Warm hands have better circulation and are less susceptible to HAVS.

☑ Smoking. This reduces oxygen supply to the extremities and increases susceptibility.

Symptoms of HAVS

HAVS can develop into a severe and potentially disabling condition. The symptoms become worse over time with continued exposure to vibration. The symptoms are accepted as being irreversible.

Damage to nerve tissue in the hand can lead to the following symptoms.

- ☑ Tingling.
- ☑ Numbness.
- ☑ Loss of sensation.
- ☑ Loss of manual dexterity.
- ☑ Painful throbbing.

Damage to muscles, bones and soft tissues can lead to the following.

- ☑ Muscle fatigue and loss of grip strength.
- ☑ Disorders of the bones (such as cysts and vacuoles).
- ☑ Joint disorders of the upper arm (such as tennis elbow and rotator cuff degeneration).

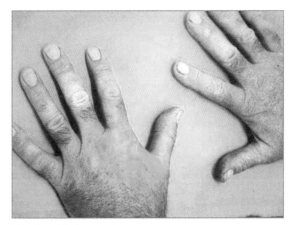

Vibration white finger

In addition, damage to blood vessels can cause finger blanching; a condition known as vibration white finger (VWF). This condition is brought on by the cold and is very painful. In severe cases the blanching of the fingers is permanent.

Hand-arm vibration can also cause carpal tunnel syndrome (CTS), which causes severe pain in the hand due to compression of the main nerve running through from the arm to the fingers.

Managing hand-arm vibration

The Control of Vibration at Work Regulations establish action and limit values for hand-arm vibration exposure. It is a requirement that employers undertake an assessment of the exposure of their workers to hand-arm vibration to estimate whether the values are likely to be exceeded.

The **exposure action value (EAV)** is a daily dose of vibration that, if reached, requires that employers put in place control measures to manage the exposure of employees and reduce it as far below the EAV as is reasonably practicable.

The **exposure limit value (ELV)** is a daily vibration dose above which employees may not be exposed.

Hand-arm vibration exposure values	
Daily exposure action value (EAV)	2.5 m/s^2 A(8)
Daily exposure limit value (ELV)	5.0 m/s^2 A(8)

(Note: A(8) refers to a time-weighted eight hour vibration dose.)

Therefore, a machine emitting a vibration level of 2.5 m/s^2 can be used for eight hours before the EAV is reached.

B 14

Examples of vibration exposure times to reach action and limit values

Vibration emission level (m/s²)	Time to reach EAV	Time to reach ELV
5	2 hrs	8 hrs
7.5	53 mins	3 hrs 33 mins
10	30 mins	2 hrs
15	13 mins	53 mins
20	8 mins	30 mins

It is important to know the vibration emission of hand-held tools and equipment. Manufacturers provide data on the vibration emission of their tools, but this should not be used for assessing individual exposure levels as part of a risk assessment, since it does not represent actual in-use vibration emission. Emission data for use in assessments must be obtained by direct measurement, which is a specialist task, or from databases of in-use data that are commercially available.

Whilst managing usage time of vibrating tools by job rotation is a common way of dealing with the risk, the ideal way of managing hand-arm vibration is to eliminate it altogether by doing jobs another way (such as using remotely controlled tools). Other ways of reducing the risk from vibration include the following.

☑ Adopting a *Buy smooth* policy, in which a commitment is made to replace old tools with new ones that incorporate low vibration technology.

☑ Ensuring the proper maintenance of tools that cause vibration.

☑ Providing suitable and sufficient information and training for employees so that they may use the equipment safely and correctly in order to minimise their exposure to vibration.

☑ Providing clothing to protect employees from cold and damp.

☑ Regularly checking and replacing worn and blunt drill bits, blades, points and chisels.

☑ Advising at-risk employees of the importance of keeping their muscles warm and adopting a good posture.

☑ Providing health surveillance for any employees thought to be at risk.

For further information on the hand-arm vibration calculator visit the HSE website.

Use of a machine-mounted pick (pecker breaker) to replace hand breakers removes the risk of hand-arm vibration

B 14

Whole-body vibration

Whole-body vibration (WBV), as its name suggests, is vibration or jolting of the whole body through the surface that is supporting the body (such as a machine seat or floor).

WBV, which often results from driving or operating some types of construction plant or vehicles, has the potential to cause back injury or make an existing back condition more painful.

Back pain can be caused by many work and non-work activities. It can lead to time off work, loss of productivity and compensation claims. Mobile machine operators and drivers (especially those who work off-road) are at increased risk from back pain.

Below are some tools and plant used in the construction industry that could cause exposure to risks from WBV.

- ☑ Rough-terrain forklift trucks and telehandlers.

- ☑ Vibratory rollers.

- ☑ Mobile crushers.

- ☑ Dumper trucks and other forms of earth-moving machinery.

Among those most likely to experience high vibration exposures are regular operators and drivers of off-road machinery, such as those listed below.

- ☑ Construction, mining and quarrying machines and vehicles, particularly earthmoving machines (such as scrapers, bulldozers, ride on rollers and building site dumpers).

- ☑ Tractors and other agricultural and forestry machinery, particularly when used in transportation, tedding (turning hay) and mowing.

WBV can be controlled in different ways, for example, improved technology in mobile plant (such as improved suspension and air-cushioned driver's seats), operator training, smooth operation of machines and job rotation.

B 14

Noise and vibration

15

Manual handling

B 15

What your employer should do for you
1. Where a risk has been identified, the first consideration must be whether the manual handling activity can be avoided.
2. Where manual handling cannot be avoided, check whether it can be automated or mechanised, or if mechanical aids can be provided.
3. Ensure deliveries are deposited and stacked safely (with the use of mechanical lifting aids) in the work area, to reduce the need for manual handling.
4. Ensure that loads have been assessed as suitable for manual handling.
5. Provide mechanical aids and provide training in the use of them.
6. Provide and maintain safe routes for carrying loads.
7. Take into account the elements of the task, individual capability, load and environment (TILE), including repetitive lifting and carrying. Ensure staff required to carry out manual handling assessments are properly trained.
8. Provide training in proper (kinetic) lifting and team lifting methods to the workforce and ensure that they understand that they should assess the load and if in doubt ask for help.
9. Ensure that personal protective equipment (PPE) is issued to protect hands, feet and so on.

What you should do as a supervisor			
Checklist	Yes	No	N/A
1. Where a risk has been identified, first consider whether the manual handling activity can be avoided.			
2. Where manual handling cannot be avoided, check whether it can be automated or mechanised, or if mechanical aids can be provided.			
3. Supervise deliveries to make sure that loads are deposited and stacked safely.			
4. Where manual handling cannot be avoided, check that loads have been assessed as suitable for manual handling.			
5. Ensure training is provided in proper (kinetic) lifting and team lifting methods to the workforce and ensure that they understand that they should assess the load and if in doubt ask for help.			
6. Supervise and manage working practices that involve repetitive lifting and carrying.			
7. Utilise mechanical lifting aids and check that training has been provided in the use of them.			
8. Organise the issue of correct PPE and make sure that it is used correctly.			
9. Monitor and maintain safe routes for carrying loads.			

B
15

Introduction

Manual handling is one of the most common causes of injury at work and is responsible for more than a third of all workplace injuries. Many manual handling injuries cause absence from work, and in the worst cases, permanent disability and physical impairment are often the result.

The **Manual Handling Operations Regulations** place legal duties and responsibilities on both employers and employees to ensure that manual handling activities are planned and carried out so that injury is avoided.

Lifting aids should be used to minimise the risk of manual handling injuries

Manual handling **relates to movement of a load by bodily force and includes lifting, lowering, carrying, pushing or pulling a load.**

The **Management of Health and Safety at Work Regulations** require employers to make a suitable and sufficient assessment of the risks to health and safety of their employees. This requirement is expanded upon in the Manual Handling Operations Regulations, which require employers to assess the risks to the health and safety of their employees arising out of manual handling activities.

The HSE has developed online tools to assist employers to carry out manual handling assessments.

Employers should find these tools useful in identifying high risk manual handling operations and helping them to complete their risk assessments.

The HSE has developed online tools to assist employers to carry out manual handling assessments.

- [✓] **Variable manual handling assessment chart (V-MAC) tool.**
- [✓] **Risk assessment of pulling and pushing (RAPP) tool.**
- [✓] **Manual handling assessment chart (MAC) tool.**
- [✓] **Assessment of repetitive tasks (ART) tool.**

Duties of the employer

The employer must identify all manual handling tasks that might involve a risk of injury and carry out a manual handling assessment of those activities. The assessment should also take into consideration the number of times the load will be lifted and moved, the distance the load will be carried, the direction of movement up and down, and any twisting, bending, stretching or awkward posture which the carrier might be forced to adopt whilst undertaking the task.

Where the assessment indicates that there are risks to employees from the manual handling of loads, the employer must take the following steps.

☑ Avoid the need for employees to carry out manual handling activities as far as is reasonably practicable, usually achieved by better planning or moving loads using mechanical means, automating the process, or the use of mechanical handling aids.

☑ Where the manual handling of loads is unavoidable, reduce the risk of injury so far as is reasonably practicable by planning how these activities can be carried out safely and putting in place suitable control measures to ensure that they are.

Manual handling assessment

An ergonomic approach to the problems of manual handling and lifting can help to overcome many of the problems.

Ergonomics is defined as 'fitting the job to the person, rather than fitting the person to the job'. A simple way to risk assess manual handling operations is to use the acronym TILE.

☑ **Task:** what has to be achieved, how and by whom?

☑ **Individual:** who will be involved in the task, their gender, build, frame, age, experience, and so on.

☑ **Load:** its size, dimensions, weight, is the weight evenly distributed, is it a live load (for example, will the centre of gravity move as with a half empty drum), is it too heavy to lift and, if so, can it be broken down into smaller loads, can two people lift it?

☑ **Environment (work conditions and location):** consider hazards of the route (such as stairs or inclines), is the travel route over good or unmade ground, is there enough room for the load to be lifted and carried ergonomically and safely?

Where the assessment indicates potential risks to the health of employees from the manual handling of loads, the employer must develop a safe system of work that avoids the risks.

The employer must consider the following.

☑ **The task.**
  - Can manual handling be avoided completely?
  - Can the distance a load has to be moved be reduced by better on-site planning?
  - Can lifting or mechanical handling aids be used?
  - Does the load have to be raised to, or lowered from, above head height?
  - Does the task involve repetitive movements?
  - Is it possible to avoid lifting from the floor?

☑ **The individual.**
  - Have they had manual handling training?
  - Do they need additional PPE?
  - Is there any known reason why they might not be suitable for the job?

B 15

B
15

☑ **The load.**
  – Can it be broken down into smaller loads?
  – Is the weight known and, if not, can it be found out?
  – Are there adequate handholds?
  – Can the centre of gravity move (fluid or live loads)?
  – Can it be carried close to the body?
  – Does it have sharp edges?
  – Should it be carried by two (or more) people due to the size and/or the weight?

☑ **The environment.**
  – Is the floor surface sufficiently level?
  – Are there any space constraints that should be removed?
  – Is the level of lighting adequate?
  – Is the workplace temperature satisfactory?

Employees must co-operate by:

☑ using the appropriate equipment supplied in accordance with their training and instructions

☑ following the systems of work laid down by their employer.

 Manual handling and lifting injuries are often for life.

Lifting and handling

The weight that can be lifted by any individual will vary according to personal physique, age, health, experience and the techniques employed. Lifting capacity declines with age and an older person may not be capable of lifting the same load as a younger person; however, this can be offset to some extent by employing a better technique.

The general rule is that the load should not be lifted if it causes any feeling of strain. Assistance should be available if required, and employees must not be required to lift loads beyond their capability.

Youthful exuberance and bravado often tempt younger employees to try to lift loads that are too heavy. While they may succeed in the short-term, long-term damage may be done to the ligaments, muscles and back.

There is a high risk of injury in the single-handed, repetitive manual handling of building blocks or other loads heavier than 20 kg. If single-person handling is needed, either blocks or other materials of 20 kg or lighter should be specified and used, or other precautions should be implemented to reduce the risk by, for example, provision of mechanical handling. With blocks or other materials weighing less than 20 kg, manual handling risks are still significant and suitable precautions should be taken to minimise these risks as much as possible.

HSE guidance recommends that women should lift a lower amount (for example, a maximum of 13 kg at elbow height, close to the torso).

Avoiding manual handling – some solutions

Placing kerbs with a mechanical suction lifter

Reducing the risk of injury can be helped by using mechanical aids such as:

- ☑ correct delivery locations
- ☑ built-in lifting attachments
- ☑ conveyor belts
- ☑ material hoists
- ☑ genie lifts
- ☑ telehandlers
- ☑ skids
- ☑ excavators and dumpers
- ☑ kerb lifters
- ☑ sack trolleys
- ☑ pallet trucks
- ☑ wheelbarrows
- ☑ stillages
- ☑ suction pads
- ☑ temporary handles and grips.

Manual handling injuries

Injuries resulting from unsafe or incorrect manual handling can affect the:

- ☑ whole body
- ☑ back
- ☑ shoulders
- ☑ arms
- ☑ hands
- ☑ feet and toes.

Back injuries are the most common, but hernias, ruptures, sprains and strains are all conditions that can result from poor manual handling techniques.

Legislation requires that adequate and appropriate protective clothing and equipment be provided by the employer and worn by the employee. Gloves, footwear, hard hats and overalls all play an important part in reducing the type and severity of accidents arising from manual handling.

The cost of physical injury can be very high for the employer through:

- ☑ legal liabilities leading to possible prosecution
- ☑ compensation payments, civil legal costs and increased insurance costs
- ☑ lost production and raised costs.

And, for the employee, through:

- ☑ immediate pain and suffering
- ☑ permanent disability, leading to lost wages and change of lifestyle
- ☑ increased pressure and stress on the family.

B 15

Anyone who believes that they have suffered a manual handling injury, particularly a back injury, should be encouraged to seek prompt medical advice.

Preparing to lift

Before lifting and handling any load, the following points should be established.

- ☑ What has to be moved?
- ☑ Does it really have to be moved?
- ☑ What does it weigh?
- ☑ Can it be broken down into smaller loads?
- ☑ Can the process that requires it to be moved be changed?
- ☑ Where is the load's centre of gravity?
- ☑ Can it be safely handled by one person?
- ☑ Will assistance be required?
- ☑ Can the move be carried out more safely with mechanical assistance?
- ☑ How far does it have to be moved and from where to where?
- ☑ Is the route clear of obstructions?
- ☑ Can it be put down safely?

Suitable protective clothing should be worn. This may include gloves, safety footwear, safety helmets, and special overalls if hot or corrosive substances are to be carried. Ensure that the lifting and lowering areas are clear of tripping hazards, and likewise check the route over which the load will be carried.

The load

Large, heavy loads should, if possible, be broken down into smaller, lighter and more manageable sizes. It is obviously easier to lift 10 kg five times than to try to lift 50 kg once.

Where the load has to be moved by a woman, the weight should be reduced by approximately 30%.

As a rough guide, the HSE has produced guidelines for the maximum weight that an individual should lift (shown in the diagram below).

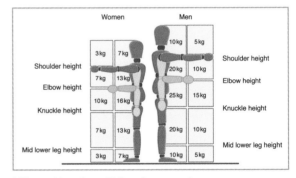

Lifting and lowering guidelines for men and women

The size and shape of a load may be as significant as its weight in determining whether assistance is required. Large, awkward loads that require the arms to be extended in front of the body place more strain on the back and abdomen than compact objects carried close to the body.

The absence of natural or designed handling points can also make it difficult to raise and carry objects without strain, so barrows or other lifting and handling aids may be required to move the load.

Not all loads need to be carried. It may be easier to roll or push them, depending on the contents. Even so, assistance might still be required to avoid the risk of injury.

Manual handling techniques

Plan the task
- ☑ What has to be moved?
- ☑ Where to, where from, and how far?
- ☑ Is the route suitable, safe and clear of obstructions?
- ☑ Is it safe for one person to do it alone?
- ☑ Will help be required? If so, how much and for what purpose?

Use your body wisely
- ☑ Let the leg and thigh muscles do the work. They cope better than the back muscles.

- ☑ Try to keep your spine straight (not necessarily vertical, but straight) and the muscles relaxed. However, slight bending of the back, knees and hips is permitted, if necessary, to maintain the natural curve of the spine, and is certainly preferable to fully flexing the back (stooping) or fully flexing the hips and knees (deep squatting).

- ☑ Once you have started to lift (taken the full weight) don't flex your back any further, which can happen if you begin to straighten before you have raised the load.

- ☑ Avoid twisting the back or leaning sideways, especially whilst the back is bent.

- ☑ Use the movement and inertia of your own body weight as you start to lift. Do not snatch the load.

Bend your knees
Feet slightly apart; one foot slightly forward; balance; keep the back straight. Avoid tight clothing that prevents you from bending your knees.

Get a good grip
Use your hands – not fingers. Tilt the load slightly to get a secure grip as close to the body as possible. Keep your elbows tucked in.

Lift with your legs
Do not jerk or snatch. Let the thigh muscles do the bulk of the work. Lift in stages, if necessary from the ground onto a low platform.

Good practice method for kinetic lifting

Putting the load down – plan before you start
- ☑ To floor level: it will probably be a reversal of the lifting process. Attention must be given to the positioning of the feet and back.

- ☑ To a higher level: depending upon the height of the surface to which the load is to be positioned, it may be less of a stress on the body to lower the load; assistance may be required.

- ☑ If loads are to be manually handled, heavier loads should be stored at waist height.

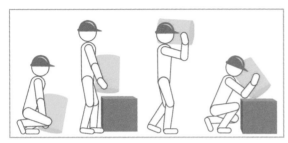

Good practice method for lifting and placing a load

Team lifting

If the load is large, heavy or awkward – get assistance, preferably from someone of about the same size and build as yourself to help maintain the balance of the load during lifting. Always plan the lift with your helper and agree who will give directions as to when and how you will lift.

More than one person may be needed to complete a job safely

Using simple mechanical aids

The use of a wheelbarrow or sack trolley will make the manual handling of suitable loads easier. Using lifting straps or hand-help suction devices will assist in moving some sheet materials.

The use of simple mechanical aids lowers the level of risk, can prevent accidents and avoids unnecessary fatigue and strain.

For further information refer to the HSE Busy Builder series leaflets:

☑ *Preventing injury from handling heavy blocks*

☑ *Preventing injury during plasterboard handling.*

For further information refer to the manual handling chapter in Section B of GE 700 *Construction site safety*.

16

Site organisation

What your employer should do for you

1. Provide information about any known hazards near your site, including information on the surrounding area (such as schools and transport restrictions).

2. Provide information about any protected species in the area, or any other environmental restrictions.

3. Devise a site management plan and advise of proposed traffic management routes.

4. Allow for visitor, contractor and staff parking where possible.

5. Provide information about any logistical issues (such as delivery times and delivery restrictions).

6. Create and communicate a materials delivery schedule.

7. Take necessary steps to prevent access by unauthorised persons, including appropriate fencing and security personnel, as required.

8. Maintain up to date records of who is authorised to be on site at any time.

9. Make specific security arrangements for particular pieces of plant, if required.

**C
16**

What you should do as a supervisor			
Checklist	Yes	No	N/A
1. Ensure entrances to and from site minimise hazards on public roads.			
2. Provide separate routes for pedestrians and vehicles, with separate entrances if possible.			
3. Monitor the location and routing of temporary electrical supplies.			
4. Ensure site and vehicle management plans are communicated to the workforce and their adherence monitored.			
5. Ensure all contractors are aware of any delivery restrictions specific to the site or surrounding area.			
6. Ensure materials are stacked appropriately and hazardous materials are stored correctly.			
7. Ensure visitors to site know where to go and are provided with safe access and egress routes.			
8. Check that visitors and the workforce sign in and out of the site.			
9. Help to monitor the site security arrangements for signs of trespass.			

C
16

Introduction

The **Construction (Design and Management) Regulations** (CDM) place specific duties on commercial clients, the contractor or the principal contractor to ensure that authorised personnel have access to appropriate information to keep them safe on site. In addition they have a duty to ensure that unauthorised persons do not gain access to site. Unauthorised persons will not be familiar with the site rules and site hazards, so access to site could expose them to hazards that they may not be aware of.

 For further information on what to do when setting up and managing a site refer to the CDM industry guidance documents for contractors and principal contractors.

In accordance with the **Occupiers Liability Act**, trespassers and non-employees have a right not to be put at risk if they enter a construction site. A higher standard of care is to be given by the site management where children are concerned, for both authorised and unauthorised access.

Site set up

The construction phase plan provides specific information on hazards that need to be considered during the setting up phase of a construction site. The information could relate to hazards in the surrounding area, as well as those present on site (for example underground services, overhead cables or asbestos). All hazards need to be identified and considered to ensure a safe site set up. The site set up needs to take into consideration any logistical issues and transport routes and restrictions.

Considerations for a safe site set up

- ☑ Suitability of ground conditions for site cabins (if they are being used).

- ☑ Design of the site hoardings and gates to withstand wind loadings.

- ☑ Material storage areas to be accessible and of sufficient size (consideration should be given to implementing height restrictions).

- ☑ Plans for traffic and pedestrian routes, parking requirements and restrictions and safe access from the highways.

- ☑ Segregation and safe disposal of waste. (Consider using lidded skips located away from any buildings to minimise risks associated with arson.)

- ☑ Securing the site, preferably with lockable gates and sufficient hoarding.

- ☑ Location of overhead and underground services.

- ☑ Presence of wildlife and other protected species in the surrounding area (such as bats and nesting birds).

- ☑ Presence of historic buildings and/or archaeological sites.

- ☑ Welfare facilities for male, female and disabled workers.

- ☑ Emergency arrangements appropriate to the hazards on site.

- ☑ Requirements for safety signs and notices and their locations.

- ☑ Existing site hazards such as asbestos, unstable structures, and adjoining properties and businesses.

- ☑ Locate site offices as near to the entrance as possible and ensure there is adequate signage.

- ☑ Requirements for the provision of information in different languages.

C 16

Security and safety considerations need to be taken into account on every part of a construction site

Site lighting

The Provision and Use of Work Equipment Regulations (PUWER) require that:

Every employer shall ensure that suitable and sufficient lighting is provided at any workplace.

CDM Regulations require that adequate lighting is provided at every place of (construction) work and approach to the workplace, and that secondary (back-up) lighting is provided where failure of the primary lighting would result in risks to health or safety.

These two legislative provisions place a duty on employers to ensure that well-planned and adequate lighting be installed on site where necessary for safe working and access.

To obtain such lighting conditions, you should consider the following.

☑ Installing suitable lighting to provide the required level of illumination for the nature of the work being carried out.

☑ Mounting the lights at a suitable height above the work level to give the required spread of light.

☑ Positioning lights to avoid glare, dazzle and reflection.

☑ Changing the position of lights as work proceeds.

☑ Screening or shielding lights from reflective surfaces, on traffic routes, neighbouring properties and so on.

☑ Routing of lighting cables to avoid tripping or damage to the cable.

☑ Installing back-up lighting where appropriate.

Certain forms of lighting can constitute a heat source and, therefore, a fire hazard. They also retain heat for a period after being switched off. Avoid locating lights in close proximity to combustible materials. Halogen floodlights get particularly hot and have been the cause of several fires.

**C
16**

Good housekeeping – cables routed along ceiling and over doors to minimise slips and trips

Site security

Unauthorised persons will probably not be aware of the hazards associated with construction sites. The site should be secured with the use of site hoarding and lockable gates. The site boundary should be secured immediately after site possession. If the whole site cannot be secured then areas with potentially hazardous operations should be appropriately secured.

A number of simple precautions can be taken to ensure that unauthorised persons cannot access the site and tools and equipment on it.

- ☑ Power tools, plant and equipment should be locked and stored when not in use, particularly out of normal working hours.

- ☑ Hazardous substances should be kept in a secure designated area.

- ☑ Gas cylinder compounds should be kept securely locked.

- ☑ Site accommodation should be locked outside working hours to prevent vandalism and theft of personal possessions.

- ☑ All ladders should be removed, locked away, or boarded up at the end of the working day, to prevent access.

- ☑ Plan and monitor routine checks of the site hoarding or fencing and address issues identified.

- ☑ Isolate and lock plant and equipment when not in use.

- ☑ Install CCTV, if appropriate.

Children trespassing on site

Children often think that construction sites are exciting places to play. It is therefore important that access to the site is controlled during and after normal working hours. Any evidence of trespass must be reported to site management immediately and appropriate action should be taken. The site management team and supervisors should monitor the situation and ensure that operatives on site are extra vigilant and report any further incidents of trespass.

 It is a good idea to visit any schools near to the site to discuss the dangers with the children and to encourage them to stay away from sites.

Involving school children in construction projects can help them to understand the dangers on site

The following information is available on the HSE website.

☑ A video in which children warn about the dangers of playing on construction sites.

☑ The HSE guidance document *Protecting the public: Your next move* (HSG151).

☑ Free to download information leaflets.

   – *Protecting the public.*

   – *Keeping your site tidy.*

   – *Running a small construction site.*

☑ A *Building site safety for children* poster, which can be used to help educate children about hazards on construction sites.

C
16

Proprietary fence bases installed to minimise the risk of small children crawling under the fence panels

Safety signs

All safety signs are colour coded, as required by the Health and Safety (Signs and Signals) Regulations.

There are five types of safety sign.

☑ Prohibition. ☑ Warning. ☑ Mandatory. ☑ Emergency escape and first aid. ☑ Fire-fighting.

Prohibition signs (must not do)

No access for pedestrians

No smoking

No escape route

No mobile phones

Children must not play on this site

Scaffolding incomplete Do not use

Warning signs

General warning sign (to be accompanied where necessary by another sign)

Industrial vehicles operating

Combustible or flammable material

Explosive material

Corrosive material

Toxic material

High voltage

Overhead load

Radioactive material

Warning Stand clear of suspended loads

Danger Asbestos removal in progress

C 16

Mandatory signs (must do)

*General mandatory sign
(to be accompanied where
necessary by another sign)*

*Safety harness
must be worn*

*Safety helmet
must be worn*

*Protective eyewear
must be worn*

*Safety boots or safety
shoes must be worn*

*Safety gloves
must be worn*

Emergency escape and first aid signs

First aid

Stretcher

Emergency shower

Emergency eyewash

C
16

Fire-fighting signs

Fire hose reel

Fire ladder

*Fire emergency
telephone*

*Fire-fighting
equipment*

Fire extinguisher

*Fire alarm
call point*

 Remember, signs should be used as a reminder. All information should be covered in the site induction.

C
16

17

Fire prevention and control

What your employer should do for you

1. Carry out a fire risk assessment and keep it up to date.

2. Inform you of the fire safety plan.

3. Provide a means of detecting fire and raising the alarm.

4. Provide and maintain safe means of escape, including appropriate signage.

5. Provide an assembly point(s), with routes to the assembly point(s) kept clear of obstructions and illuminated, if required.

6. Provide a procedure to be followed in case of a fire emergency, included in site induction training and in the construction phase plan, and supply 'Action in the event of fire' notices to inform all interested parties.

7. Identify any workers who require a personal emergency evacuation plan (PEEP) and make additional arrangements, as required, for their safe evacuation.

8. Provide and arrange for the siting of sufficient numbers of suitable fire extinguishers, including a reserve stock.

9. Train the appropriate number of site staff in the correct selection and use of portable fire-fighting equipment.

10. Provide suitable storage areas for flammable, highly flammable and oxidising substances and materials (such as petrol, diesel, oils, solvents, LPG and paints).

11. Provide a hot-work permit procedure, including the appointment of a hot-work permit officer.

12. If smoking is permitted on site, monitor smoking areas and appropriate fire prevention and fire safety measures.

13. Appoint a person to make contact with the emergency services, to establish what information the emergency services will require, and to liaise with them throughout the life of the project to ensure they have sufficient project information to deal with an emergency situation if it arises.

C
17

What you should do as a supervisor

Checklist	Yes	No	N/A
1. Ensure a suitable and sufficient fire risk assessment has been carried out and is kept up to date.			
2. Inform all relevant parties of the fire safety plan.			
3. Ensure that a means of detecting fire and raising the alarm is provided.			
4. Ensure a safe means of escape, including appropriate signage, is provided and maintained.			
5. Ensure that an assembly point(s) is provided, and routes to the assembly point(s) are kept clear of obstructions and illuminated, if required.			
6. Make sure there is a procedure to be followed in case of a fire emergency and ensure this is included in site induction training and in the construction phase plan. Ensure 'Action in the event of fire' notices are displayed throughout the site, particularly at high fire risk areas.			
7. Identify and provide for any worker who requires a personal emergency evacuation plan (PEEP) and make additional arrangements, as required, for their safe evacuation.			
8. Ensure there are sufficient numbers (including a reserve stock) of suitable fire extinguishers and the extinguishers are sited, as required.			
9. In accordance with company procedures, ensure that an appropriate number of site staff are trained in the correct selection and use of portable fire-fighting equipment.			
10. Ensure suitable storage areas are provided for flammable, highly flammable and oxidising substances and materials (such as petrol, diesel, oils, solvents, LPG and paints).			
11. Provide a hot-work permit procedure, and ensure that a hot-work permit officer has been appointed.			
12. If smoking is permitted on site, monitor smoking areas and appropriate fire prevention and fire safety measures.			
13. Ensure a designated person has been appointed to make contact with the emergency services, to establish what information the emergency services will require, and to liaise with them throughout the life of the project to ensure they have sufficient project information to deal with an emergency situation if it arises.			

C
17

Introduction

Every year there are a number of large fires on construction sites. Many are in buildings that are undergoing alteration and refurbishment. The move towards timber frame and system-build housing has also been the cause of several serious fires. All can have serious consequences: people are injured and buildings so badly damaged that they have to be demolished. Some irreplaceable buildings burn and are lost forever.

The risk of fire is greater during the construction, refurbishment or demolition of buildings than at any other time, and the resultant loss of equipment, working time and financial implications can be severe.

There have been several serious fires on such sites, attributed to arson by third parties and the workforce. For this reason, effective site security and a fire safety management plan is an absolutely essential part of fire risk management.

Serious fires are devastating

Most fire fatalities are caused by people being overcome by smoke and being asphyxiated. Smoke and toxic fumes are equally as dangerous as the heat from flames.

Conditions required for a fire to start

Fire requires three elements: fuel, heat and air. Without any one of the three, combustion cannot be sustained.

Everyone on site must be aware of the following.

- ☑ There is nothing that can be done about excluding the **air** around us.

- ☑ Flammable materials **(fuel)** will be present on site for much of the time.

- ☑ On most projects there will be sources of **heat** at some time (for example, an office heater or someone using a grinder).

The fire triangle

Given that it may well be impractical to exclude any of the above elements of a fire, the practical method of preventing fires is to ensure that flammable materials and sources of heat are kept well apart.

Management of fire risks

The Regulatory Reform (Fire Safety) Order is the main piece of fire legislation in the UK and applies to construction sites. Details for Scotland and Northern Ireland differ from those for England and Wales. Construction projects operating in any of the UK countries should be checked against the relevant legislation for that country. The Regulatory Reform (Fire Safety) Order requires that, during the construction phase, the principal contractor or contractor must identify a responsible person. The responsible person must make sure that a fire risk assessment is conducted and kept up to date.

The Construction (Design and Management) Regulations (CDM) also cover the following.

- ☑ Prevention of risk from fire.
- ☑ Emergency procedures.
- ☑ Emergency escape routes and exits (which must be designated and kept clear).
- ☑ Fire detection and fire-fighting.
- ☑ The structure compartmentalised at the earliest opportunity.
- ☑ Suitable and serviceable fire extinguishers provided around the site.
- ☑ Good housekeeping to prevent the build-up of combustible waste.
- ☑ An emergency fire-action plan.
- ☑ Effective site security to prevent arson, particularly out of normal working hours.

Additional fire risks arise from work processes that form a part of the job, such as the following.

- ☑ The bulk storage of flammable substances or materials, prior to them being used.
- ☑ Any type of hot works.
- ☑ Work on high risk projects (such as timber frame and multistorey structures), because of the high fire-loading until they can be compartmentalised and fire-engineered solutions are installed.

The HSE indicates that it regards large timber frame construction and multistorey (new-build or refurbishment) jobs as particularly high risk.

The enforcing authorities for fire safety on construction sites will be the HSE and the Local Authority fire and rescue service (FRS).

For further information refer to the HSE guidance *Fire safety in construction* (HSG168).

Identifying fire risks

Many fires on site are caused by tools and equipment that produce a naked flame, sparks or hot metal (such as blowlamps, oxyacetylene or oxypropane torches and arc welding); this is true irrespective of whether the work on site is new work, maintenance, repair or demolition.

C
17

A build up of combustible material causing a fire risk

Hot works are carried out by on-site fabricators and steel erectors, plumbers, roofers and painters, sometimes in confined spaces and often near to flammable materials.

Many substances used on site (such as LPG, solvents or paint) are either flammable or give off a flammable vapour.

Protective coverings can contribute to the overall fire load – install vulnerable features as late as possible and ensure coverings conform to flame-retardant specifications wherever reasonably possible.

High energy, halogen flood lamps can produce sufficient heat to ignite dry materials and have been the cause of many fires. Where possible, alternative methods of lighting should be used (such as LED), otherwise consider the use of hot-work permits where halogen lamps are used.

Fire risk assessment

A fire risk assessment must be carried out by the responsible person. You, as a supervisor, should be aware of the findings of the fire risk assessment.

There are five steps to carrying out a fire risk assessment.
1. **Identify the hazards.** Consider how a fire could start and what could burn.
2. **Identify the people at risk.** Employees, contractors and visitors.
3. **Evaluate the risks and take necessary action.** Consider the hazards and people identified and decide what actions to take to remove and reduce the risk to people and the premises.
4. **Record, plan and train.** Keep a record of the risks and actions taken. Make a fire safety plan and make sure that people know what to do in the event of a fire.
5. **Review** the assessment regularly and check it takes account of any changes on site.

Fire prevention

The precautions necessary to prevent the outbreak of fire must be actively managed; it cannot be left to chance.

A fire safety plan should be drawn up by someone competent to do so and it should be updated as the project progresses (for example, if new hot-works activities start or escape routes are changed). A competent member of the management team should be nominated as the fire safety co-ordinator.

Construction projects have a risk of fire at all stages due to the following.

☑ Many activities involve the use of flammable materials whether they are solid (such as timber), liquid (such as vehicle fuels) or gaseous (such as LPG).

☑ Some activities require or produce a source of heat, including equipment that has a naked flame.

Examples of fire prevention measures

☑ Carrying out a fire risk assessment for the whole site and paying particular attention to areas where there is a significant or increased risk of fire (such as highly flammable liquid stores and canteens).

☑ Implementing control measures to eliminate the risk of fire or reduce it to an acceptable level.

☑ Wherever possible, using alternative, non-flammable or less flammable materials for the job. (Under the Building Regulations, designers and specifiers have a part to play in this.)

☑ Storing highly flammable and flammable materials and substances in compounds, as required by the Regulatory Reform (Fire Safety) Order, the CDM Regulations and the Dangerous Substances and Explosive Atmosphere Regulations (DSEAR).

☑ Keeping flammable materials (solids, liquids or gases) away from sources of heat, such as:

– welding and other hot work

– heaters in site cabins

– electrical or other sparks.

☑ Keeping only enough highly flammable or flammable materials or substances at the point of work for immediate work needs.

☑ Not allowing waste materials (especially not highly flammable or flammable materials, or materials that may have been contaminated by highly flammable or flammable substances) to accumulate and removing them to a designated, flammable waste store as soon as possible.

☑ Not allowing any equipment that incorporates a flame (such as blow lamps or bitumen boilers) to be left unattended whilst the flame is lit or the equipment is hot and therefore a potential source of ignition.

☑ Ensuring that fire stop doors are not propped open and are able to close as designed.

☑ Continually monitoring risk to ensure control measures remain effective as the project progresses.

☑ Keeping ventilation equipment clean, unobstructed and properly maintained.

☑ Training staff in fire awareness and the use of fire extinguishers.

Hot-work permits

Activities that increase the risk of fire should be controlled by a hot-work permit. The conditions of the permit will specify the methods of work and prevention measures that must be taken before, during and after the work.

Examples of fire prevention measures

☑ The need for fireproof screens or mats to protect people nearby and adjacent flammable materials.

☑ Provision of a serviceable fire extinguisher of an appropriate type, located where the work is being carried out.

☑ A requirement that the person carrying out the work has been trained in the use of fire extinguishers (*see also Staff training on page 217*).

☑ The need for continuous, active fire checks during the work and for a period of at least one hour afterwards (or more depending upon the risk assessment and the site rules and procedures).

☑ Processes in place to isolate smoke and heat detectors near the location of the hot works and for these to be reactivated at the end of each working shift.

Site fire safety plan

A fire safety plan must be drawn up to outline the measures that must be taken to:

☑ reduce the chances of a fire breaking out to the lowest practical level

☑ ensure the safe escape of everyone on site if a fire occurs.

Elements to be included in the plan

☑ Arrangements for the storage of highly flammable material.

☑ Fire escape routes.

☑ Locations of assembly points.

☑ Locations and type of fire-fighting appliances and alarm call points.

☑ The easy identification of staff with responsibility for fire safety by the addition of red fire marshal helmet stickers.

☑ Details of any hot-works permit scheme.

An example of a good fire point on site

 A construction site will change every day. Ensure that the fire point positions reflect these changes and the emergency escape plan and 'Action in the event of fire' notices are prominently displayed.

Emergency procedures

In the event of a fire occurring, it is essential that the alarm is raised as quickly as possible so that everyone is aware and can quickly and safely reach the designated assembly point.

- ☑ A means of fire warning must be provided on site and in site offices (hand bells, klaxons and manually or electrically operated alarms may be suitable if they are clearly audible above background noise in all areas and can be readily identified as being a fire alarm).

- ☑ 'Action in the event of fire' notices must be displayed next to fire alarm call points, external exit doors and in prominent locations (such as offices and canteens), giving (local) actions in the event of a fire. The 'Action in the event of fire' notice should contain the following.

  – Instructions for raising the alarm.

  – Information as to the whereabouts of the assembly point.

  – Instructions to report to the assembly point.

  – The locations of fire escape routes.

In case of fire – no matter how small – or if a fire is suspected:

- ☑ raise the alarm

- ☑ call the emergency services

- ☑ evacuate the site

- ☑ make sure that everyone is accounted for.

Anyone can call the emergency services when the alarm is heard, giving the address of the site and any directions that are necessary. It is better that the emergency services are informed of the fire by several people, rather than not at all.

Means of escape

Adequate means of escape must be provided to enable all employees and visitors to reach a place of safety should a fire occur.

When considering the means of escape from a building, an employer should consider the following points.

- ☑ As part of a fire safety plan, dedicated escape routes should be identified, clearly signed and adequately lit.

- ☑ All emergency exit and directional signs should be clearly visible and kept unobstructed.

- ☑ If the escape route changes for any reason, due to work being carried out, emergency escape direction indicating signs should be re-positioned to indicate the changed route.

- ☑ Signage and routes must be regularly reviewed to ensure they remain effective.

Fire escape routes can be blocked unintentionally

As well as providing emergency exit or directional signs, additional fire escape routes can be marked on the floor using a simple template

**C
17**

Burning waste

Bonfires should not be allowed on any high risk development (such as timber frame).

Bonfires are only acceptable in limited situations, such as to burn vegetation as part of site clearance for road-building projects. Where bonfires are permitted, they must be authorised and controlled by the use of a hot-work permit or other written authorisation.

There should be alternative arrangements for the proper disposal of rubbish and waste. Environmental factors and/or the Local Authority may prohibit the burning of rubbish on site.

Smoking restrictions

Across the UK, regulations enforce a ban on smoking in enclosed and substantially enclosed workplaces.

This includes all forms of normal site accommodation such as offices, canteens, toilet units and other areas of the site that are categorised as enclosed or substantially enclosed, as defined in the legislation.

☑ An *enclosed* workplace is one that has a roof or ceiling and (except for passageways, doors and windows) is wholly enclosed, whether on a temporary or permanent basis.

☑ A *substantially enclosed* workplace is one that has a roof or ceiling but there are permanent openings in the walls, the combined area of which is less than 50% of the total wall area. When calculating the total open area of any workplace, doors and/or windows that can be closed must not be counted.

Since smoking in the open air is allowed by law, provision for the safe disposal of smoking materials still has to be made. Carelessly discarded cigarette ends and matches have the potential to cause fires on site and, therefore, smoking in the open air should only be allowed in areas where it is acceptable from a fire-safety point of view.

An official 'No smoking' notice must be clearly displayed in any area where smoking is not allowed, including all entrances to enclosed work areas and all work plant and vehicles.

Site rules should state that designated smoking areas are checked at the end of each working day to ensure that any developing fire is discovered and dealt with before the site closes.

Site security and protection against arson and trespass

Children and other trespassers may start fires on site. Sites should, as far as possible, be secured against trespassers. In every case, combustible materials should be cleared away on a regular basis (daily) and not left lying around. Storage areas for flammable liquids and gases must be secured during non-working hours.

Everyone should know the correct action to take if they discover a trespasser on site during working hours.

Site offices and other accommodation

The risk of fire can arise from the use of heating and cooking appliances if they are not located, installed and maintained correctly or if they are unsuitable for the intended use.

C 17

Fuel supplies for gas-fired appliances, especially propane or butane, should be kept secured outside the building and piped in through fixed pipework. Any flexible pipework should be kept as short as possible, and used only for the final connections.

Combustible material should be kept well away from heaters and stoves. The practice of drying wet clothing in front of heaters must be prohibited. Care must be taken to see that newspapers, clothing or other combustible materials are not allowed to build up around heaters.

All heaters, cookers and any other gas-powered appliances must be turned off at the end of each working day. Portable electrical apparatus should be switched off, unplugged and disconnected from the mains supply.

Fire action notices and fire escape signs should be positioned in accordance with the fire safety plan.

Fire-fighting

Knowing what to do in the event of a fire is essential. Using the wrong fire-fighting equipment can turn an already serious situation into a deadly one. It is crucial that only people who have been trained to select and use fire extinguishers attempt to fight fires, and they can recognise when the situation is sufficiently serious that fire-fighting must be left to the fire and rescue service (FRS).

Staff training

The following points should be emphasised to all staff with regard to fire extinguishers and fire-fighting training if the fighting of small fires is to be allowed.

The decision to allow the safe fighting of fires should be taken via a risk assessment, taking into account requirements of CDM and the need to protect life from fire.

Fire safety regulations across the UK require that employers should ensure that all tasks related to fire safety are allocated only to employees with the necessary skills, knowledge and experience to carry them out safely. This will inevitably require that appropriate training is provided for those engaged in hot works, and for fire wardens, site managers and so on.

If the fighting of small fires is allowed by staff who have been trained to use fire-fighting equipment, the following points must be emphasised.

10 suggested rules for fighting fires
1. Do not put yourself in danger.
2. If you discover a fire, raise the alarm first and ensure that an evacuation is underway before fighting the fire.
3. Only use an extinguisher if it is safe and you have been trained to do so.
4. Do not let the fire come between you and your escape route. You may become trapped if the fire develops.
5. If the extinguisher does not appear to be working or is ineffective on the fire get out immediately.
6. If the fire starts to develop or gets out of control get out immediately.
7. Do not misuse fire extinguishers (for example, in boisterous play or dampening down).
8. Do not move fire extinguishers from their allocated positions.
9. Do not use fire extinguishers as door stops.
10. Immediately report (or replace) any fire extinguishers that appear to have been used, misused or damaged.

C
17

To comply with Regulation 32(5) of CDM, based upon a risk assessment, workers must be instructed in the correct use of fire-fighting equipment where it has been identified that they may need to use such equipment.

Portable fire extinguishers

Where there is a realistic possibility that staff may have to use a fire extinguisher, they should be trained in their use. In selecting staff for training, thought must be given to the size and weight of extinguishers.

There are several different types of fire extinguisher, each indicated by a different colour panel on the extinguisher body. The colours indicate the different substances that they contain and the different types of fire for which they are most effective.

With older fire extinguishers, the contrasting colour covers the whole of the body. Both old and new type water-filled extinguishers are completely red.

The fire extinguisher chart *(page 219)* shows which types of fire extinguisher should be used on different types of fire and, equally as important, which fires some extinguishers must not be used on.

All fire-fighting equipment must be maintained and inspected regularly, and all such inspections recorded in the appropriate register.

Fire blankets

Fire blankets are normally found in catering facilities. They are usually sufficient to deal with small, contained fires involving frying pans or other cooking vessels.

Anyone who may have to use a fire blanket should be trained to do so, because it involves placing the blanket gently over the burning pan of oil, which requires getting close to the fire and behaving in a controlled manner. Before a fire blanket is used, the gas or electricity supply should be turned off where circumstances permit.

A fire blanket can also be used to put out clothing that is on fire.

Fire hydrants

Adequate water for fire-fighting must be available. This should be achieved by utilising the fire hydrants fixed to street mains or by providing a separate supply. The amount of water likely to be required should be discussed with the FRS and the water supply company as part of the liaison process.

All fire hydrants must be clear of obstructions and suitably marked. Particular care should be taken to ensure that site plant, delivery lorries or workers' cars are not parked close to or over hydrants.

It should be noted that it is an offence for any vehicle to obstruct a fire hydrant and that the FRS have the power to initiate the prosecution of offenders.

Fire hydrant. The upper number indicates the size in mm of the main serving the hydrant (100 mm in this instance). The lower number indicates the distance from the sign to where the hydrant is located (3 m in this instance)

C
17

Fire wardens

Where the complexity of the site and/or the accommodation units make it difficult to establish that everyone has been evacuated from the site, it will be necessary to appoint fire wardens. It is generally accepted that a fire warden manages an area whereas a fire marshal manages a site.

A warden will 'sweep' and report to the marshal, who, in turn, reports to and advises the responsible fire officer. Each fire warden should be allocated an area to 'sweep' in the event of an evacuation to make sure that no-one remains on site. Fire wardens can also be used to monitor the effectiveness of the general fire precautions and contribute to the ongoing development of the fire safety plan.

Types of portable fire extinguisher and what to use them on

Extinguishing medium	Water for wood, paper, textile and solid material fires	Foam for liquid fires	Powder for liquid and electrical fires	Carbon dioxide for liquid and electrical fires	Wet chemical for wood, paper, textile, cooking oil and solid material fires
Colour of panel	Red	Cream	Blue	Black	Yellow
Where not to use	Do not use on liquid, electrical or metal fires	Do not use on electrical or metal fires	Do not use on metal fires	Do not use on metal fires	Do not use on liquid, gas or electrical fires

Note: – where the term 'electrical' is used it should be read as 'fires involving electricity or electrical equipment'
– dry powder extinguishers may be provided in addition to or substituted for water, foam or carbon dioxide extinguishers
– extinguishers used to control Class B fires (flammable liquids) will not work on Class F fires (cooking oils) because of the high temperatures generated.

 Ensure that you read the instructions on a fire extinguisher before using it.

Highly flammable liquids and liquefied petroleum gases

Highly flammable liquids (HFLs) and liquefied petroleum gases (LPG) are used extensively in the construction industry.

A spillage, escape or leak of HFLs or LPG will create a significant risk of fire if the vapour or gas comes into contact with a source of ignition. The following must be carried out to maintain fire safety when dealing with HFLs and gases.

- ☑ Handle and transport them safely.
- ☑ Store them safely.
- ☑ Use them safely.

All three situations require that suitable fire extinguishers are located nearby to aid escape.

Highly flammable liquids

Any liquid that gives off a vapour that can be ignited at a temperature below 32ºC is classed as a highly flammable liquid. Common examples include those listed below.

- ☑ Petrol.
- ☑ Thinners.
- ☑ Solvents.
- ☑ Adhesives.

The following precautions should be observed when using HFLs.

- ☑ Only get out the quantity that is likely to be used in one day, or less, if practical and keep the remainder in a fireproof store.
- ☑ Keep containers closed at all times.
- ☑ Dispense or decant HFLs in designated areas and over drip trays to avoid spillage.

- ☑ Quickly clean up any spillages that occur and safely dispose of the material used to soak up the spillage.
- ☑ Provide suitable fire-fighting measures in case of emergency.
- ☑ Prohibit anything that could create naked flames, sparks or other means of ignition.
- ☑ Treat empty drums and containers with care (they will contain a mixture of vapour and air that could be explosive).
- ☑ HFLs or solvents should not be used to clean floors or surfaces as they could evaporate and create a flammable atmosphere – always use a detergent cleaner instead.
- ☑ When using a HFL or solvent to clean or soak brushes, always use a container with a lid, and keep it closed and carry out the cleaning in a well ventilated area.

Do not bring petrol into a timber frame or enclosed building. Use designated refuelling points or preferably equipment powered by another means

C
17

Liquefied petroleum gases

Liquefied petroleum gas is stored in cylinders at high pressure, which keeps it in a liquid state. When released to the air, the pressure is reduced and it reverts to a gas. Because it is stored as a liquid it is essential that LPG cylinders are secured in an upright position when being used, transported or stored.

LPG is used extensively in the construction industry as a means of producing heat during some work processes (such as heating bitumen boilers, soldering, or as a means of heating or cooking).

There are two types of LPG: propane and butane, which operate at different pressures. It is, therefore, essential that no attempt is made to use equipment designed for use with propane on butane or vice versa.

Another hazardous feature of LPG is that it is heavier than air. If allowed to leak, the gas will sink to the ground and find the lowest point (such as drains, excavations, cellars and so on). It will form an explosive reservoir just waiting for a source of ignition.

LPG and air in the correct concentration can form an explosive mixture. One litre of liquid LPG can produce more than 250 litres of gas. If that quantity were to be ignited, the resultant explosion could destroy a building. If LPG cylinders are being engulfed by a fire there is a serious risk of the cylinders exploding. The area should be evacuated and a cordon formed to keep people out of the area.

When not in use, cylinder valves must be closed to prevent the possibility of leakage. Gas cylinders must be kept in a store that will allow any leakage to disperse safely.

Frosting on the body of the cylinder may indicate that the gas discharge rate is too high and there is a need to reduce the gas flow or couple-up another cylinder by means of a manifold. Seek advice if there is any doubt.

An LPG leak can be detected by the smell of the gas or by frosting around the leak. If the leak can be isolated or turned off, do so. However, if that is not possible, and it is safe to do so, the cylinder should be moved into an open, unoccupied space and the fire service called. If the cylinder is involved in a fire, evacuate the area immediately and inform the fire service of the situation.

Never use a naked flame to detect a leak.

For further information refer to the Construction (Design and Management) Regulations chapter in Section A and the fire prevention and control chapter in Section C of GE 700 *Construction site safety*.

C
17

C
17

18

Electrical safety

What your employer should do for you

1. Put arrangements in place to check for overhead and underground power cables and provide appropriate safety measures.

2. Implement permits to work and isolation systems for work to electrical supplies, and ensure that they are monitored regularly.

3. Ensure that isolation points are clearly identified.

4. Put controls in place to prevent unauthorised use, alteration or repair to the electrical supply, tools and equipment.

5. Ensure that the electricity supply is tested and inspected regularly in line with regulations.

6. Plan that the preference for using 110 V or battery-powered tools is followed by the company.

7. Provide you with information on the hazards associated with the use of electrical tools and equipment.

8. Arrange for electrical tools and equipment to have regular inspections and portable appliance testing (PAT), and that records are kept.

9. Provide the work team with training in actions to be taken in the event of electrocution.

10. Provide and maintain adequate site and task lighting.

11. Ensure that the length of trailing cables is minimised to prevent danger.

12. Ensure that in the event of power failure there is an emergency escape plan in place to ensure safe egress.

C
18

What you should do as a supervisor

Checklist	Yes	No	N/A
1. Mark up and maintain warnings for overhead and underground power cables.			
2. Issue permits to work and isolations systems for work to electrical supplies, and ensure that they are used correctly.			
3. Check that isolation points are clearly identified and unobstructed.			
4. Prevent unauthorised use, alteration or repair to the electrical supply, tools and equipment.			
5. Test and inspect the electricity supply regularly in line with procedures.			
6. Use 110 V or battery-powered tools as a preference, and in line with procedures.			
7. Ensure that workers are provided with information on the hazards associated with the use of electrical tools and equipment.			
8. Present electrical tools and equipment for regular inspections and portable appliance testing (PAT), and keep records up to date.			
9. Check that the work team have training in actions to be taken in the event of electrocution.			
10. Maintain site and task lighting.			
11. Minimise the length of trailing cables to minimise danger.			
12. Check that the emergency escape plan is in place to ensure safe egress in the event of an emergency.			

C
18

Introduction

Each year, construction industry workers are killed or injured as a result of unsafe electrical installations, unsafe practices or defective tools. The danger arises as follows.

Danger of death

- Electricity is invisible; it never tells you it is there or it is coming, and it can kill you.

- During an electric shock low levels of current (just 1 mA (milliamp)) can be enough to throw you off balance and make you fall. Higher levels of current cause muscles to spasm and can make it impossible to let go of the object you are holding. At 50 mA, the skin will burn at the point of contact and the heart can be affected, which may result in fatal injury.

- Electricity can cause sparks (arcing). In places where there is airborne dust or flammable vapours, those sparks can cause explosions.

- Site electrical distribution systems are temporary, often operate in harsh (including wet) conditions and are often modified as the demand for supplies change.

- Overhead cables are often uninsulated, meaning that the electricity will flow through anything that will conduct electricity (such as a raised excavator bucket or scaffold poles).

- Overhead cables often carry high voltage supplies, which means that the electricity can jump (arc) to anything nearby that will conduct electricity without it actually touching the cable.

- The higher the voltage, the greater the risk of the electrical energy jumping (arcing). In addition, if there is more moisture in the air, it is more likely that the energy will arc and it may arc further.

- The existence of underground cables is sometimes not established, or they are not accurately located before excavation of the ground starts.

 A little knowledge is often sufficient to make electrical equipment function, but a much higher level of knowledge and experience is always needed to ensure safety.

Definitions used in connection with electricity

- *Conductor* means any substance or material capable of carrying electrical energy.

- *Live* means equipment that is at a voltage by being connected to a source of electricity.

- *Charged* means that the item has acquired a charge, either because it is live or it has become charged by another means, such as static or induction charging.

- *Dead* means a conductor is neither live or charged.

- *Isolated* means secured disconnection (for example, the circuit, circuit conductor or conductor has been separated from the source of electrical energy, and the form of disconnection is secured in such a way that the person working on the system has control over the point of disconnection). It must be understood that disconnecting or isolating a circuit, a circuit conductor or a conductor does not mean or equate to that circuit, circuit conductor or conductor being dead.

Disconnection means physical detachment of a circuit, circuit conductor or conductor from a source of electrical energy. Disconnection does not mean or equate to that circuit, circuit conductor or conductor being dead.

Relevant legislation

Management of Health and Safety at Work Regulations

These regulations require that employers carry out a suitable and sufficient risk assessment of the work they do and put in place measures to control the risks arising from the work. In the context of this chapter, this will mean that procedures and practices are put in place to eliminate or reduce the risk of anyone being harmed as a result of coming into contact with electricity.

 For further information on carrying out risk assessments refer to Chapter A04 Risk assessments, method statements and permits to work.

Provision and Use of Work Equipment Regulations (PUWER)

Electrical equipment and hand tools are classified as *work equipment* as defined under PUWER. As such, employers have a duty to ensure that electrical hand tools and equipment:

- are suitable for their intended purpose
- are well-maintained and inspected as necessary
- are fitted with suitable controls
- are fitted with guards as necessary
- can be effectively isolated from the supply
- carry appropriate markings and warning notices.

Furthermore, employers have a duty to ensure that users of work equipment receive adequate health and safety information, including written instructions, where appropriate, on the use of the equipment.

 For further information on PUWER refer to Chapter C20 Work equipment and hand-held tools.

Electricity at Work Regulations

The requirements of these regulations cover fixed and temporary electrical distribution systems rather than electrical hand tools and equipment. The supply system that feeds mains power onto the site and distributes it to site offices, canteens and so on, must be installed, inspected and maintained in accordance with these regulations.

Managing the risks

Treat electricity with respect. Always assume that an electrical supply is live unless you have proof that it is not.

Do not tamper with, work on or near the site electrical distribution system unless you are competent to do so and you have been authorised to make the necessary changes.

The electricity supply company must install the main supply to the site distribution board. Further distribution to site offices and other accommodation must be installed by competent electrical contractors. All mains (230 V) circuits should be supplied through residual current circuit breakers located in the main distribution board.

C
18

Safe systems of work

A risk assessment should identify any risk of electric shock and the measures that must be taken to ensure that work can be carried out safely. In some circumstances a permit to work system will be necessary to ensure that the electrical supply is isolated and remains isolated until the work is complete. All circuits at the point of work must be proved dead by the use of a suitable test lamp and proving unit. Power should only be restored on the express authority of the site's electrical authority (permit to work (electrical) issuer).

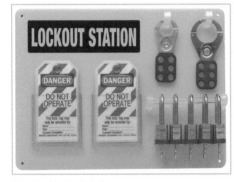

Electrical lock-off devices

Wherever practical, work should not be carried out on live equipment or near to a live electrical supply. If possible the power should be isolated. The Electricity at Work Regulations require that work on or near exposed live electrical conductors can only be carried out in the following conditions.

☑ When it is unreasonable for the supply to be made dead.

☑ When it is reasonable for live working to be carried out.

☑ When suitable and sufficient precautions are taken (for example, appropriate tools, screening and PPE).

Low-voltage hand tools

The safest electrical hand tools operate from low-voltage batteries. An increasing range of battery-powered hand tools are becoming available.

All non-battery electrical hand tools used on building or construction sites should operate from a 110 V supply. The way that the system is wired results in a supply voltage of effectively 55 V. This will reduce the severity of any electric shock.

The 110 V supply will usually be derived from a transformer that is plugged into a 230 V (mains) supply or from a portable generator. The power lead, casing or plug will be yellow in colour signifying that it is 110 V equipment. A round, blue plastic plug or a domestic 3 pin plug signifies that the equipment is 230 V (mains) powered. 400 V (three-phase) cable casing and plugs and sockets should be red.

Plugs and sockets should be manufactured to BS EN 60309-2:1999. This standard will prevent accidental or intentional connection of tools to power supplies of the wrong voltage.

Mains-powered hand tools and equipment

Wherever possible, the use of electrical hand tools that operate directly off the mains supply should be avoided and battery or 110 V tools used instead.

However, where the use of a mains-operated tool or other equipment is unavoidable, possibly because there is not a 110 V version, a portable residual current device (RCD) should be used. RCDs are often known as power breakers; they plug into the mains socket and have an inbuilt socket into which the tool is then plugged.

C
18

An RCD will detect an electrical fault and disconnect the supply to the tool quickly, and before an electric shock would be sensed by the user.

 RCDs have a test button that should be operated before each use (daily user check), so the operator connecting to that RCD proves the effectiveness of the RCD for themselves.

Proprietary battery banks can be hired to facilitate safe and secure recharging

The supplies for other mains-operated electrical equipment (such as office and catering equipment), should be fed through a fixed RCD at the main distribution panel. **Fixed** RCDs should be subject to daily user checks, a formal weekly inspection and a combined inspection and test before first use, and then every three months. **Portable** RCDs should be subject to daily user checks, a formal weekly inspection and a combined inspection and test before first use, and then every month.

Care of electrical hand tools and other equipment

Working with damaged electrical tools or equipment can cause harm. Before starting work, a visual inspection should always be made to check for:

☑ damaged casings

☑ cables that are cut, abraded or pulled from the plug

☑ damaged plugs

☑ the condition of the socket.

Wires being pulled from a plug can be caused by:

☑ pulling or dragging cables across the ground

☑ picking the tool up by its cable

☑ overstretching the cable

☑ flex clamps in the plug not secured tightly enough.

 If a fault is found the equipment should be repaired or replaced.

**C
18**

Electrical hand tools should be subjected to a periodic test of their electrical safety, known as portable appliance testing (PAT). PUWER does not specify what testing needs to be done, by whom or how frequently. This allows the duty holder to select precautions appropriate to the risk. Electrical hand tools used in a construction environment can be roughly treated and it is recommended that they should have a combined inspection and test before they are first used and then as follows.

☑ Every month for 230 V tools and portable RCDs.

☑ Every three months for 110 V tools and fixed RCDs.

☑ Every year for equipment in site offices. (The RCD at the mains distribution board should have an electrical and mechanical test every three months.)

These suggested frequencies for inspection and testing are not legal requirements.

 For further information refer to the HSE publication *Maintaining portable electrical equipment* (HSG107).

If an electrical hand tool becomes defective whilst it is in use, the user should stop work immediately and disconnect the tool from the supply. It should not be used again until it has been repaired by a competent person, who should test the item and declare it safe for use.

In many cases a user will be capable of replacing a blown fuse in the plug of a 230 V tool. However, the question that must first be asked is 'Why did the fuse blow?'. Repairs must only be carried out by someone who is competent to do so. If a fuse blows, and you are competent and authorised to replace it, carry out the followng steps.

☑ Unplug the tool from the supply.

☑ Look for obvious signs of damage.

☑ If there are no obvious signs of damage, replace the fuse with another fuse of the correct rating.

☑ If a repair has been carried out or a new tool has been issued and the fuse blows for a second time, report the occurrence to the site's electrical engineer.

☑ If a tool is defective, label the tool as such and put it where no-one else will be able to use it until an authorised repair by a competent person has been carried out. (Sites and contractors should have a means of quarantining defective equipment.)

Dealing with electric shock

☑ Could you help someone who has had an electric shock?

☑ Do you know that what you do could make the difference between life and death?

☑ Do you know how to apply resuscitation correctly?

☑ Have your employees been trained to do it correctly?

☑ If you were the casualty, is there anybody who could treat you?

☑ Do you have the 'Danger of electric shock' notices available?

☑ Can these notices or posters be seen by everyone? Are they well positioned?

☑ Are they read and, more importantly, understood?

C
18

Electric shock action

If the casualty is in contact with what could be a live electrical supply, switch off the power if possible and shout for help. Never assume the power has been turned off.

If the power cannot be switched off, you must respond in the following way.

☑ Do not touch the casualty with bare hands.

☑ If practical and safe, move the casualty clear of the electrical source, or the source away from the casualty, with a broom or something else wooden – never use an object which could conduct electricity (such as a metal pole).

☑ Seek prompt help from a first aider and get qualified medical assistance.

Electricity can kill. The correct information, instruction, training and supervision helps keep workers and others from coming into contact with unsafe electricity. Never put yourself in danger.

☑ **For further information refer to the electrical safety chapter in Section C of the GE 700 *Construction site safety*.**

☑ **For further information on working close to overhead cables refer to Chapter D26 *Underground and overhead services*.**

C
18

C
18

19

Temporary works

What your employer should do for you

1. Have procedures for managing temporary works, including the appointment of temporary works co-ordinators and temporary works supervisors, if appropriate.

2. Tell you the name of the temporary works co-ordinator if one is appointed.

3. Tell you the name(s) of the temporary works supervisor(s), how their activities might affect your work area, and their duties.

4. Provide access to a register of temporary works.

5. Ensure you have the appropriate information, training and experience before appointing you in any formal capacity in relation to temporary works.

6. Clarify your supervisor role in relation to temporary works.

7. Tell you who to ask if you have a concern or query about temporary works which you are not able to answer or deal with.

C
19

What you should do as a supervisor

Checklist	Yes	No	N/A
1. Ensure you know whether a temporary works co-ordinator has been appointed.			
2. Ensure you are aware whether you have been appointed as a supervisor (in the normal sense of the word) or, more formally, as a temporary works supervisor.			
3. Ensure you are clear about your duties in relation to temporary works.			
4. Ensure you are aware of what temporary works are under your remit (these should be listed in the register of temporary works).			
5. Whatever your role, ensure you have the skills and experience to undertake the task.			
6. Ask if you are unsure about anything relating to temporary works.			

C
19

Introduction

 Temporary works is defined in BS 5975 as: 'Parts of the works that allow or enable construction of, protect, support or provide access to, the permanent works and which might or might not remain in place at the completion of the works.'

Temporary works are a vital element of most projects. Despite not being part of the final structure, they often have the potential to cause harm or delays. It is essential to ensure that they are competently designed, used, maintained and dismantled.

Temporary works can take many forms, such as hoardings, access roads, excavations, propping and building supports. It is important that, whatever the form, it is clear who is responsible for each temporary works structure, and that those with the responsibility for them have the appropriate skills to deal with them safely and effectively.

Temporary works showing piling to facilitate civil engineering works

Examples of temporary works

	Example	Comment
1.	Site hoardings	These should be designed to the guidance contained in *Hoardings: a guide to good practice* (TWf2012:01), published by the Temporary Works Forum.
2.	Site cabins	Foundations need to be suitable and, if stacked, checked for stability.
3.	Access roads, granular platforms	These should be designed to recognised standards.
4.	Propping	All these examples require an engineered solution.
5.	Excavation support	
6.	Building support	
7.	Formwork, falsework	

Your responsibilities as a supervisor

You should be satisfied that temporary works within your area of responsibility are safe. If you are in any doubt about the competencies required to ensure that temporary works remain safe, or of the action needed if they are not safe, the temporary works supervisor should speak to the temporary works co-ordinator or their manager.

C 19

Temporary works supervisors should not accept any instructions or attempt any action to try to make the temporary works safe if they do not have the required competencies.

Temporary works co-ordinator or supervisor

In recognition of the safety-critical nature of temporary works, it is established practice, but not a legal requirement, for contractor organisations to designate appropriate individuals as temporary works co-ordinators (appointed by the principal contractor) or temporary works supervisors (appointed by contractors). Temporary works supervisors need to understand what has to be done to ensure temporary works are safe, as well as when the actions need to be taken, by whom and when. Temporary works supervisors are specifically appointed to the role and are given a written schedule of their duties by the temporary works co-ordinator.

This does not mean that any supervisor can act as a temporary works supervisor. You should not be offered nor accept such appointments unless you are authorised to do so and fulfil the competency criteria.

Requirements

As temporary works can cause harm to people, they are covered by legislation in the same way as other site activities. The main legislation relevant to all site activity is the Construction (Design and Management) Regulations (CDM).

Certain forms of temporary works need to be inspected. These include working platforms, which require inspection by competent persons before use, after any significant event that may have disturbed the platform, and at intervals not greater than seven days.

The precise requirements are complex and should be discussed and confirmed with the temporary works co-ordinator.

The temporary works co-ordinator may require other temporary works to be inspected. The temporary works supervisor should discuss the necessary competencies for these inspections with them.

Duties of the temporary works supervisor

The temporary works supervisor's role and duties should be in accordance with the industry standard BS 5975. Their specific duties will be confirmed by the temporary works co-ordinator; it is likely that they will include the following.

☑ **Supervision and checking.** This is the core role, applicable to all temporary works supervisors.

☑ **Issuing load/unload permits.** These are key stages in the construction process that will be undertaken by the temporary works supervisor, if and when requested, to do so by the temporary works co-ordinator.

☑ **Assisting the temporary works co-ordinator** in discharging the responsibilities that the temporary works co-ordinator is permitted to delegate. This is only permissible if the temporary works supervisor selected has the necessary skills and experience for each individual task delegated to them.

The Temporary Works forum (TWf) consists of several construction organisations and provides guidance and information about temporary works. It has produced a number of publications on a range of related issues, including legislation, design and erection. For further information visit the TWf website.

C
19

C
19

20

Work equipment and hand-held tools

What your employer should do for you

1. Ensure that all plant and work equipment is inspected, maintained in good working order and tested, where required, to ensure that it is fit for purpose.

2. Ensure that statutory and other records are kept up to date and ensure that all work equipment is marked with a unique identification.

3. Set up a procedure to allow for defective equipment (including equipment that has either failed a statutory inspection or whose statutory inspection report or certificate has expired) to be removed from service and securely quarantined, to prevent it being brought back into service until it passes a thorough examination and/or is provided with a valid inspection report or certificate.

4. Implement procedures for the inspection and repairing or replacing of faulty or damaged work equipment and tools and rectify any faults developed through misuse or neglect.

5. Ensure that operators are suitably trained on specific plant or equipment and are aware of hazards associated with its operation.

6. Maintain up to date lists or registers of authorised drivers and operators.

7. Provide relevant information in relation to specific items of plant or work equipment where restrictions of use apply, where such information is kept and by whom.

8. Monitor that plant and equipment is being used safely and as intended.

9. Ensure that traffic routes are suitable and are observed by site vehicles as applicable.

10. Prevent any instance of overloading or over-stressing of plant.

11. Ensure that roll-over protective structures (ROPS), falling object protective structures (FOPS) and operator restraint systems are fitted, subject to inspection, and used in line with manufacturer's guidance, and training is provided.

12. Monitor that operators of mobile or self-propelled plant have adequate visibility in all directions and all visibility aids are in good order.

C
20

What you should do as a supervisor

Checklist	Yes	No	N/A
1. Ensure that all plant and equipment under your control is appropriately maintained, thoroughly examined, inspected and tested, with the correct certification issued in line with manufacturers' guidance and legal requirements.			
2. Ensure that any equipment that fails a statutory inspection, examination or test, or if its certification date has expired, is placed in quarantine and its use prevented until such time as it passes the required inspection and a valid test certificate is issued by a competent person.			
3. Maintain statutory records, keep registers updated and ensure that all work equipment is marked in a unique and identifiable way.			
4. Arrange for the repair or replacement of equipment and tools and rectify any faults reported by the operator.			
5. Check that operators are suitably trained on specific items of plant or equipment and are aware of hazards associated with its operation and the need to report shortfalls, and are authorised to use the item of plant.			
6. Update lists or registers of authorised drivers and operators.			
7. Retain and provide relevant information in relation to specific items of plant or equipment where restrictions of use apply, where this information is kept and by whom.			
8. Check that plant and equipment is being used safely and stop work where necessary.			
9. Ensure that traffic routes are suitable, safe and kept clear of obstructions.			
10. Manage the prevention of any instance of overloading or over-stressing of plant.			
11. Check that roll-over protective structures (ROPS), falling object protective structures (FOPS) and operator restraint systems are used properly and inspected accordingly.			
12. Ensure that operators of mobile or self-propelled plant have adequate visibility in all directions.			

C 20

Introduction

Work equipment is defined as any equipment used in the course of carrying out work. The following are included within this definition.

- [✓] Hand tools (such as hammers, trowels and handsaws).

- [✓] Small plant (such as cement mixers and portable generators).

- [✓] Construction plant (such as excavators, dumpers and mobile compressors).

- [✓] Access equipment (such as ladders and mobile towers).

Legislation

Provision and Use of Work Equipment Regulations

The Provision and Use of Work Equipment Regulations (PUWER) apply to all work equipment and sets the standards for the provision and use of work equipment. The primary objective is to provide all workers with equipment that is safe for use.

The following is a list of duties on the employer.

- [✓] Ensure that any equipment provided is safe and is constructed or assembled so that it is safe and fit for purpose.

- [✓] Ensure that any adapted equipment is adapted in such a manner that the item is safe and fit for purpose. Any adaptation shall meet with all necessary and essential health and safety requirements.

- [✓] Prior to providing work equipment, consider where it will be used and the working conditions, to ensure that neither the work equipment nor the conditions in which it is to be used pose a risk to the health or safety of the operator or any other person when the item is being used as intended and within its design parameters.

- [✓] Ensure that work equipment is properly maintained, inspected, and tested, as necessary, by a competent and authorised person.

- [✓] Ensure that all dangerous parts of a machine or an item of equipment are guarded so far as it is practicable to do so.

- [✓] Provide or ensure adequate and appropriate information, instruction, training, and where necessary, supervision for the safe use of the equipment.

- [✓] Ensure, where appropriate, that work equipment is fitted with effective and clearly marked controls and that it can easily be disconnected and isolated from all sources of energy (power).

The regulations also require that, where necessary, mobile plant is fitted with the following.

- [✓] Roll-over protection (a roll-over cage or frame) for the operator where, otherwise, there would be a danger of injury if the machine were to roll over.

- [✓] Seat belts (restraints) where, otherwise, there would be a danger of the operator being thrown from the machine, or being crushed by it, if it were to roll over.

- [✓] Falling object protection where, otherwise, the operator would be at risk of injury from falling objects or materials.

Suitable and sufficient arrangements shall be made to ensure that mobile equipment is not operated by untrained, unqualified or unauthorised persons.

These control measures and safety devices should be identified in the employer's suitable and sufficient risk assessment, which must be completed prior to the provision of the equipment.

**C
20**

Plant must be well maintained, suitable for the job in hand and used or operated only by trained, competent and properly authorised persons

Management of Health and Safety at Work Regulations

Every employer shall make a suitable and sufficient assessment of the risks to the health and safety of their employees, to which they are exposed whilst they are at work, and the risks to the health and safety of persons who are not in their employment but are at risk of injury or harm arising out of, or in connection with, the conduct of their business activities. The employer must put such control measures in place to eliminate the risks or reduce them, so far as is reasonably practicable, to a safe level. In the context of work equipment this process will often involve the following.

☑ Selecting the most suitable piece of work equipment for the work to be done, considering the conditions under which it will be used.

☑ Ensuring that it is adequately inspected and maintained and used in a safe manner.

☑ Ensuring that those who will use the work equipment are properly trained, competent, authorised and appropriately supervised. The degree of formal training required will depend on the following.

– The complexity of the work equipment.

– The potential for harm if it is not used correctly.

Establishing a person's competency may involve checking that they hold valid competency cards.

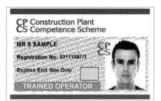 

Written procedures, information and instruction

Adequate levels of information and instruction must be provided to operators of any equipment, along with written procedures that are easily understood. These could include the following.

☑ Possible risks that may be found and subsequent precautions to be taken.

☑ The conditions in which, and methods by which, the equipment shall be used.

☑ Any foreseeable abnormal conditions that might arise and the appropriate action to be taken.

☑ Any conclusions that can be drawn from experience with the equipment.

**C
20**

☑ Safe methods of working.

☑ The inspection regime, including pre-use and frequency of formal documented inspections.

Associated legislation

Other chapters in this book provide details on legislation that is specific to work equipment in the following situations.

☑ Working at height (for example, fragile roofs, ladders and scaffolds).

☑ Mechanical lifting operations (for example, cranes, slings and telescopic handlers).

☑ Confined spaces (for example, cellars, manholes and service tunnels).

☑ Personal protection (personal protective equipment (PPE) and respiratory protective equipment (RPE)).

Mobile plant and vehicles

Accidents involving plant and vehicles that result in serious injuries and fatalities are all too common. Many of these accidents are as a result of the following.

☒ The operator's limited range of vision when at the controls.

☒ Semi-automatic quick hitch releasing devices not having the retaining pin or bar replaced after attachment changes, or automatic devices not being checked for closure.

☒ Passengers being carried on plant that is not designed to carry them.

☒ Untrained and/or unauthorised operators using mobile plant.

As a minimum, all mobile plant should be equipped with the following.

☑ A reversing audible alarm.

☑ At least one amber beacon that is switched on when the machine is in operation.

☑ Fully working lights and indicators.

☑ Extra operator vision aids (such as additional mirrors or CCTV), to give all round visibility or as near as possible to it.

☑ Roll-over protection, seat belts (restraints) and falling object protection where appropriate.

☑ Cab guards, where required (such as demolition excavators).

Prevention and control measures

☑ Unauthorised use of machines, both during and out of site working hours, is easily prevented by implementing a system of close control for keys and other starting devices, along with shutters to prevent vandalism and theft.

☑ Recorded pre-user checks by the operator before start-up coupled with the weekly recorded inspections of plant.

☑ Avoiding fuel and other spills by ensuring mobile plant refuelling only takes place at designated refuelling points, using refuelling pumps and nozzles, or funnels where refuelling has to be carried out manually. Providing spill kits and making sure any spills are promptly cleaned up, reported and investigated.

**C
20**

☑ Where static equipment is located, giving consideration to refuelling and replenishment of consumables as part of the siting assessment. Static equipment should ideally be set up on impervious platforms so that any spillage or leak is easily detectable and is contained within drip trays or similar containment devices (such as spill mats). Drip trays and spill kits should be provided. Refuelling or other replenishments (such as oil) should be carried out using a safe system of work that limits the potential for spills, such as using bowsers or hand pumps with nozzle type dispensers or, where that is not practicable, using funnels.

☑ Preventing overloading and handling of unsafe loads.

☑ Stopping work if you suspect a problem.

 For information on (logistics) plant movement, pedestrian segregation and traffic management refer to Chapter C21 Site transport safety.

Abrasive wheels

Diamond blades, angle grinders and disc cutting tools

 These tools can cause serious injury if not used correctly by trained and competent staff. Nearly half of all accidents involving abrasive wheels are due to an unsafe system of work or operator error.

They can inflict a severe injury to the user, and others, in an accident. They operate at high speeds and can cause serious personal injury in several different ways.

☑ The operator's hand coming into contact with the revolving wheel or disc.

☑ Particles (such as hot metal or sparks) being thrown off while in use.

☑ Disintegration (shattering or loss of segments) caused by a damaged, incorrectly fitted or overspeeding disc, or improper use (such as using the wrong disc or wheel for the task).

☑ Loose or ill-fitting clothing or PPE becoming entangled in the rotating wheel or disc.

☑ The wheel or disc shattering and fragments projecting beyond the work area.

Injuries to hands through contact with a rotating wheel or disc can be severe. Users should remember that guards are only effective when the equipment and the guard are used in the correct manner.

The most common causes of accidents involving abrasive wheels are listed below.

☑ Using the wrong type of disc or wheel.

☑ Incorrect mounting.

☑ Ignition from the stream of hot sparks and the heat generated in the material being worked on.

☑ Failure to properly secure the item being worked.

☑ Overspeeding due to an incorrect disc, blade or wheel being used.

☑ Misuse by the operator.

☑ Diamond blades losing segments, particularly if not used in line with employer and manufacturer instructions and training provided.

C 20

Using the wrong blade

A worker used a concrete blade to cut a series of post holes through an asphalt surface to receive concrete fence posts.

The blade failed and several 50 mm-long segment blade tips broke off at high speed, two of which embedded deep within his knee cap. He suffered high blood loss, was airlifted to hospital and the embedded blade tips were removed during reconstructive surgery. He was off work for over six months and never fully recovered.

Providing and using an asphalt blade would have avoided the accident.

Using abrasive wheels

Abrasive wheels should only be mounted by a trained and competent person appointed (in writing) by the employer.

Operators must ensure the following.

- ☑ They have been trained and authorised to use the abrasive wheel.

- ☑ They are wearing the appropriate PPE, including eye protection and a face shield.

- ☑ The rest is set as close as possible to the wheel (maximum gap 3 mm), on a firm, clean and unobstructed underfoot base.

- ☑ The spark guard is set.

- ☑ The wheel is started and observed as it comes to operating speed.

- ☑ Plan their own working posture and position to avoid injury in case of slippage or other unintended movement.

- ☑ Maintain a firm grip when operating.

- ☑ Use adequate protection from flying debris (such as a screen or exclusion zone) to protect others in the vicinity.

- ☑ Ensure adequate support and stability of the material being worked on by the correct use of the work platform or rest.

- ☑ Be aware of the health hazards (such as flying debris, dust, noise and vibration). This will usually involve the following.

  - Keeping other people out of the area.

  - Wearing suitable RPE, hearing protection, high-impact eye protection and suitable, well-fitting gloves.

  - Not working in an area with restricted ventilation so dust and fumes cannot disperse.

  - Using a dust collector (on-tool extraction) or wet cutting that collects or dampens down the dust.

  - Ensuring that guards are in place, adjusted and secure.

  - Doing the job in short spells or by job rotation if hand-arm vibration has been assessed to be an issue.

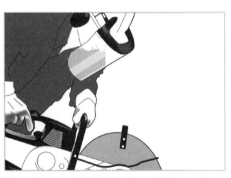

Wear the appropriate PPE and ensure the guards are properly set

C
20

For further information refer to the plant and work equipment chapter in Section C of GE 700 *Construction site safety*.

Portable fixing tools

Cartridge-operated tools

These tools have the potential to be highly dangerous in untrained hands as they look and perform like guns.

Cartridge-operated tools may be used for installing repetitive fixings on site and are either piston-operated by the cartridge (indirect) or with a cartridge operating the fixing device (direct). They may be high or low powered.

The hazards most commonly associated with cartridge tools are listed below.

☑ Lack of knowledge and training.

☑ Deliberate misuse, including boisterous play, by pointing the tool at someone.

☑ Poor inspection and maintenance.

☑ Incorrect storage and disposal of spent nail gun caps or cartridges.

There are two particular problem areas associated with the use of these tools – **penetration** and **ricochets**.

Causes of penetration

☑ The cartridge being too powerful resulting in the fixing passing through the background material, often at high speed.

☑ Thin materials or voids in the structure being worked on.

☑ Changes in density of the material being worked on.

☑ The material density not being ascertained before starting work.

Causes of ricochets

☑ The fixing passing straight through the material being secured.

☑ Second attempts at the same hole.

☑ Working on excessively hard materials (hardened steel or welded areas).

☑ Not holding the tool square.

☑ Working too close to the edge of the material.

☑ Obstructions inside the material (reinforcing rods or dense aggregate).

Precautions

In the event of a misfire, keep the tool pressed against the workface for at least 30 seconds then follow the manufacturer's instructions closely to ensure the tool does not fire unexpectedly.

Operatives must be adequately trained in the use of equipment and made aware of the hazards. They should be tested for colour blindness, as cartridges are colour coded for identification.

Safety helmets, high impact eye protection and hearing protection should be worn at all times when cartridge-operated tools are being used.

C
20

247

Take care when using the tool since any recoil could lead to loss of balance. Always work from a suitable working platform, where loss of balance will not create a secondary risk.

 Never use a cartridge tool while on an unsecured ladder.

Select the correct cartridge, carry out trial fixings and check behind the structure to be worked on to prevent these hazards. Also carefully align tools, examine structures and use low-powered, indirect-acting tools.

Gas-powered tools

Poor practice and lack of concentration can lead to injuries

Many of the principles for the safe use of cartridge-operated tools also apply to gas-powered fixing tools, which use a canister of pressurised gas (a fuel cell) as a propellant. Generally, gas-powered fixing tools are used for firing fixings into softer materials (such as timber). However, in untrained hands they can be as dangerous as cartridge-operated tools.

The implications of a misfire when using a gas-powered fixing tool are not as serious as when using a cartridge-operated tool and it is usually safe after a misfire to attempt to make the next fixing immediately.

The battery and fuel cell **must** be removed prior to attempting to remove a blockage.

 Only mature individuals over the age of 18 should be selected to use cartridge or gas-powered fixing tools.

Woodworking machinery

Woodworking machines (such as portable bench circular saws, portable hand-held circular saws and planing machines) are all found on building and construction sites.

They are also the cause of many accidents. Poorly adjusted guards and the failure to use push-sticks have contributed to many injured hands and lost fingers.

Only competent and authorised persons or trainees under the direct supervision of a competent colleague should operate any woodworking machine.

Woodworking machines should be set up on a firm and level base with a clear and well-ventilated working area established prior to work starting.

All guards and safety devices should be fitted, tested, correctly adjusted and fully operable all the time the machines are running. The safety distances of the guards from the blades should be closely monitored.

It is a requirement that all woodworking machines with a rundown time of 10 seconds or more must be fitted with a braking device, unless the effect of braking could be detrimental to the integrity of the machine.

Machines must not be left running unattended. The operator should not leave a machine until it has fully run down and stopped rotating. The machine should then be isolated.

Compressed air tools

Compressed air tools are attached to a compressor using air hoses. Tools include heavy duty breakers, soil picks, concrete scabblers and pokers.

Always check hose fittings are tight and secure before use. High pressure air hoses can cause serious injury if they break away from the compressor or tool.

 Air hoses should not be in contact with any part of the body. Failure of a hose close to the body can cause serious injuries.

Compressed air tools should be checked before and after use

Whip checks should be used on every hose joint to prevent break away

Other tools and equipment

Petrol-driven hand tools

If petrol must be kept on site it must be kept in low quantities in approved containers. Petrol-driven machines should only be refuelled in a well-designed, well-ventilated area using a funnel, without the engine running and after the machine and its parts have cooled down. Exhaust fumes are toxic and must not be allowed to accumulate in enclosed or confined spaces. Petrol must not be stored at the immediate workplace.

Electrical hand tools

All electrical hand tools used on site should ideally be battery powered or 110 V. Before every use the user should carry out a visual inspection of the item to ensure it has had an appropriate portable appliance test and the casing, switches and triggers are all undamaged. The power lead should be in good condition, not showing signs of damage or cuts to the outer insulation, and the plug itself should be in good condition, the cable grips in place and the inner wires should not be seen where the outer insulation enters the plug. Operators must switch off and remove the plug before carrying out any adjustment.

Non-powered hand tools

These may seem low risk, but they are the cause of many injuries; they need to be well maintained and regularly inspected. Well used or poorly used chisels and bolsters can form mushroom heads. When they are struck, fragments can fly into the air and into the eye. Loose handles, blunt blades and worn parts all pose a risk.

C
20

Lasers

If used correctly lasers should not pose a health or safety hazard.

A rotating laser means it is difficult to look directly at the beam for more than an instant. Static lasers (such as pipe lasers) pose more of a risk.

Exclusion zones and warning signs must be in place if high-powered lasers are being used.

**C
20**

21

Site transport safety

C
21

	What your employer should do for you
1.	Implement a traffic management plan.
2.	Design a safe site and plan and provide safe vehicle and pedestrian routes, which are physically segregated, where possible.
3.	Ensure that daily and pre-use checks, weekly inspections and statutory examinations are undertaken, and keep records.
4.	Implement procedures for the safe delivery, off-loading and movement of plant and materials onto and around the site, including planning around busy times or congestion (such as school drop off and pick up times).
5.	Maintain up to date lists of authorised drivers and operators.
6.	Ensure plant operators and drivers are competent and have the required experience. (Familiarisation training may be required if new plant is delivered to site.)
7.	Plan vehicle movements to minimise the risks at access and egress points and avoid reversing, if possible, by creating one-way systems.
8.	Monitor the movement of plant to ensure that it is in line with the traffic management plan.
9.	Ensure that drivers receive instruction on vehicle reversing procedures.
10.	Ensure that traffic routes and restrictions are observed by site vehicles at all times.
11.	Select and provide mobile or self-propelled plant ensuring that it has adequate visibility in all directions and all visibility aids are in good order.
12.	Provide the most appropriate vehicle for the task and environment and the people who will use it.
13.	Investigate any accidents and near misses involving vehicles and plant so that corrective action can be taken.
14.	Let you know when deliveries are scheduled to arrive and any unloading requirements or restrictions.

What you should do as a supervisor

Checklist	Yes	No	N/A
1. Organise vehicle movements under your control to minimise the risks at access and egress points.			
2. Liaise with site management and other contractors to plan deliveries and avoid potential clashes or issues.			
3. Monitor and maintain separate pedestrian and vehicle routes.			
4. Supervise the site and your workers to minimise the risk of any potential interface between people and vehicles.			
5. Liaise with managers for the safe delivery, off-loading and movement of plant and materials onto and around the site.			
6. Follow the traffic management plan for vehicle movements, loading, off-loading and storage.			
7. Ensure daily checks, weekly inspections and statutory examinations are undertaken and keep records up to date.			
8. Manage traffic routes to ensure they are observed and followed by site vehicles.			
9. Check drivers are competent and demonstrate the correct behaviours when operating plant, including reversing under the control of a vehicle marshal.			
10. Ensure that only authorised drivers and operators move and operate plant.			
11. Check that operators of mobile or self-propelled plant have adequate visibility in all directions and all visibility aids are in good order.			
12. Ensure that defective equipment is isolated and taken out of service.			
13. Ensure that all incidents and near misses involving vehicles and plant are investigated so that corrective action can be taken to prevent recurrence.			

C
21

Introduction

A good site management traffic plan promotes project efficiency, reduces nuisance and, most importantly, keeps people safe.

Each year there are fatalities and injuries in the construction industry. Many are as a result of working with, or being struck by, mobile plant. These incidents not only impact on the individual but they can also be devastating to their families, friends and work colleagues.

Managers, supervisors, workers, authorised and unauthorised visitors (trespassers) to sites and members of the public visiting the site can all be at risk if construction vehicle activities are not properly managed and controlled.

The majority of construction transport accidents result from the inadequate segregation of pedestrians and vehicles. This can usually be avoided by careful planning, particularly at the design stage, and by controlling vehicle movements and operations during construction work. Vehicles commonly travelling and being used on construction sites include excavators, telescopic handlers, mobile elevating work platforms, delivery vehicles and dumper trucks.

Traffic management

The CDM Regulations stipulate that vehicles and pedestrians should be organised on site so they can move around safely. Pedestrian and traffic routes need to be in suitable positions, sufficient for the number and size of vehicles that can be used.

The term *vehicles* includes cars, vans, lorries, low-loaders and mobile plant (such as excavators, lift trucks and site dumpers).

A traffic management plan should be in place. This should be communicated to workers and visitors on site during their site induction.

The traffic management plan should ensure the following.

- ☑ Any pedestrian doors or gates that lead onto a traffic route are situated so that pedestrians can see any approaching vehicle.

- ☑ Protection for pedestrians is provided.

- ☑ Warning arrangements are in place for any person who could become trapped or crushed if a vehicle approached.

- ☑ Loading bays have at least one exit used exclusively for pedestrians.

- ☑ Traffic routes are suitably signed, regularly checked and maintained.

- ☑ Traffic routes are clear from obstructions and have sufficient clearance.

Pedestrian and vehicle segregation

Where work space permits, establish pedestrian routes on site that provide safe access to work areas. Pedestrian routes should be located a safe distance away from areas of vehicle activity or provided with appropriate physical protection (such as barriers and/or kerbs). This will prevent pedestrians being struck by vehicles or their loads.

Criteria of pedestrian routes

- ☑ Have clearly marked, separate access for pedestrians at loading bays and site gates used by construction vehicles.

- ☑ Be clearly separated from vehicle routes by barriers and/or a kerb, or other suitable measures.

C
21

☑ Be adequately lit where light is not provided by natural means.

☑ Be wide enough to safely accommodate the number of people likely to use them at peak times.

☑ Allow easy, safe and unhindered access to work areas.

☑ Be clearly marked and kept free from obstructions and tripping hazards.

☑ Ensure pedestrian safety where they cross main vehicle routes, by the introduction of designated and clearly indicated crossing points.

☑ Provide pedestrians with a clear view of traffic movements at crossings and where gates used by pedestrians lead onto traffic routes.

The safe separation of construction plant and pedestrians avoids accidents

C
21

Deliveries, loading and storage areas, and distribution

In some situations it may not be possible to phase certain jobs to keep plant and pedestrians apart, which increases the likelihood of an accident. Where it is inevitable that plant and people will be operating in close proximity even for a short period (for example, a telehandler delivering a pack of bricks for the bricklaying gang or a skip lorry reversing to pick up or drop off a skip), it is essential that the following are complied with.

- ☑ Any additional hazards are identified and eliminated or controlled.
- ☑ The plant operator is fully competent.
- ☑ The activity is under the control of only one person who instructs the others what to do.
- ☑ Everyone involved is informed of, and fully appreciates, the potential for danger and keeps out of the danger area.

Work on site should be planned to minimise vehicle movements, and to avoid unnecessary deliveries and the double handling of materials. Therefore the location of loading and storage areas requires careful planning. Where there is little on-site storage space, off-site areas may be required for the temporary storage of materials. Loading and storage areas should be planned with consideration of the following.

- ☑ Located away from pedestrian-only areas and main pedestrian routes.
- ☑ Have sufficient room for vehicle movements.
- ☑ Exclude pedestrians so far as reasonably practicable.
- ☑ Have one-way systems and safe exit points.
- ☑ Have adequate fixed lighting, signs and appropriate visibility aids for drivers (for example, convex mirrors positioned on corners).

 Anti-collision devices can be fitted to vehicles such as dumpers. They are a useful aid to the operator but should not be relied on exclusively in place of operator vigilance and a safe system of work.

Vehicles should be loaded and unloaded on level ground in areas away from passing traffic, pedestrians and overhead hazards (for example, bridges, pipelines or electrical cables). Climbing onto vehicles should be prohibited unless fall prevention/arrest measures are provided. Loads need to meet the following conditions.

- ☑ Be of suitable height and width for the vehicle and road conditions on site.
- ☑ Be positioned on vehicles and transported so that they do not adversely affect vehicle stability.
- ☑ Be evenly loaded and distributed to keep the centre of gravity as low as possible and to prevent stresses on vehicle structures.
- ☑ Be secured to prevent movement.
- ☑ Be checked to ensure they will not fall uncontrollably when restraints are removed during unloading.

No vehicle should be loaded beyond its safe working capacity. Loads that project out from the body of the vehicle should be indicated by a warning beacon, flag or sign.

Site rules should dictate that visiting drivers inform site management of any hazardous loads on their vehicles. Appropriate fire precautions need to be implemented for loads that contain substances with specific fire hazards (such as fuels and solvents). Information about the hazards of dangerous loads and necessary precautions in the event of an accident should be issued to all site drivers.

Loading and off-loading areas should be of sufficient size to allow vehicles to move, without striking obstructions or causing hazards to others. A significant number of incidents have occurred through uncontrolled movement, or machines slipping off the side of trailers.

For further information refer to the following HSE documents.

☑ *The safe use of vehicles on construction sites (HSG144).*

☑ *Protecting the public: your next move (HSG151).*

Reversing vehicles

Vehicle reversing operations cause a third of all fatal transport accidents in the construction industry. The most effective way of managing the risks from reversing is to avoid the need for reversing manoeuvres by providing one-way systems, turning areas and drive-through loading and unloading areas.

It is good practice to follow a hierarchy of control when planning vehicle movements.

1. Segregate vehicles and pedestrians.

2. Eliminate the need to reverse.

3. Reduce reversing operations.

4. Provide warnings when vehicles are reversing and limit reversing, except when under the control of a marshal or in a designated area.

Vehicles required to reverse should have adequate visibility around the vehicle for the driver to ensure safety. Safe systems of work need to be devised and followed for all reversing operations, particularly when vehicle marshallers are used to control third-party vehicles or to assist in the accurate positioning of a vehicle.

Warning systems offer the lowest level of protection in the hierarchy and, if they are the only precaution used, should only be used for low-risk situations.

Vehicle marshallers

Ensure that all vehicle marshallers, who are used to safely direct vehicle movements, are appropriately trained and are positioned safely to avoid them being hit by the vehicle.

C
21

Plant safe zones

The following diagrams are for guidance purposes and provide information on the safe zones applicable to a range of plant machinery likely to be used on site.

- ☑ Always signal the plant operator and wait for a positive response before entering Zone 1.

- ☑ Keep out of Zone 2 at all times.

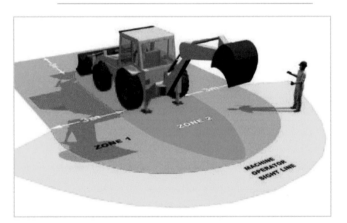
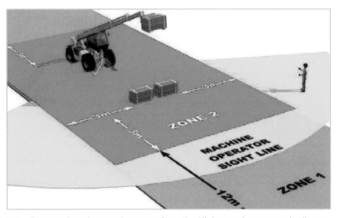

(Reproduced from the Delivery hub health, safety and environment – Raising the bar 1 – Plant and equipment document from the Highways Agency, under licence of the Controller of Her Majesty's Stationery Office.)

For further information refer to the mobile plant and vehicles chapter in Section C of GE 700 *Construction site safety*.

Perimeters, interface with highways and public rights of way

For most sites the perimeter is an area in which construction work will be carried out.

Identifying and establishing this perimeter is an important aspect of managing risks to public safety.

Three issues should be considered when deciding on the type of perimeter guarding.

1. **Planning** what form the perimeter will take (solid hoarding, fence panels and so on).

2. **Providing and constructing** the perimeter.

3. **Maintaining** the perimeter and the facilities and procedures provided (such as entry and exit points and delivery times).

Sometimes construction work can create risks to the public outside the site perimeter.

These risks might include materials falling from access platforms, materials stored temporarily off site, the operation of cranes and other lifting equipment either on or off site, vehicles blocking the footway, vehicles or plant obstructing the roadway or obscuring lines of site, and congestion.

 Any work undertaken outside the site perimeter must be properly planned, resourced and carried out under strict control due to the direct interface with members of the public.

The site entrance is an interface between the site and the highway, the general public, their rights of way, and the rights of way of other road users. Therefore, all such work areas must be properly planned, resourced and executed as a priority in order to reduce the risks of incidents and accidents as far as is practicable. Site entrances must be clearly marked by signs and ideally there should be separate access for vehicles and pedestrians. Vehicle and pedestrian access and egress must be strictly controlled.

The site team will need to liaise with the local highways authority as they may need authorisation should the work involve the closure or obstruction of public footpaths or roads to facilitate complex deliveries or the erection of scaffolding. A licence may be required before work can commence. A number of precautions can be taken, including those outlined below.

☑ Fence off the area and provide alternative routes which are clearly signposted.

☑ Exclude the public from the work area whenever possible.

☑ Provide wheel-washing facilities to avoid public roads becoming muddy or dusty.

☑ Ask for protective measures to be put in place at an early stage during erection and have them removed as late as possible during dismantling.

☑ Fans, tunnels and sheeting are a useful means of protection (the scaffold must be designed to take the extra loading and wind resistance).

☑ Make sure the working platform is constructed to prevent materials falling through it; double-board scaffold platforms and insert a layer of strong polythene between the two sets of boards (a few small punctures will allow rainwater to drain away).

C
21

☑ Make sure scaffold components do not project where there is a risk to people or vehicles.

☑ Use brick guards, netting or other suitable protection to prevent materials falling.

☑ Bolts on couplings should face away from the public or be wrapped.

☑ Erect, modify and dismantle equipment when there will be fewer members of the public in the area and always use warning notices.

☑ Consider enclosing the base of the scaffolding to prevent climbing, especially on or near occupied residential premises and schools.

☑ Lighting may be necessary in tunnels.

☑ Out of hours, remove ladders from the scaffold; secure them in a compound or in locked storage containers.

☑ Make sure that doors to buildings or those allowing access to the roof, lift motor rooms and so on are locked at all times when work is not in progress.

☑ Consider using alternatives to scaffolding (such as a MEWP, cradle, or mast climber where work is of a temporary nature).

☒ Do not allow the dropping or throwing of components during erection or dismantling.

A licence may be required if you are obstructing the highway

C 21

22

Lifting operations

What your employer should do for you

1. Ensure that there are no restrictions on airspace or oversailing rights.

2. Survey the site and implement checks for underground services, voids and overhead power lines.

3. Ensure that lifting equipment selected is suitable for the task to be undertaken.

4. Ensure that lifting equipment and accessories are properly marked (with an identity number and safe working load) and are within their examination period.

5. Put procedures in place to ensure that personnel are trained, competent and appointed.

6. Plan the lift, including carrying out risk assessments to identify hazards and control measures.

7. Provide lifting plans and ensure that the work team are briefed.

8. Ensure that if excavators, loaders or combined excavator loaders are used for lifting, they have the necessary features, information and documentation.

9. Put procedures in place to prevent people or materials falling during the off-loading of vehicles.

C
22

What you should do as a supervisor

Checklist	Yes	No	N/A
1. Check that a survey of the site for underground services, voids and overhead power lines has been completed.			
2. Follow employer guidance on restrictions on airspace or oversailing rights and ensure the work team are aware of any restrictions.			
3. Ensure that lifting equipment and accessories are properly marked (with an identity number and safe working load) and are within their examination period.			
4. Follow procedures put in place, to ensure that personnel are trained, competent and appointed for the work in hand.			
5. Ensure that if excavators, loaders or combined excavator loaders are used for lifting, they have the necessary features, information and documentation.			
6. Review the lift plan before the lift commences to ensure that it is still valid.			
7. Follow lifting plan requirements and ensure that the work team are briefed and follow the plan.			
8. Implement measures to prevent people or materials falling during the off-loading of vehicles.			

C
22

Introduction

The Lifting Operations and Lifting Equipment Regulations (LOLER) cover all aspects of mechanical lifting operations. They are accompanied by an Approved Code of Practice (ACoP) and guidance notes. Any employer who carries out any mechanical lifting operations using lifting equipment must comply with the regulations. LOLER cover all safety aspects of using lifting equipment and lifting accessories, including planning.

Competence in lifting operations

Where it is necessary to hire in lifting equipment, the employer must decide whether there is adequate competency available within the company to plan, organise and perform the lift(s). If this is not the case, the employer will need to arrange for the crane hire company to appoint competent people and take responsibility for the lift(s). This option is known as contract lifting.

However, the company will still need to manage and control the site in which the lifting operation will take place and provide such things as preparing and testing the ground and enforcing exclusion zones.

Safe system of work (Lift plan)

Principles

Inadequately planned lifting operations are often responsible for accidents that result in fatalities and injuries to those involved, and other persons in the area (such as members of the public), especially if the lift involves moving (sailing) over occupied areas or the potential for structural failure or overturning of the lifting equipment.

Employers have a duty to ensure all lifting operations are managed as outlined below.

- ☑ Properly planned by a competent person.
- ☑ Adequately supervised.
- ☑ Carried out in a safe manner.

The employer should appoint a competent person in writing (normally referred to as the appointed person) with responsibility for ensuring that the above duties are carried out.

Each lifting operation should be the subject of a risk assessment, although where a lifting operation is repeated in the same circumstances with the same hazards and level of risk (such as stacking materials using a forklift truck), an initial, generic risk assessment should satisfy the legal requirements for a suitable and sufficient risk assessment.

The findings of the risk assessment should be used as a basis for developing the safe system of work. A method statement should be written for the job, which will also form part of the safe system of work.

The safe system of work should be effectively communicated to all those involved in the lifting operation. The lifting plan will incorporate the aforementioned risk assessments and method statements and should also include the following points.

- ☑ Thorough planning of the operation, including the selection and provision of suitable and sufficient lifting equipment and accessories.
- ☑ Procedures to ensure that the suitable and sufficient lifting equipment and accessories provided are used in a safe and competent manner.
- ☑ Procedures to ensure that all equipment is inspected, maintained and thoroughly examined, as necessary.

Lifting operations, no matter how large or small, must be properly planned

The safety of all persons, both those involved in the lift as well as those not involved but who may be affected by the lifting operation is dependent on the operation being properly planned, resourced and executed by trained and competent persons. Therefore, there must be procedures that ensure the following.

☑ The provision of all relevant documentation, including copies of the examination reports.

☑ Equipment is only operated by trained, competent and authorised persons.

☑ All lifting operations are overseen (supervised) by a competent person, with authority to stop a job if necessary.

☑ The prevention of unauthorised use or movement of equipment by suitable security measures.

 For further information refer to Chapter A04 Risk assessments, method statements and permits to work.

Failure

During lifting operations accidents can occur as a result of the following.

☒ Using lifting equipment of the wrong type or lifting capacity.

☒ Failure of the ground or structure supporting the lifting equipment.

☒ Using lifting equipment in an incorrect manner (unsafe technique).

☒ Trying to lift a load of an unknown weight and/or centre of gravity.

☒ Incorrect slinging of the load.

☒ Lack of training of the crane operators, slingers and signallers.

☒ Poor maintenance of the equipment.

☒ Rushing to carry out the task.

☒ Lack of co-ordination of crane movements when more than one crane is operating and their arcs of movement overlap.

C
22

The collapse, overturning or failure of lifting equipment is a notifiable dangerous occurrence, which must be reported to the HSE even if no-one is injured.

Siting of cranes

The siting of cranes will usually be carried out by site management in conjunction with the lift supervisor and crane operator. Site management must also ensure the following.

- ☑ The crane does not encroach into the safety distance from overhead cables.

- ☑ The stability of the crane will not be adversely affected by unstable ground conditions, or the presence of excavations, manholes, cellars, or other underground voids.

- ☑ Oversailing rights (a licence that permits the jib of a crane to encroach on the air space above adjacent property) must be agreed (tower cranes mainly).

- ☑ Suitable clearance (minimum 600 mm) is maintained between any mobile or slewing crane and any fixture. Examples include guard-rails and adjacent buildings to ensure there are no crush zones.

- ☑ Airspace restrictions must be checked (tower cranes mainly).

- ☑ The position corresponds to those approved in any lifting plan.

- ☑ Safe access is available for refuelling or other service vehicles.

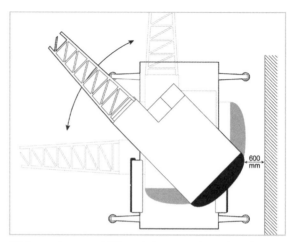

Minimum clearance of 600 mm between moving parts and other structures to avoid crush zones

Assistance of a slinger/signaller

Lifting operations involving the use of a crane will usually require the assistance of a slinger/signaller to safely secure the load to the crane and give direction to the operator. An effective system of communication between them is essential. Hand signals are generally used unless the line of sight between the operator and signaller is restricted or blocked. In this case, radios should be used with an agreed set of signals.

Signals

The giving of signals by untrained persons is extremely dangerous and must be prohibited. Where hand signals are to be used, they should be those detailed in the Health and Safety (Safety Signs and Signals) Regulations (also shown in BS 7121-1).

Care must be exercised by those giving and receiving signals and, if there is any doubt, movement of the load must be stopped and the signal repeated if necessary.

Operators

Operators of cranes and other lifting appliances, and any other people involved in lifting operations, including slingers and signallers, must be trained, experienced and (it is recommended) aged 18 years or over unless under the direct supervision of a competent person for the purposes of training.

Overhead hazards

For further information refer to Chapter D26 Underground and overhead services.

Modern lifting equipment can be equipped with sensors that limit the height the jib or boom will reach and how far a machine can slew. Rated capacity indicators are fitted to the majority of lifting equipment (particularly mobile-type cranes) which use amber lights and an alarm to warn the operator and others when the machine is approaching overload and when it has been exceeded (alarm plus red light). Motion restrictors can be fitted to equipment such as tower cranes to keep the slewing arc within predefined limits. These safety features must not be overridden or disabled.

Loads

All lifting must be planned by a competent person who will use their theoretical and practical knowledge and experience to plan for and safely conduct a lifting operation. The weight of the total load, the centre of gravity of the load and the safe working load (SWL) of the lifting equipment must all be considered. The SWL of the lifting equipment must never be exceeded.

Never allow a load that has not been assessed for weight and centre of gravity to be lifted.

Loads must be slung correctly by an authorised load handler (slinger) using the lifting accessories that are specified in the lift plan. The slinger must ensure that all loads are secure for lifting by having the load raised slightly clear of the ground and then stopping to check its stability, security and safety.

Information and instructions

Several pieces of legislation require employers to provide suitable and sufficient information, instruction and training that is easily understood and proportional to the complexity of the equipment being used. Employers must also ensure that there is adequate and appropriate supervision at all times.

The information should include the following.

☑ How and when the equipment may be used.

☑ Possible abnormal conditions and the action to be taken should such conditions arise.

☑ Conclusions drawn from experience of using the equipment.

The Construction Plant-hire Association (CPA) has produced a series of best practice guides that give detailed guidance for supervisors and managers involved in lifting operations.

Publications are available as free downloads from the CPA website.

C
22

23

Lifting equipment

What your employer should do for you

1. Ensure that all lifting equipment selected is suitable for the task to be undertaken.

2. Ensure that the equipment and accessories in use have been inspected, maintained and thoroughly examined.

3. Ensure that all lifting equipment and accessories are properly marked (with an identity number and safe working load) and are within their examination period.

4. Put procedures in place to ensure that personnel are trained, competent and appointed.

5. Provide lifting plans and ensure that you are briefed and understand the lifting plans.

6. Ensure that suitable equipment and procedures are in place to prevent people or materials falling from lifting equipment, especially during the off-loading of vehicles.

7. Ensure that if excavators, loaders or combined excavator loaders are used for lifting, they have the necessary features, information and documentation.

C
23

What you should do as a supervisor

Checklist	Yes	No	N/A
1. Check that the equipment and accessories in use are suitably inspected, maintained and thoroughly examined (including any fall prevention equipment or measures).			
2. Check that all lifting equipment and accessories are properly marked (with an identity number and safe working load) and are within their examination period, and reject non-complying equipment.			
3. Follow procedures put in place, to ensure that personnel are trained, competent and appointed for the work in hand.			
4. Ensure there are procedures and/or equipment to prevent unauthorised persons from accessing lifting equipment and/or the unauthorised use of lifting equipment.			
5. Check that if excavators, loaders or combined excavator loaders are used for lifting, they have the necessary features, information and documentation.			

C
23

Introduction

The Lifting Operations and Lifting Equipment Regulations (LOLER) apply to lifting equipment. Additionally, the Provision and Use of Work Equipment Regulations (PUWER) consider lifting equipment with regard to such factors as suitability, maintenance, keeping in good order and the use of trained and competent operators.

Lifting equipment is any work equipment (such as cranes (mobile and static), hoists, telehandlers and excavators) that is used for mechanically lifting or lowering any load, including people.

The definition includes all attachments used for anchoring, fixing or supporting the lifting equipment and hand-operated lifting equipment (such as gin wheels and hand-operated hoists).

Lifting accessories are items of equipment used for attaching the load to the lifting equipment (such as chains, ropes, slings, hooks, spreader-beams, shackles and eye bolts).

The regulations do not apply to shovels, crowbars, wheelbarrows or anything else that would be regarded as equipment for assisting the manual handling of loads.

Tower cranes

A conventional tower crane is defined in the regulations as a slewing jib type crane with its jib located at the top of a vertical tower and which is assembled on a construction site from components. This includes, but is not limited to, cranes with horizontal or luffing jibs and slewing rings at the base or top of the tower. These tower cranes are usually installed (and dismantled) with the assistance of another crane and, as a result, are sometimes referred to as assisted erected cranes.

There are four key aspects to the safe use of lifting equipment and accessories.

1. Planning the lifting operation.

2. Developing the safe system of work for the lifting operation.

3. Supervision of the lifting operation.

4. Maintenance, inspection and thorough examination of the lifting equipment and accessories. *(See page 276 for more information on carrying out thorough examinations.)*

Where several tower cranes are close together, their operation must be co-ordinated to avoid collisions

Excavators used for lifting

Excavators and backhoes are primarily designed for earth moving operations and not lifting operations as a main function. Therefore they are subject to the requirements and provisions of PUWER and LOLER when being used for lifting operations.

C
23

At selection stage the lift planner should consider whether such equipment is suitable for the required lifting activity. All lifting operations are subject to suitable and sufficient planning by a competent person, including ensuring that the risk assessment and a safe system of work takes into account the capabilities and suitability of the equipment for the task.

When considering using an excavator for a lifting operation the weight of the bucket (if fitted), plus the weight of the quick hitch coupler and lifting accessories, must be added to the weight of the load to establish if the machine will be working within its safe working load. Unless required, the bucket should be removed to improve the excavator operator's visibility.

 A rated object handling capacity table must be available in the cab.

The risk assessment must address the following.

☑ The need for the lifting operation to be segregated from other work activities taking place in the vicinity, particularly where it is necessary for the lifting equipment to travel with a suspended load.

☑ Ground conditions, particularly where an excavator or similar type of equipment will carry out the lifting operation, which should be on a level, firm surface. Where a pick-and-carry operation is required, the intended route must be checked (for both tracked and wheeled types) so that there are no voids or trenches.

The risk assessment and method statement should take into account the fact that when an excavator is in the object-handling mode (being used as a crane), it will be necessary for the slinger to approach the machine to attach or detach the lifting accessories.

This puts the slinger in a hazardous area (for example, in the slewing arc of the boom and dipper) and at risk of being struck by the load, bucket or excavator arm.

Excavator operators and slingers must be made aware of these dangers; effective communication and constant vigilance are essential. If the slinger has to enter the area of the slewing arc of the machine's boom to attach or remove lifting accessories, the operating controls of the machine must be isolated.

If the rated lifting capacity for an excavator (or the backhoe of a backhoe loader) is greater than 1 tonne (or the overturning moment is greater than 40,000 Nm), the machine must be fitted with the following.

☑ A boom-lowering control device on the main boom cylinder(s) (a safety check valve), which meets the requirements of BS ISO 8643*.

☑ An acoustic or visual warning device that indicates to the operator when the object handling capacity or corresponding load moment is reached.

* Machines first supplied after July 2012 must be fitted with a boom-lowering device on the dipper arm cylinder as well as the main boom cylinders.

Chains or slings for lifting must not be placed around, or on, the teeth of the bucket. Accessories for lifting may only be attached to a purpose-made point on the machine.

Where the risk assessment shows that there is a significant risk of the excavator overloading or overturning, a rated capacity indicator may need to be fitted.

 For further information download the CPA guidance *Lifting operations in construction when using excavators.*

**C
23**

A proprietary manhole lifting attachment

Telescopic handlers

Also known as telehandlers, these are commonplace on construction sites. The ability of telehandlers to raise loads to greater heights increases the hazard of overturning. To counteract this, some types are fitted with stabilisers and chassis-levelling devices.

Many machines are used with a variety of attachments that may affect their stability. The manufacturer's recommendations for fitting and using attachments should be followed.

Lift planners and operators should be aware that attachments will alter the rated lift capacity and centre of gravity of the machine.

Standard telehandlers are normally fitted with load moment indicators (LMI) and in some cases, load moment limiters (LML), which prevent components such as the boom from extending if an overload situation is indicated. However, the LMI should never be relied on as a way of checking whether the machine is safe to pick up a load.

The operator must refer to the lift plan and lift capacity charts of the machine at all times. LMI units only warn of longitudinal instability and can become inaccurate. They require resetting by a competent person on a regular basis.

A lifting plan is required for all telehandler operations, specific to the site conditions, the load to be lifted or transported and the attachments to be used (as is the case with other lifting accessories). The attachments should be regularly inspected and checked.

Travelling with suspended loads is particularly hazardous and requires careful planning by the competent person. Travelling with a suspended load means that the boom is raised to keep the load clear of the ground, and extended to prevent the load from striking the machine's chassis. This can make the telehandler much less stable so travel routes must be carefully selected to ensure that all operations are undertaken on firm, level ground and at speeds slow enough for the operator to maintain control. The position of the slinger must also be considered as they are at risk when in close proximity to a moving machine.

☑ **For more information refer to the HSE document** *Rider-operated lift trucks: operator training and safe use. Approved Code of Practice and guidance* **(L117).**

☑ **Also refer to the Strategic Forum for Construction Plant Safety Group's good practice guidance** *Lifting and travelling with suspended loads using telehandlers* **and the** *Safe use of telehandlers in construction.*

A lifting plan is required for all telehandler operations

Gin wheels

It is often necessary to raise tools and light materials manually up to a working platform. A simple way of achieving this is to employ a gin wheel. The following provisions and requirements apply to the use of gin wheels supported by or fixed to a scaffold.

☑ Poles and hooks should be strong enough to take the load that is to be lifted and be properly secured to prevent movement.

☑ All ropes should comply with the relevant BS EN standards and fit the wheel correctly. They should be marked with a tag confirming their safe working load.

☑ Proper fixings for suspending the gin wheel from the scaffold should be used. This could be achieved through a purpose built bracket system or a ring type fixing with a swivel eye fitted over the tube and secured by fittings to prevent any lateral movement.

☑ Any joints in standards should be made with sleeve couplers.

☑ Gin wheels should be suspended not more than 750 mm from the outer support.

☑ Hooks used for raising the load should be safety hooks and spliced into the hauling rope.

☑ The maximum loading should be no more than 50 kg at 750 mm from the outer support.

☑ Where appropriate, lifting equipment should be fitted with suitable devices (such as inertia brakes) to minimise any risk of the load falling freely.

☑ Gin wheels must be visually checked on a regular basis, thoroughly examined after installation and then every 12 months and a report of thorough examination issued. *(See page 276 for more information on carrying out thorough examinations.)*

**C
23**

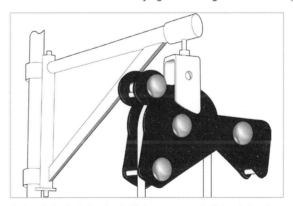

An inertia braked gin wheel utilising a purpose built bracket system. Inertia braked wheels are now more common and far safer than traditional gin wheels

Lifting accessories

Lifting accessories are pieces of work equipment used to attach loads to machinery for lifting. Lifting equipment means work equipment used for the lifting or lowering of loads and includes any attachments used for anchoring, fixing or supporting a load.

Lifting accessories include items such as chains, slings, hooks and spreader bars.

Machinery and accessories for lifting loads must be clearly marked to indicate their safe working load. Accessories used in lifting operations must be clearly marked to indicate the characteristics necessary for their safe use.

Lifting accessories are subject to a competent person's thorough examination every six months, and a record of the findings of the examination must be kept.

If it cannot be shown that a lifting accessory has been examined by a competent person in the previous six months, the lifting accessory cannot be used.

Maintenance, checks and inspection

Maintenance, checks and inspection of lifting equipment and accessories are essential if they are not to deteriorate over time, break down and fail. All maintenance should be carried out by a competent person who is familiar with the equipment and has the knowledge and experience to detect and repair existing or potential faults. The maintenance should be in accordance with the manufacturer's instructions, carried out at the recommended intervals and recorded in a log.

Both lifting equipment and accessories should have a pre-use check carried out daily or at the start of each shift and any defects reported to a supervisor. This is normally undertaken by the operator who should be trained to carry out the checks.

In addition to pre-use checks, inspections should be carried out at appropriate intervals, either as part of the maintenance process or at more frequent intervals (such as the weekly inspection of mobile cranes or slings). The frequency of inspections will depend on assessment of the risk of failure of the equipment and should be guided by the manufacturer's instructions.

The results of all checks and inspections should be recorded and there should be a system in place to ensure that all reported defects are rectified and recorded.

Thorough examination

LOLER requires all lifting equipment to be thoroughly examined by a competent person. The competent person must be sufficiently independent and impartial to allow objective decisions to be made.

Lifting equipment must be thoroughly examined as follows.

- [x] Before being put into use for the first time.

- [x] After installation on a new site, after installation in a new location on the same site or where significant changes have been made to the lifting equipment (such as an extension of a tower crane's jib).

- [x] After exceptional circumstances have occurred, such as high winds, overload or shock loading (for example, vehicular impact or impact from a load being dropped).

- [x] At intervals not exceeding 12 months.

C
23

Lifting equipment used for lifting persons, and all lifting accessories, must be thoroughly examined every six months.

Thorough examination reports

For every thorough examination, the competent person must record the following information.

☑ Who performed the examination.

☑ The name and address of the employer for whom the thorough examination was made.

☑ The address of the premises where the thorough examination was carried out.

☑ The identification of the equipment examined.

☑ The date of last thorough examination.

☑ The SWL of the equipment.

☑ The date of the thorough examination.

☑ The type of examination that has been carried out.

– First examination.

– Post-installation examination.

– Periodic six-monthly examination.

– Annual examination.

– Examination under an examination scheme.

– Examination after exceptional circumstances.

☑ Details of any defects found and whether they require immediate rectification, or the date by which they must be rectified.

☑ Particulars of any repairs or alterations needed to remedy the defect.

☑ The date by which the next thorough examination must be carried out.

☑ The particulars of any test carried out.

☑ The name, address and qualifications of the competent person carrying out the thorough examination.

☑ The signature of the person and date of the report.

Records can be kept in writing, or electronically on a computer, but must be capable of being reproduced in hard copy form.

For further information refer to the chapters on lifting operations and lifting equipment in Section C of GE 700 *Construction site safety*.

A thorough examination before first use is not required for new lifting equipment where the owner has received an EC declaration of conformity not more than 12 months before the lifting equipment is first put into service. However, if the equipment was *installed* on site (for example a goods hoist), it would still need to be thoroughly examined before being put into service.

**C
23**

C
23

24

Working at height

What your employer should do for you

1. Plan all work at height activities. This includes minimising the need to work at height wherever possible.

2. Carry out a suitable and sufficient risk assessment and brief everyone involved in the work on the findings.

3. Use collective protection methods (those that protect more than one person) in preference to personal protective methods.

4. Ensure that adequate fall protection systems are in place for all work at height activities.

5. Provide you with the most appropriate equipment in the circumstances for working at height.

6. Ensure that suitable rescue plans, procedures and rescue equipment are in place, as part of the safe system of work, and that rescues are practised.

7. Ensure that there are adequate levels of supervision and that work is carried out by a suitably trained and competent workforce.

8. Survey the surrounding area for the existence of overhead power lines (OHPL) and other high level hazards.

9. Avoid working on fragile roofs by working from underneath, when possible. If this is not possible, a safe system of work must be planned, implemented and followed, which may involve the use of specialist access equipment.

10. Make arrangements for scaffolding to be erected, altered and dismantled by competent person(s).

11. Arrange for the statutory inspection of scaffolding and other equipment provided for work at height to be carried out by a competent person at the appropriate intervals.

12. Check that ground conditions are suitable for the use of the selected access plant and equipment, including investigating for the existence of cellars, drains and other underground voids.

13. Provide training to ensure that competent operators will be available to operate access plant and equipment (such as mobile elevating work platforms (MEWPs)) and assist with a rescue if required. Employers should consider the use of anti-entrapment devices (secondary guarding) on MEWPs during the planning and risk assessment stage.

14. Restrict the use of ladders to tasks where it is not reasonably practicable to use an alternative, safer means of access.

D
24

What you should do as a supervisor

Checklist	Yes	No	N/A
1. Ensure that all work at height will be carried out using the most appropriate means of access and in accordance with the risk assessment and method statements provided.			
2. Ensure that anyone involved with working at height or using access equipment has the right skills, knowledge, training and experience. Provide any additional information, instruction, training and supervision for the equipment being used and the task in hand.			
3. Ensure that working on or near fragile roofs is avoided and adequate arrangements are put in place to provide a safe place of work.			
4. Ensure that the workforce is briefed on the position of any overhead power lines (OHPL) and other high-level hazards.			
5. Ensure that rescue procedures are in place, as described in your safe system of work, and are rehearsed.			
6. Supervise and monitor all working at height activities, report any previously unidentified hazardous situations and deal with deviations from the given methods of work, as appropriate.			
7. Check the arrangements for scaffolding to be erected, altered and dismantled by suitable qualified and competent person(s).			
8. Monitor ground conditions to ensure that they do not deteriorate from those described in your safe system of work. This should also include monitoring the standards of housekeeping.			
9. Ensure that the statutory inspection of scaffolds and plant is carried out by a competent person in accordance with the statutory requirements.			
10. Monitor interface between trades, activities, members of the public and the public highway and instigate the necessary control measures.			
11. Monitor the use of ladders and ensure they are only used as a last resort and in accordance with a risk assessment.			
12. Ensure that all fall-arrest equipment is visually inspected prior to each use, at the start of each shift. It should also receive a weekly, detailed inspection and a statutory examination at least every six months.			

D
24

Introduction

Falls from height continue to be the main cause of fatalities and serious injury within the construction industry. Many of these falls were from low levels, yet still had serious consequences.

Around 33% of all specified injuries in the construction industry are caused by workers falling from height. In addition, many construction workers have sustained life-changing injuries due to a fall from height. Such events affect lives and livelihoods.

Many serious injuries occur during low-level work of short duration and where procedures have not been correctly followed, due to the perceived benefit of saving time and completing the job more quickly. It should be remembered that a safe system of work is always required, regardless of the duration of the work.

Work at height should be regarded as working in any place at, above or below the ground, where a fall in the vertical plane could cause or result in injury.

Falls resulting from the use of ladders, and work on or near to roof edges or fragile materials, continue to figure prominently amongst the industry's accident statistics. Falls such as these make up a large proportion of Health and Safety Executive (HSE) prosecutions. A risk assessment must be carried out and a safe system of work produced before any work at height activity is undertaken.

Legislation

All work at height must be carried out in compliance with the **Work at Height Regulations**. Employers, managers and supervisors should note the following key provisions of the regulations.

☑ Where it is reasonably practicable, avoid the need to carry out work at height. This can be achieved, for example, by carrying out assembly work at ground level and lifting the assembly into position, using high reach equipment from ground level to complete final connections.

☑ Where work at height cannot be avoided, select the most appropriate work equipment for the task. This includes equipment that will provide a temporary safe place of work at height.

☑ Ensure that the way that any work is carried out is based upon the findings of a risk assessment.

☑ Organise work at height so as to prevent falls and falling objects (such as tools and materials). This may involve using a scaffold fitted with brick guards, sheeting or debris netting.

☑ Give priority to the use of collective fall-protection measures (such as safety nets) over those that protect only the person using it (for example, safety harnesses).

☑ Reduce the distance and potential consequences of any fall that does occur. If it is not possible to prevent a fall then the consequences of a fall from height should be reduced by using fall-arrest equipment or a soft-landing system.

☑ Ensure that those who have to work at height are competent and also medically and physically fit to do so.

☑ For scaffold edge protection, the minimum height of the top guard-rail is 950 mm. The maximum gap between it and a mid-rail, and between a mid-rail and the top of a toe-board, must not exceed 470 mm.

☑ Ladders and stepladders must only be used where it can be shown, by a risk assessment, that it is not reasonably practicable to use alternative forms of access equipment and the remaining risks are low.

D 24

☑ Each working platform must be wide enough for its intended use (for example, BS EN 12811, which relates to scaffolding, recommends a minimum width of 600 mm).

☑ Ensure that adequate provisions are made for emergency situations. Consider the location and points of work for the work activities taking place, the work equipment in use, and ensure that the rescue plan can be initiated without delay and without reliance on the emergency services.

Hierarchy for working at height

Any person planning work at height should always consider options at the top of the hierarchy before moving down.

Step 1. Avoid working at height
e.g. assemble on the ground and lift into position using a crane or by fixing guard-rails to structural steelwork on the ground before lifting and fixing at height

▼

Step 2. Prevent falls from occurring
Use an existing safe place of work e.g. parapet walls, defined access points, a flat roof with existing edge protection

▼

Step 3. Prevent falls through providing *collective* protection
e.g. scaffolding, edge protection, handrails, podium steps, mobile towers, MEWPs

▼

Step 4. Prevent falls through providing *personal* protection
e.g. using a work restraint (travel restriction) system that prevents a worker getting into a fall position

▼

Step 5. Minimise the distance and/or consequences of a fall using *collective* protection
e.g. safety netting, airbags or soft-landing systems

▼

Step 6. Minimise the distance and/or consequences of a fall using *personal* protection (The last resort)
e.g. industrial rope access (working on a building façade) or a fall-arrest system (harness and fall-arrest lanyard), using a suitable, high anchor point

 Ensure that people with sufficient skills, knowledge and experience are selected to perform any task. Any person being trained should be under full supervision at all times.

D
24

Preventing falls

Ideally, falls should be prevented by physical barriers and equipment. This may include using scaffolding, mobile towers, MEWPs, suitably selected podiums, edge protection systems and brick guards. Edge protection should be of sufficient strength and rigidity to serve its intended purpose and, therefore, rope or other lightweight materials are not suitable.

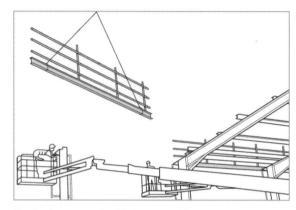

Pre-fixed crane guard-rail being installed by crane

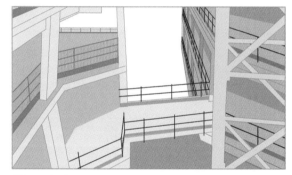

Edge protection

For further information on the selection and use of edge protection refer to the Edge Protection Federation's Code of Practice.

Proprietary edge protection

Holes in floors, slabs, roofs and open shafts

Where holes have been cast or cut in (for example, floor slabs and roofs, and around open stairwells, service voids and lift shafts) erect securely anchored edge protection, complete with toe-boards, or fix suitable load-bearing covers with warning signage. Covers should be regularly inspected for integrity.

D
24

Employee prosecuted for dangerous work at height

An employee of a steel erection firm has been sentenced at Manchester Magistrates' Court after he admitted working unsafely at height on a hotel development in central Manchester.

Manchester Magistrates' Court heard on the 21 January 2015 that a member of the public contacted the Health and Safety Executive (HSE) claiming that a man had been seen balancing on scaffold tubes in the rain while working on the roof of the multistorey hotel. HSE inspectors subsequently found the employee working on the roof.

An investigation by the HSE found that the employee had climbed up the scaffold to hammer the steel beams into place and had not used the tower scaffold that had been made available for him. There was also a full time scaffolder on site, available for any of the contractors to utilise, to ensure safe working platforms were in place.

The employee in question pleaded guilty to breaching Section 7 of the Health and Safety at Work etc. Act 1974 and was sentenced to six months imprisonment, suspended for 18 months, fined £1,400.00 and ordered to pay costs of £2,939.18.

After the case the HSE inspector said: 'This case dealt with a serious work at height risk, which could have led to a fatal incident. The particular employee failed in his duty to protect his own safety while at work and also placed others at risk had he dropped any tool from the position he was seen in, some 27 m above street level. During the HSE's investigation he said that he did not appreciate how high he was. Never before in my career as an HSE inspector have I seen such a staggering disregard for personal safety. It is a matter of pure luck that no-one was injured or killed. My thanks go to the member of the public who reported their concern to us, as they have been instrumental in saving a life and arguably that of anyone below him at that time'.

D
24

Roof work

Working at, above or below ground level, at any height from which a fall is possible, should be regarded as hazardous and the necessary precautions should be taken.

Working at height in a safe environment

Safe systems of work

Before work starts a risk assessment must be carried out to identify the hazards and enable suitable control measures to be put in place. A safe system of work should be derived from a suitable and sufficient risk assessment considering the location of the work, the task to be undertaken, and the hazardous substances, tools, plant and equipment involved in the task. This process will assist a competent person to draft a safety method statement, sequencing the operations required for the work to proceed.

The safe system of work must be communicated to everyone involved in the task to ensure that they understand the precautions to be taken. Signatures of acknowledgement should be obtained from those involved to show that they have attended the briefing and have **understood** the safe system of work. The person delivering the briefing should also ask questions to check understanding.

If the work is to be sub-contracted, site management must ensure that the sub-contractor understands this requirement.

Equipment

All equipment used for work at height must be safe and well maintained. It must also be tested and inspected at the required intervals. It must be the right equipment for the task and must be used as intended.

☑ The booklet *Health and safety in roof work* (HSG33) contains advice from the HSE and is a useful source of further information for companies that carry out roof work.

☑ The Advisory Committee for Roofsafety (ACR) represents roofing trade associations and provides industry guidance.

Training

Training is imperative to ensure work can be carried out in a safe manner. Without proper and specific training in roof work, employees could endanger themselves and their co-workers through a lack of knowledge and appreciation of the inherent risks.

D
24

Supervision

Always ensure that all roof workers are adequately supervised. A roof is no place for an unsupervised trainee. In some circumstances it may be necessary to maintain a one-to-one supervisory approach for young and/or inexperienced workers.

Handling of materials

The handling of materials at height can create a falling material hazard that could impact on other workers and members of the public. For this reason, the planning process must consider the implications and establish the safest means of handling in the particular circumstances. The use of telehandlers and up and over loading bay gates is becoming more common because they go someway towards ensuring that fall protection is maintained throughout loading activity.

Flat roofs

If it has been established that the work cannot be avoided and there is no integral safety rail, parapet wall or other effective barrier to prevent falls from a roof edge, some form of protection must be provided. In preferential order, this may take the form of:

- ☑ a working platform around the external perimeter of the roof complete with guard-rails and toe-boards, or

- ☑ securely anchored double guard-rails and toe-boards, positioned on the roof and set as far back from the edge as possible whilst allowing the work to take place, or

- ☑ a fall protection system that offers a suitable anchor point to which employees can attach fall restraint equipment.

Counterweight temporary edge protection system
Image courtesy of Kee Safety Ltd

Sloping and curved roofs

Falls from sloping roofs can occur at any time but are more likely when the surface is slippery or in windy conditions. Moisture, ice, snow, moss and lichens will all increase the risk of slipping and this becomes greater still as the roof slope increases.

In most situations, work on sloping or curved roofs means that edge protection must be installed. As the roof slope increases, the specification of the edge protection should be changed to accommodate the potential loading of the edge protection by increased fall heights. All reputable scaffolding contractors should be able to assist with providing edge protection of the required specification.

**D
24**

Additional considerations include the following.

- ☑ If work extends to within 2 m of gable ends, edge protection should be provided to those edges too.

- ☑ A scaffold platform level with the eaves is an ideal way of providing access and storage space. When provided, this form of protection should be located no more than 300 mm below the level of the eaves.

On particularly steep roofs, work positioning equipment may need to be installed, such as abseiling rope anchor points. In this situation, a specialist sub-contractor must be employed.

Weather conditions

Avoid roof work in high winds. Remember that the eddying and funnelling effects of wind, which can be caused by nearby buildings and pitched roofs, can make a roof dangerous in windy conditions. The handling of sheeting and cladding at heights in windy conditions can be dangerous – for those on the roof and on the ground. Work should also be stopped at the first sign of localised thunder and lightning.

Roof ladders

Roof ladders must not be considered as a standalone item of equipment. They should only be used for access when accompanied by edge protection.

It is essential that roof ladders are:

- ☑ the correct type – Class 1 industrial

- ☑ in good condition, well maintained and strong enough for the job

- ☑ properly supported

- ☑ securely fixed against slipping or being dislodged

- ☑ long enough to span across supports.

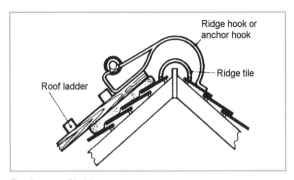

Erecting a roof ladder

 Do not set ridge hooks onto ridge or capping tiles as the downward pressure of the ladder and a person's weight will cause the tiles to loosen.

Temporary work platforms

Temporary work platforms should be a minimum of 600 mm wide and fitted with double guard-rails and toe-boards on both sides, unless the nature of the work requires that they are left off one side, in which case alternative fall-protection measures must be taken.

When moving across a roof, where one temporary work platform is not sufficient, use two platforms: one to work from and one to move across, ready for your next change of position.

Roof scaffolds

Where access for chimney repairs is required, the best form of access is often a fixed access scaffold. This is because those that are properly built are structurally stable and offer safe access and a sufficient storage area for tools and materials.

Example of a TG20 compliant chimney stack and access scaffold

 Chimney repair work must never be attempted by standing directly on the roof or standing a free-standing ladder on the roof and leaning it against the chimney.

 For more information on good practice download the free HSE leaflet *Roof repair work*.

Fragile roofs

On average, seven people are killed each year as a result of falls through fragile roof material during small, short-term inspection, maintenance and cleaning jobs. People who fall and escape death often suffer life-changing injuries.

 Visit the CITB website for a fragile roofs video highlighting the dangers of unsafe working on fragile roofs.

When working on roofs be aware of fragile surfaces that may fail under a person's weight, including the following.

- ☑ Glass.
- ☑ Plastic.
- ☑ Asbestos and new technology cement profile sheets.
- ☑ Corroded metal sheets.
- ☑ Rotten chipboard (or similar materials).
- ☑ Liner panels on built-up sheet roofing.
- ☑ Roof lights (which may be difficult to see in certain conditions).

Fragile surfaces may not be immediately obvious as they may be dirty, weathered, covered in moss, grime or debris or they may have been painted. Reports of accidents show that skylights are a particular problem. Signs placed in a prominent position should identify all fragile roofs.

D
24

Remember: fragile roof incidents can be prevented by careful planning, using trained and experienced workers with suitable equipment and a high level of supervision.

A clear indication of a fragile roof and the measures necessary to work safely upon it

Management should ensure that work does not proceed on or near to a fragile surface until the appropriate measures, as highlighted by the findings of a risk assessment, have been taken. A safe system of work should be devised to enable the task to be carried out without anyone having to go on to the roof. Improvements in technology mean that roof sheets can be replaced from beneath. Working methods such as this should be adopted wherever possible.

 ## Before work starts

☑ Ensure that a suitable and sufficient risk assessment has been undertaken and the findings of the risk assessment have been taken into account, the working party briefed on its content and suitable risk control measures are in place.

☑ Ensure that a competent person has assessed the roof and the surrounding environment.

☑ Ensure that the work is properly planned in advance.

☑ Plan to use non-fragile assemblies for new and replacement roofs where possible.

☑ Give due consideration to others who may be affected by the works, for example building occupants and the general public.

☑ Satisfy yourself that you have allowed sufficient time to carry out the work safely.

 ## During work

☑ Ensure the planned safe system of work is implemented and that those carrying out the work follow the system.

☑ Monitor progress and maintain safe systems of work, adapting it where necessary, if authorised to do so.

D 24

Where it is necessary for someone to go on the roof make sure of the following.

- [✓] Install perimeter edge protection and use a stable, temporary working platform, complete with guard-rails, on the roof surface to spread the loads.

- [✓] All work and access platforms are fitted with guard-rails. If this is not possible, install safety nets or air bags underneath the roof or use a harness system.

- [✓] Physical load-bearing edge protective barriers should be fitted around skylights and other fragile areas, or load-bearing covers that cannot be dislodged should be fitted over skylights, particularly where fragile skylights are fitted to an otherwise load-bearing roof. Safety signage should also be displayed in line with the safe system of work.

- [✓] Where demarcation barriers and signs are used, they must be set at least 2 m from a leading edge or fragile surface.

- [✓] Measures must be taken to spread the loading on the roof sufficiently to prevent failure of the roof material (for example, a stable, temporary working platform with guard-rails).

- [✓] If it is possible that someone will fall through a fragile surface, a collective fall-arrest system (such as safety nets or airbags) or a protection platform (such as a birdcage scaffold) should be positioned below the area where work will be carried out. Debris nets may also be needed to protect those working below from falling debris.

- [✓] Where harnesses and lanyards are used, make sure they have adequate anchorage points and they are properly fitted and worn.

- [✓] Increase supervision and monitoring of the work activity.

Proprietary covers, which can serve as either a temporary or a permanent installation, are available to prevent someone who is passing by, or working near, fragile material from falling through.

For further information refer to the following HSE publications.

- [✓] *Working on roofs* (INDG284).

- [✓] *Fragile roofs. Safe working practices* (GEIS5).

For further information refer to the safe working at height chapter in Section D of GE 700 *Construction site safety*.

Working above other people

When working at height above an area where other people have access, it is important to implement a safe system of work, to prevent people below from being struck by falling objects. This may be achieved in the following ways.

- [✓] Implementing a system of work that prevents anything falling (such as tethering tools).

- [✓] Using physical containment measures, including containment barriers, sheeting or netting, brick-guards, protection fans, pedestrian tunnels and crash decking or a combined safety/debris net to catch falling objects.

- [✓] Where possible, excluding people from the area below.

For further information refer to the safe working at height chapter and fall arrest and suspension equipment chapter in Section D of GE 700 *Construction site safety*.

It is important to ensure that the wind speed is measured at the same height at which work is being carried out. Wind speed can increase with height.

Also consider that obstructions, such as nearby buildings, can cause wind eddies which may create differing or higher wind speeds and forces.

Wind

High wind speeds can create unsafe working conditions. Winds can funnel and swirl around buildings, causing turbulence, which may make work places unsafe, particularly where items are being stored or handled at height.

The measurement of wind speed can be carried out using a hand-held anemometer, as shown in the image below.

Typical hand-held wind meter (anemometer)
(Image supplied by Kestrel Weather & Environmental Meters by NK)

D 24

Beaufort wind scale for use on land (Numbers 1–9)

Windforce number	Description of wind	Wind locally	Speed mph	Speed m/sec
0	Calm	Calm, smoke rises vertically.	1	0–1
1	Light air	Direction of wind shown by smoke drift, but not by wind or weather vanes.	1–3	1–2
2	Light breeze	Wind felt on face. Leaves rustle. Wind or weather vanes move.	4–7	2–3
3	Gentle breeze	Leaves and small twigs in constant motion. Wind extends light flags.	8–12	3–5
4	Moderate breeze	Wind raises dust and loose paper. Small branches move.	13–18	5–8
5	Fresh breeze	Small trees in leaf begin to sway. Little crested wavelets form on inland waters.	19–24	8–11
6	Strong breeze	Large branches in motion. Umbrellas used with some difficulty.	25–31	11–14
7	Near gale	Whole trees in motion. Becoming difficult to walk against the wind.	32–38	14–17
8	Gale	Twigs break off trees. Progress is generally impeded.	39–46	17–21
9	Strong gale	Chimney pots, slates and tiles may be blown off.	47–54	21–24

D
24

Ladders and stepladders

Traditionally, ladders and stepladders have been used in the following ways.

- ☑ As a way of getting up to or down from a place of work at height (for example, the means of access to a roof or scaffold).

- ☑ As a place of work at height (work carried out whilst standing on a ladder or stepladder, for example, painting first floor windows).

Ladders and stepladders must be inspected before use to ensure there are no defects and they are fit for purpose. A good practice approach would be to include them as part of a documented tagging system.

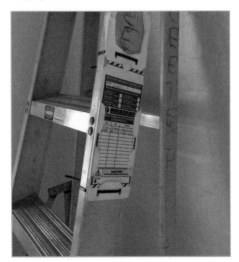

Good practice is to tag ladders and stepladders to record inspections

The Work at Height Regulations require that employers give adequate consideration to the safety of the user before selecting a ladder or stepladder as either a means of access to a place of work at height, or as a place of work at height.

Ladders are classified into the following three grades.

Class 1	Industrial.
EN 131	Light trades (may include scaffolding ladders).
Class 3	Domestic.

 In November 2017, the British Standards and regulations for ladders and steps changed. BS 2037 Class 1 Industrial and Class 3 Domestic standards were withdrawn to create two European-wide categories: EN 131 Trade and Industrial – heavy duty and industrial use (for professional users) and EN 131 Domestic (for non-professional users). The new standards will ensure products are built with additional safety standards, such as wider bases and stabilisers on ladders over 3 m in height. *(For further information on these changes visit the companion website.)*

Prior to deciding whether or not a ladder or stepladder should be used, a risk assessment must be carried out. The results must clearly demonstrate that it is not reasonably practicable to use any other means of access and that the risks from using a ladder or a stepladder are low.

HSE guidance recommends that ladders and stepladders should only be used as a means of access to a place of work at height, or as a place of work, when the nature of the work is as follows.

- ☑ Is of short duration (less than 30 minutes is recommended).

- ☑ Is of a light nature (requires no heavy lifting, carrying or a destabilising pressure applied by the user or equipment in carrying out the work – minimal manual handling).

- ☑ Allows one hand to be available at all times for holding onto the ladder or stepladder.

- ☑ Requires nothing to be carried that would cause instability of the ladder, stepladder or user.

- ☑ Does not necessitate using the top three treads of any stepladder unless they are designed for use.

 For further information refer to the HSE guidance *Safe use of ladders and stepladders* **(INDG455).**

Additionally, when stepladders are used as a place of work they should be positioned so that the user faces the work as the stepladder is climbed. A stepladder must not be positioned in such a way that the worker is side on to the work, because there is the potential for the work to require or create a sideways pressure and cause the stepladder to become unstable.

Ladders should:

- ☑ be subjected to periodic inspections with written inspection reports kept

- ☑ be individually identifiable (ladder tag) and proof of inspection must be able to be demonstrated

- ☑ be visually checked by the user for obvious defects before use and not used if found to be defective

- ☑ be set up at an angle of 75° (1 m out for every 4 m up)

- ☑ be positioned on a firm, level surface, where they are not exposed to being struck by pedestrians or vehicles

- ☑ be used in accordance with the manufacturer's instructions

- ☑ be the right ladder for the task (for example, long enough with enough of an overrun, if necessary)

- ☑ ideally, be secured at or near the upper point of rest by the stiles, not the rungs

- ☑ extend at least 1 m above the stepping-off place unless an alternative handhold is provided that enables a safe transfer between the ladder and stepping-off place

- ☑ be secured at the bottom or footed* if securing at the top is not possible

- ☒ not be rested against fragile or flexible items (such as plastic guttering); a ladder stay or stand-off device must be used as necessary

- ☒ never be painted to an extent that the paint could conceal defects.

* HSE research has shown that to be most effective, the person footing a ladder should stand on the bottom rung with both feet at all times. Even then, footing is not an effective method of stopping a long ladder from slipping sideways. Ideally a ladder will only be footed when it is climbed for the first time for the purpose of tying it off.

D 24

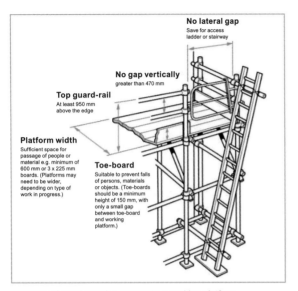

Example of good practice access to a working platform

 Users should face the ladder at all times when climbing up or down, and not carry anything that would interfere with their safety, balance or ability to grip the ladder.

Podium steps

Over recent years, the use of stepladders has reduced because improved technology offers alternatives for tasks where a stepladder or hop-up would previously have been used.

These alternative methods are becoming popular because they offer a collective means of protection and a greater degree of safety than stepladders. Podium steps offer a stable working platform, complete with wheel-brakes, guard-rails and in many cases stabilisers to increase the load bearing footprint, in contrast to the potential instability of ladders and stepladders. A number of manufacturers of podium steps have designed them with a view to improving safety by incorporating anti-surf features (for example, to prevent those using the equipment from pulling the equipment along when they are on the working platform) and by adding power so that height can be adjusted easily.

 New podium steps and other low-level access equipment should comply with the standard specification (PAS250/BS 8620), which is available from the British Standards Institute (BSI).

Podium steps in use, wheels locked and correctly assembled

Lightweight staging and trestle scaffolds

This type of access equipment should only be used where all of the requirements of the Work at Height Regulations can be met. Modern trestle systems are lightweight, stable in use and must be fitted with guard-rails, toe-boards and safe access and egress, as necessary.

- ☑ Trestles should only be erected by someone who has been trained and competent to do so.

- ☑ They should be of sound construction.

- ☑ They should only be erected on a surface that is sufficiently level and will bear the weight of the trestle plus any loading of persons and materials.

- ☑ Trestles should be subject to an inspection regime (such as before first use, after alteration and at regular intervals thereafter). A good practice approach would be to include them as part of a documented tagging system.

 The use of loose scaffold boards supported on split-head trestles or other older trestle systems with no means of preventing falls is totally unacceptable and should be prohibited for working at height.

Mobile access towers and access platforms

The use of prefabricated aluminium mobile access towers (mobile towers) has become a common alternative to other means of access to height for construction and maintenance work.

However, mobile towers have some limitations and should only be used when they can satisfy both legislative and general site requirements.

Any person erecting a mobile tower must be competent and authorised to do so, having received adequate training or, if not fully competent, be under the direct supervision of an experienced, competent and appointed person.

The Prefabricated Access Suppliers' and Manufacturers' Association (PASMA) operates a well-recognised competency scheme for lightweight mobile towers. The collective fall protection methods recommended by PASMA and the HSE must be used to erect, alter or dismantle towers. They are known as advanced guard-rail technique (AGT) and the through-the-trap (3T) methods.

It is good practice that anyone working on a tower holds a current PASMA qualification, which is valid for the type of tower in use. Where this is not achievable, then each working party using mobile towers (such as mechanical and electrical workers, plasterers and dryliners, painters and decorators) should have sufficient workers (one per tower is recommended) who hold a current PASMA card or its equivalent. For those individuals who will be working on but not involved in erecting, altering or dismantling a mobile tower, formal work at height awareness training is required, more comprehensive than that normally given during a toolbox talk. A record of such training should be kept, including details of who gave the instruction, who attended and any action taken to confirm participants' understanding.

 A toolbox talk does not give a worker the authority to erect, adapt or dismantle a mobile access tower.

A risk assessment must be carried out to determine whether or not a mobile access tower is suitable for the environment in which it is to be used and for the type of work that is to be carried out. The following factors should be considered when deciding whether or not it is safe to use a mobile tower.

☑ Is there a safer method, as far as is reasonably practicable, of carrying out the work at height?

☑ Are ground conditions suitable (flat and firm)?

☑ Will the tower provide sufficient height and working space? The manufacturer's instructions must be followed with regard to the maximum height to which a tower may be built, the loading of the tower and the purpose of the tower including, where necessary, the need to fit outriggers. Reference must be made to the manufacturer's instructions when erecting a mobile tower. The maximum permitted heights information will be stated there.

☑ Are there adjacent overhead power lines, other overhead obstructions or obstructions that reduce working head room?

☑ Is a mobile tower suitable and safe to use in all other respects?

☑ Will the tower be able to take the required loading of people, tools, equipment and materials?

☑ Could high winds, the nature of the work being carried out or hoisting materials up from below impose forces on the tower that may cause it to overturn?

☑ If the weather, hoisting materials or the nature of the work could cause a problem, can the tower be tied to the adjacent structure and if so, is it safe to do so?

☑ Is there a chance of the tower being struck by mobile plant or other vehicles?

☑ Is there a chance of the tower being an obstruction or danger to the public or others, or of the tower being interfered with by others?

When a mobile tower is in use the following basic safety requirements must be met.

☑ Pre-use inspections and checks by the user and statutory inspections of the tower must be carried out by a competent person and inspection reports compiled as necessary.

☑ The working platform must be fully boarded with guard-rails and toe-boards fitted.

☑ The brakes should be effective and set in the ON position at all times that the tower is not being moved.

☑ Access to the working platform must be gained by using the built-in ladder sections, with users climbing the ladder on the inside of the tower, never by using a freestanding ladder or by climbing the outside of the tower.

☑ The hatch on the working platform must be in the closed position before any work takes place.

☑ Attempts to gain extra height by using a ladder, stepladder or other forms of hop-up systems are unacceptable and must be prohibited.

☑ If the work cannot be reached from the platform of the tower erected to its full height, it is the wrong form of access equipment for the job.

☑ The tower must not be moved whilst anyone is on the working platform (equipment, tools and materials should also be removed).

D
24

☑ Mobile towers must not be moved by someone on the platform pulling the tower along using the adjacent structure (known as surfing).

☑ Exclusion zones with suitable barriers and safety signs should be set up to prevent others entering the work area.

For further information refer to the common access equipment chapter and the scaffolding chapter in Section D of GE 700 *Construction site safety* and the PASMA Code of Practice.

Safe working on a mobile access tower, with toe-boards and guard-rails in position and wheels locked

Mobile access towers can now be supplied with an advanced guard-rail. These are fitted at a lower level and provide edge protection at the level above so a safe place to work is created without placing the operative at risk during erection and dismantling.

Mobile elevating work platforms

Mobile elevating work platforms (MEWPs) provide a temporary working platform where ladders would be unsafe and scaffolding is not economical or reasonably practicable.

Any work involving the use of a MEWP is classified as a *lifting operation* as defined in the Lifting Operations and Lifting Equipment Regulations (LOLER). The requirements of those regulations must be complied with, and supplemented with the guidance provided by the MEWP manufacturer and the International Powered Access Federation (IPAF), the trade body for the powered access industry.

For further information refer to the HSE document *The selection, management and use of mobile elevating work platforms* (GEIS6).

The limits of elevation and outreach (the operating envelope) are described in manufacturers' handbooks. The work must always be planned and executed within those guidelines. It is essential, therefore, that the correct machine is chosen for the task.

Ground conditions are critical to safe operation. Many platforms are fitted with outriggers or stabilisers and these must be used in accordance with the manufacturer's instructions.

D
24

MEWP in use

When positioning a MEWP, the following safety factors must be considered.

- ☑ How firm is the ground? Will it support the MEWP and its expected loading?

- ☑ Are there cellars, basements, sewers, drains, manholes, old trenches, un-compacted backfill or anything else that might collapse under the weight of the MEWP and its load?

- ☑ Are there any overhead services that could create an unnecessary hazard (for example, overhead power lines or telephone lines)?

- ☑ Is the machine level and, if not, can it be levelled up?

- ☑ What are the weather conditions? Windy and/or icy conditions or thunder and lightning may mean that work at height cannot be carried out safely.

- ☑ Are there any other activities taking place (such as other trades at work) in the area where the MEWP is to be used?

Safety harnesses must be worn by all individuals working from a MEWP when this is identified as necessary by the risk assessment. In some circumstances the risk assessment may indicate that users should not wear a harness, for example, when working in a MEWP over or in the immediate vicinity of water, as specified in IPAF guidance. The decision should be based upon the assessed risk of falling from the machine, the machine toppling and the implications of being clipped to the machine in the event of an incident of this kind.

When a safety harness is worn it must be used in conjunction with a work restraint lanyard and attached to a dedicated anchor point on the machine's platform. Fall-arrest lanyards are **not** suitable for this purpose, unless a combination adjustable type lanyard is used. The length of lanyard used will depend upon the range of movement required, allowing free movement within the basket or about the platform, yet preventing a fall from the basket or platform.

The free end of the harness must **never** be attached to a point on an adjacent structure, as this would lead to difficulties if the platform were to be inadvertently lowered with the operator still attached to the structure, or if the ground-level controls had to be used because the operator was unable to use the platform controls for any reason.

Detail of this nature should be included in the risk assessment and method statement and should extend to the arrangements for carrying out a rescue if the operator becomes incapacitated or if the MEWP suffers mechanical problems.

Sheet materials and cladding will act like sails in windy conditions and can affect the stability of the platform and safety of the worker in the platform.

Never use a MEWP in the following circumstances.

- ☒ As a jack or prop to support anything else.
- ☒ For the transfer of goods.
- ☒ As a crane or lifting appliance.
- ☒ As a means to transfer a worker from one level to another (for example, using a scissor lift as a lift and then getting out to work on the roof).

 Only trained, competent and authorised operators should use MEWPs.

Operators should be trained, competent and familiar with the type of machine they are required to use and:

- ☑ be registered with the Construction Plant Competence Scheme (CPCS) or another industry-recognised scheme
- ☑ be issued with a company licence or authority.

Personnel being considered as operators should meet certain requirements.

- ☑ Be sufficiently fit and mobile to climb in and out of platforms.
- ☑ Have a good head for heights, good hearing and colour vision.
- ☑ Be able to judge space and distance.
- ☑ Have good eye/hand co-ordination and manual dexterity.
- ☑ Be generally in good health.

Any medical history of fainting or dizziness may make a person unsuitable for operating a machine like a MEWP.

Maintenance and inspections should be properly scheduled, and include the following.

- ☑ A pre-use inspection by the operator who must be trained and competent to do so.
- ☑ A recorded weekly inspection by a maintenance fitter or trained and competent operator.
- ☑ A thorough examination every six months, as defined by LOLER. A certificate of conformity that is delivered with a new platform is the equivalent of a thorough examination for the six months from date of issue.

Employers are required to keep records of thorough examination under LOLER.

Emergency controls

Both ground and work platform controls should be checked as part of the pre-use inspection to ensure they are working correctly. This check should also include the emergency lowering controls that are provided to enable the work platform to be safely lowered to ground level.

The supervisor should ensure that a responsible person who is familiar with the emergency lowering system, is always in close proximity to the MEWP to lower the work platform, in the event that rescue is required.

Even experienced operators sometimes have difficulty locating the emergency descent controls that every mobile elevating work platform is fitted with.

 You should be able to easily find this symbol *(on the next page)* **on any MEWP. It helps identify the location of the emergency descent controls.**

D 24

Emergency descent symbol

The emergency descent symbol is a practical visual aid and a prime example of an industry initiative to make access equipment even safer.

Emergency descent systems can be found on all types of mobile elevating work platforms. They differ in terms of where they are located on specific machines and how they operate. It is therefore vital that familiarisation training is given when a machine is delivered to site and before an operator's first use.

 The emergency descent symbol is available to download for free from the IPAF website.

Controls shrouded and fitted with anti-crush protection measures (note tool clip)

Personnel must be instructed to never attempt to climb out of an elevated MEWP if the emergency back-up system fails to work, but should stay in the work platform until rescued by other means.

Secondary guarding

A secondary guarding device is a piece of equipment that can be fitted to a MEWP in addition to the primary guarding systems. It is intended to further reduce the risk of entrapment and/or provide an alert that an entrapment situation has occurred. When formulating the safe system of work (SSoW) for the use of a MEWP, secondary guarding should be given due consideration.

Scaffolding

Competence

The design, erection, alteration and dismantling of scaffold should only be carried out by competent workers (such as CISRS qualified scaffolders), or be carried out under the supervision and direction of competent persons. It is an offence for anyone else to erect, modify or dismantle a scaffold.

 For further information refer to the HSE's website and to the National Access and Scaffolding Confederation's website.

D 24

Installation

Where a scaffold will be erected for you by a scaffolding contractor, it should be constructed in accordance with a TG20 compliance sheet or a bespoke scaffold design, or for system scaffolds, the manufacturer's guidance.

On completion of the scaffold site management should receive a copy of the scaffold handover certificate, which provides details of the safe loading of the scaffold, design references and the last inspection date. The scaffold should not be used until such time that site management, the contractor and scaffolding company representatives have inspected the scaffold and the handover certificate has been issued.

☑ **For further information on safe working at height for scaffolders refer to the NASC publication *Preventing falls in scaffolding* (SG4).**

☑ **For further information and details on scaffolding configuration, refer to the NASC guidance, TG20.**

All equipment used for work at height must be checked before use to ensure that it is safe to use and work from.

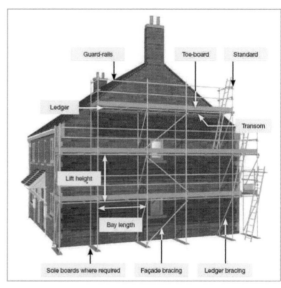

Scaffolding terminology

Basic safety requirements

Foundations should be level, firm and able to withstand the loading to be imposed, with uprights located upon base plates. Wooden sole pads are required for most construction applications.

Standards (uprights) are vertical scaffold tubes and should be spaced closely enough to provide an adequate support for the proposed load. In most circumstances they should not be more than 2.7 m apart.

D
24

Ledgers are horizontal scaffold tubes, linking the standards along the scaffold, and provide the support for board bearers (the transoms).

Transoms are horizontal scaffold tubes that sit on top of ledgers, supporting the scaffold boards that form the working platform.

Structural transoms are used to connect opposing façades of the scaffold and are specified by some designs. Connection must be made with load-bearing couplers from standard to standard or ledger to ledger.

Ties provide vital stability and are needed to prevent collapse or overturning of a scaffold. The number, type and positioning of the ties will be detailed within the bespoke scaffold design, TG20 compliance sheet or, if proprietary scaffold is being used, in the manufacturer's instructions. A percentage of the ties should be subject to a pull test in accordance with the NASC, TG4:11. This process should be recorded and a record of the test kept on site.

Bracing is the method by which scaffold structures are made rigid and are installed diagonally. Bracing is an integral part of any scaffold.

Façade bracing is the scaffolding tubes that run across the face of the scaffold. The bracing tubes may be a continuous diagonal from the top to the bottom of the scaffolding, or may be installed in a zigzag configuration.

Ledger bracing runs from ledger to ledger, usually from front to back or back to front on independent scaffolds.

Platforms must be wide enough to provide a safe place of work and enable other people and equipment to pass. British Standard BS EN 12811-1 recommends a minimum width of 600 mm for working platforms and 500 mm for access only scaffolds.

Stability of boards: there should be at least three supports for each scaffold board, normally not more than 1.2 m apart or 900 mm for heavy duty scaffolding. Boards should overhang each end support by at least 50 mm but by not more than 150 mm.

Guard-rails should be placed along the outside edges and at the ends of each working platform from where a person could fall. Occasionally, guard-rails are necessary on the inner edge of working platforms, perhaps across window openings or other internal areas where falls are possible. It should be noted that the Work at Height Regulations make no distinction between internal and external guard-rails.

In most circumstances a minimum of two guard-rails should be installed. The top guard-rail should be at least 950 mm above the working platform and the other mid-way (the mid-rail) between the top guard-rail and the top of the toe-board. There should be no unprotected gap of more than 470 mm.

If a guard-rail has to be moved, it must only be done with the permission of the responsible person and only by a trained and competent person. The guard-rail must be replaced as soon as possible and alternative fall protection measures may be required until it is replaced.

Toe-boards should be fitted to all working platforms and are usually formed by securing a scaffold board on edge. BS 12811 requires a 150 mm toe-board. There should not be more than a 470 mm gap between the top of the toe-board and the mid guard-rail.

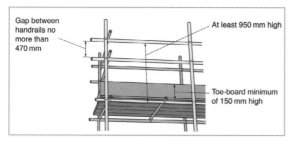

Required edge protection dimensions

Access: Ideally access to a scaffold will be via a purpose-built stair tower. However, where the decision is taken to use a ladder, the scaffold should be designed to incorporate internal ladders in preference to external ladders. If an external ladder is used it should be positioned at right angles to the scaffold to allow users to step on and off the scaffold with ease. Ladder gates should be installed at all access points. Scaffold users should not be expected to duck beneath guard-rails or step through unprotected gaps.

Ideally, loading bays should be provided with a purpose-made gate that allows access for materials whilst at the same time offering protection against falls for users of the scaffold.

A proprietary scaffold staircase tower

D
24

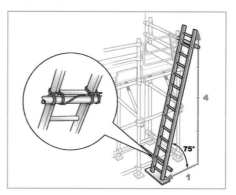

External access ladder and safety gate

Protection of the public

Particular attention should be paid to protecting the public and users of the highway, where necessary. Where scaffolds are erected over or next to pavements or other public places, the use of debris nets, brick guards or protective fans are essential. There should be adequate lighting and guarding of the scaffold at night. The types of protection to be installed may be specified by the Local Authority's highways and pavement licence. Checks should be made to ensure Local Authority requirements are met.

To mitigate the risk of a member of the general public being struck by falling work equipment, scaffolding companies and others should consider the use of tool lanyards to secure tools when working at height.

Working on scaffolds

Before starting work on scaffolds you must check that the scaffold has been inspected within the previous seven days, that the access route is safe (stair towers and ladders) and there are no gaps exceeding 50 mm between boards.

 50 mm gaps are only permissible to allow the vertical passage of a scaffold upright through the working platform. If a risk of falling materials remains it may be necessary to close off these gaps, using plywood or proprietary gap fillers.

Measures should be in place to prevent boards from splaying, which can be a danger to those using the working platform.

Loading on scaffolds

Care should be taken to ensure scaffolds are not overloaded. Detail relating to the safe loading of scaffolds can be found on the bespoke scaffold design, the TG20 compliance sheet, the scaffold tagging system and the handover certificate.

Scaffolds designed to receive a specific load (such as loading or specially strengthened sections for installing lifting equipment) should display signs showing the load rating.

A proprietary access system incorporating ladder access, working platform, guard-rails and hoist

Inspections and reports

Scaffolding must be inspected by a competent person. It is a legal requirement of the Work at Height Regulations that every working platform must be inspected as outlined below.

☑ After installation or assembly in any position.

☑ At suitable intervals (not exceeding seven days).

D 24

☑ If exposed to conditions that may cause deterioration.

☑ Each time that exceptional circumstances, which are likely to jeopardise the safety of the work equipment, have occurred.

Where a person can fall 2 m or more, a scaffold or working platform must not be used in any position unless it has been inspected in that position or, in the case of a MEWP, inspected on the site within the previous seven days.

Results of these inspections must be recorded.

Scaffold inspection in progress

Fall-arrest systems

Where it is not possible to devise a safe system of work that would prevent a fall from height, it is necessary to put measures in place that will ensure the following.

☑ Any fall that does occur is arrested.

☑ The distance that anyone could fall is limited to the lowest reasonably practicable distance.

☑ Injuries resulting from a fall are minimised as far as reasonably practicable.

Safety nets

Safety nets are designed to catch and then absorb the energy from a falling person. To do this it is important that they are rigged immediately below where people are working and that they are free from obstruction (such as plant and machinery, building materials and debris).

When nets are used they should be installed by qualified and competent net riggers who hold the appropriate fall arrest safety equipment training (FASET) qualification. Nets should only be provided where an assessment demonstrates that the use of working platforms is not reasonably practicable.

 It is recommended that nets are only installed by FASET member companies.

Nets should be:

☑ tested and fitted with a tag confirming that the inspection has been carried out

☑ inspected before first use and weekly thereafter by a competent person

☑ issued with a handover certificate before they are put into use for the first time

☑ maintained and inspected when rigged

**D
24**

☑ reinspected after a fall has occurred

☑ overlaid with fine mesh netting where protection from falling objects is required.

Safe systems of work devised for netting should consider the rescue of casualties who may have fallen into the net. It may be possible for casualties to walk out of the net, but this will not be possible in all situations.

Safety nets installed prior to roof works commencing

Soft-landing systems

Soft-landing systems do not prevent falls but they do reduce the potential consequences of any fall and they have the following benefits.

☑ They are **passive** safety systems. This means that once they are installed there is nothing that the people working above them have to do to make the system effective.

☑ They are **collective** safety systems that are designed to protect everyone working above them. As such, they are much preferred to safety harnesses and lanyards that are **personal** protection systems and only protect the individual wearing them, and then only when properly worn, adjusted and anchored.

Air or beanbags

Designed to be used in buildings with a storey height of up to 2.5 m, these systems comprise large polypropylene bags that are located at ground floor level and either inflated with air from a pump (airbags) or pre-packed with polystyrene chippings (beanbags). The depth of the bag cushions the fall and reduces the distance and consequences of the fall.

The bags are linked together with plastic snap-clips to completely fill the ground floor area without gaps. (To be effective and afford the level of protection required, the bags **must** be clipped together.) They can also be used on the first or subsequent floors providing that the floor joists supporting the bags are boarded over. The bags must be flame retardant and fully tested for resistance to flammability. This information will be identified on the label or data information sheet supplied by the manufacturer or installer.

Where soft-landing systems are used, due consideration should be given to the loading that may be applied to newly constructed block and brick walls.

 It is important that these systems are installed and used in strict accordance with the manufacturer's instructions.

D
24

Safety harnesses and lanyards

If fall-prevention measures (working platforms, barriers, guard-rails and so on) or collective fall-arrest measures (safety nets or other soft-landing systems) are not practical, an alternative safe system of work must be implemented. This safe system may require the use of safety harnesses and lanyards, but these should be regarded as the **last resort.**

Care must be taken when planning to use a safety harness, lanyard and energy-absorbing system, since, depending on where the lanyard is anchored, a falling person may fall a distance or swing before the fall is arrested.

The use of personal fall protection equipment requires a high degree of training, competence and supervision. Safety harnesses must not be used in any lone-working activity as there would be no means of carrying out a rescue.

Inspection

Fall protection equipment must be formally inspected, at intervals not exceeding six months, and the inspection results must be recorded. However, many internal procedures reduce the interval between inspections to as little as three months.

In addition to formal checks carried out by a competent person, the user of the equipment must inspect the equipment for damage prior to each period of use.

Items to be checked during inspection of fall protection equipment include the following.

- ☑ Stitching for completeness.

- ☑ Webbing for signs of damage. This can include chemical damage, heat damage, cuts and abrasions.

- ☑ Buckles and metal components for cracks or distortion.

- ☑ Friction damage.

- ☑ Excessive contamination (by grease, dirt, and so on).

If any of these faults are identified, the equipment must be withdrawn from service immediately.

 For comprehensive information on inspections refer to the HSE publication *Inspecting fall arrest equipment made from webbing or rope* (INDG367).

Types of safety harness

There are many types of safety harness and the employer's risk assessment will determine the correct type of harness to be used for any particular job.

Rescue

In all situations, when a worker has fallen and their fall has been arrested by fall protection equipment, the individual should be retrieved as quickly as possible to prevent the onset of suspension syncope, more commonly known as fainting. In many cases, the casualty may be able to assist either fully (self-rescue) or partially. When they have been rescued, the casualty should be referred to a medical practitioner for a professional medical assessment, even if it seems the fall has caused no harmful effects.

**D
24**

First-aid procedures

Information which was previously widely accepted within the construction industry, relating to the condition that was known as suspension trauma, is now considered misleading. Current guidance suggests that standard UK first-aid procedures should be adopted for anyone who has been suspended in a safety harness.

Manufacturers of fall-arrest equipment have developed several types of rescue system that either enable the suspended person to relieve the pressure on their legs or allow them to be quickly and safely raised back to the working platform or lowered to the ground.

D
24

25

Excavations

What your employer should do for you
1. Plan for excavation work.
2. Provide suitable and sufficient risk assessments and method statements for the work, including a permit to work system.
3. Ensure staff are trained in safe excavation techniques to expose underground services.
4. Arrange for the monitoring of any changes in the ground, soil and atmospheric conditions surrounding the excavation.
5. Plan for any possible anticipated surcharging and actions in the event of a surcharge.
6. Locate underground services and provide relevant information to the site management team.
7. Provide the correct type of excavation supports, where needed, and provide information and instruction on safe use.
8. Provide safe access to and egress from the excavation.
9. Plan for vehicles and/or plant to approach the excavation safely.
10. In accordance with the findings of the risk assessment, carry out pre-entry gas monitoring of the excavation prior to each entry and ensure continuous monitoring of the excavation. Ensure that an attendant is in place whilst the excavation is occupied.
11. Provide (where necessary) an individual gas monitor and appropriate RPE for each entrant.
12. Restrict vehicles, scaffolds, plant (either mobile or parked) or materials from becoming too close to the edge.
13. Provide barrier material, warning signs and lights for the excavation.
14. Ensure that statutory inspections are carried out.
15. Ensure that any occupational health issues, as a result of the excavation work, are controlled.
16. Provide suitable welfare facilities for the type of work being undertaken.

D
25

What you should do as a supervisor			
Checklist	Yes	No	N/A
1. Continuously check for underground services and take note of relevant information.			
2. Ensure the work team are briefed on the contents of the relevant safe system of work, including permit to work procedures.			
3. Check that there is safe access to and egress from the excavation.			
4. Monitor any changes in the soil condition surrounding the excavation and report any areas of concern, including withdrawing workers.			
5. Ensure that the excavation remains supported and use the correct supports.			
6. Brief the team in the location of underground services and ensure they have been trained in the correct excavation techniques to expose any services.			
7. Avoid any possible surcharging and understand the actions to be taken in the event of surcharging.			
8. Install and maintain barrier material, warning signs and lights for the excavation.			
9. Organise for vehicles and/or plant to approach the excavation safely.			
10. Prevent vehicles, scaffolds, plant and materials from being stored or working too close to the edge.			
11. In accordance with the findings of the risk assessment, carry out pre-entry gas monitoring of the excavation prior to each entry and ensure continuous monitoring of the excavation. Ensure that an attendant is in place whilst the excavation is occupied.			
12. Provide (where necessary) an individual gas monitor and appropriate RPE for each entrant.			
13. Check that any occupational health issues, as a result of the excavation work, are monitored.			
14. Ensure suitable welfare facilities are provided.			
15. Check that the excavation is safe at the start of each shift, before the workers enter.			

D
25

Introduction

Every year people die and many others are seriously injured as a result of excavations collapsing. Most deaths occur in excavations that are less than 2.5 m deep.

Planning for work in excavations must be carried out by competent and authorised persons, including arranging for the installation of suitable trench support systems as necessary.

The diagram below is an example of the typical safe slope angles and should be used for guidance purposes only. If there is any doubt regarding soil conditions, the site engineer or shoring provider should be consulted.

Different types of ground composition and soil, and to an extent the prevailing weather conditions, will dictate how a trench may be dug and supported.

Where possible, it is far better to shore or batter back the sides of an excavation to a safe angle, based upon the chart on this page, in an effort to eliminate the chances of the sides collapsing inwards.

 A small collapse of earth into a trench may only involve a cubic metre of soil, but that will weigh over a tonne. If the ground is heavy clay and waterlogged, it will weigh much more. In most cases, digging someone out who has been buried by a fall of material will not be a quick or easy task.

The sides of a trench may look firm, but looks can be deceptive. Besides the inherent nature of the ground being excavated, additional factors that can cause what was thought to be a stable excavation to collapse include the following.

☑ Heavy rain waterlogging the ground.

☑ The ground drying out and shrinking.

☑ Excess pressure (known as surcharge) caused by nearby vehicles, materials or structures, including scaffolds.

The longer an unsupported excavation is open, the more chance there is of a collapse.

 You can download the free leaflet *Excavation: what you need to know as a busy builder* from the HSE website.

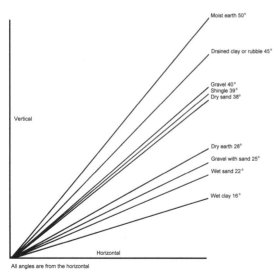

Moist earth 50°
Drained clay or rubble 45°
Gravel 40°
Shingle 39°
Dry sand 38°
Vertical
Dry earth 28°
Gravel with sand 25°
Wet sand 22°
Wet clay 16°
Horizontal
All angles are from the horizontal

Typical safe slope angles. The vertical distance should not exceed 1.2 m

D
25

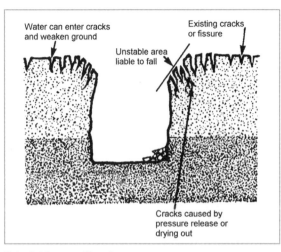

Potential dangers of trenches

Health and safety regulations no longer stipulate a depth at which the sides of a trench must be supported; the decision must be based on the findings of a risk assessment. In some cases, shallow trenches may not need support, providing the type of ground is firm and self-supporting.

Safe systems of work

Work in an excavation has the potential to be a hazardous activity. A risk assessment must be carried out to establish the inherent hazards and how they can be overcome.

Depending on the nature of the work to be carried out, it may be necessary to draw up a method statement and/or implement a permit to work system.

For further information on method statements and permits to work refer to Chapter A04 Risk assessments, method statements and permits to work.

In addition to the collapse of the sides, other potential hazards that may need to be addressed are listed below.

- ☑ Falls of materials, people, plant and vehicles into the excavation and deliberate (fly) tipping.

- ☑ Undermining the foundations of nearby structures, including scaffolds and other temporary works structures.

- ☑ Accidental or deliberate contact with underground services.

- ☑ Ingress of water or other fluids, standing water and pumping out.

- ☑ The presence of naturally occurring gases (such as hydrogen sulphide (H_2S)).

- ☑ The accumulation of gases which are heavier than air (such as H_2S and liquefied petroleum gas (LPG)).

Supports

Selection

There are many types of trench support systems available in preference to traditional timber supports. These include metal proprietary support systems, with or without hydraulic adjustment, sheet piles and props, drag boxes, trench and manhole boxes. The decision as to what is adequate support will depend on the type of excavation and the nature of the ground. Initial risk assessments, ground and soil surveys and planning must be carried out by trained and competent people.

D 25

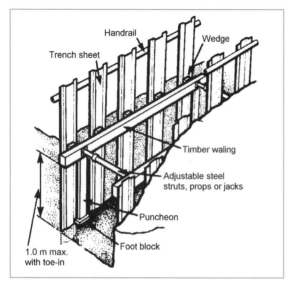

Example of a trench support system

Safe working in a deep excavation using trench boxes

Stability of adjacent structures

The stability of adjacent structures (such as nearby buildings or scaffolding) must be considered, not only at the planning stage but throughout the whole job. If an excavation is dug adjacent to the wall of a building, the removal of earth or undermining may cause the foundations and wall to slip or collapse.

Installation of trench supports

The placing, alteration and removal of trench supports must be carried out by competent workers or workers under the strict supervision of a competent person.

Inspection and examination

To comply with the Construction (Design and Management) Regulations, a person with the correct skills, knowledge, training and experience and who fully understands the dangers and necessary precautions **must** inspect an excavation in the following circumstances.

- ☑ Before any person carries out any work in the excavation.
- ☑ At the start of every shift.

☑ After any event likely to have affected the strength or stability of the excavation.

☑ After any accidental fall of rock, earth or other material.

Guarding

Barriers

It is necessary to erect barriers around most excavations, particularly those that are in places to which the public has access. If identified by the findings of a risk assessment, barriers must be erected around any excavation into which a person could fall and suffer personal injury. On many sites it is common practice to install guarding around all excavations. An unprotected excavation presents a fall risk in exactly the same way as an unprotected edge at height does (for example, the potential for injury resulting from a fall in the vertical plane). Particular attention must be given to the guarding and even covering of excavations, with suitable, robust covers (such as steel plates) if there is a likelihood of children gaining access to the site.

Excavation edge protection barriers

Excavations may be guarded by the installation of a substantial barrier, comprising double guard-rails and toe-boards or fencing on all sides to prevent the accidental fall of pedestrians. To prevent vehicles being driven into or too close to an excavation a barrier may be formed by depositing the excavated spoil in an extended heap along the length and width of the excavation. However, this earthwork barrier will add weight to the ground surrounding the excavation and must therefore be sited so as not to pose a risk of slippage into or surcharging the excavation.

Lighting

During the hours of darkness or other periods of reduced natural light, excavations and the guarding surrounding them will need to be illuminated, particularly if the excavation is in a place to which the public has access.

Access

There must be adequate and safe arrangements for getting into and out of excavations. This is usually with ladders, properly located and fixed with adequate overruns or other handholds, but adjustable, lightweight staircases or towers are becoming increasingly common and are safer and quicker to use. Under no circumstances should anyone use the side supports or underground services that cross or run along the trench as footholds to climb into or out of an excavation.

D
25

Safe access into a deep excavation, together with all round secure edge protection

Surcharging

The layout of the site must be planned to avoid and prevent, so far as practicable, the surcharging (the result of excess pressure being applied) to the sides of any excavation. This will involve planning for vehicle routes, parking areas and material lay-down areas to be kept well away from areas where excavations are to be dug. Where surcharging is inevitable, the way in which the sides of the excavation are supported must be designed and installed to accept the load.

Vehicle and plant movements

Where it is necessary for plant or vehicles to approach an excavation (for example, to tip materials or actually dig the excavation), adequate measures must be taken to ensure that the activity can be carried out safely.

The following are examples of safe practice.

- ☑ Ensuring that vehicle drivers and plant operators are competent.

- ☑ The installation of anchored stop-blocks to prevent the vehicle wheels over-running and getting too close to the edge.

- ☑ Using a vehicle marshaller to give directions to the driver or plant operator.

Personal protective equipment

The need for personal protective equipment (PPE), particularly specialist PPE, will be indicated by the findings of the risk assessment.

It may be necessary to wear respiratory protective equipment (RPE) in excavations where the air quality cannot be guaranteed as safe to breathe, particularly where, because of its nature, the excavation is designated as a confined space.

 For further information on PPE and RPE refer to Chapter B10 Personal protective equipment.

Occupational health issues

Leptospirosis (Weil's disease)

Leptospirosis is a potentially fatal disease that can be contracted through contact with the urine of, or water that has been contaminated by, rats or cattle. Rats will be attracted to wet places (such as the bottom of trenches) and they are likely to be a problem if sewers or other underground pipes have to be broken into as part of the work.

 For further information refer to Chapter B08 Health and welfare.

Asphyxiation/poisoning

An excavation could be designated as a confined space due to any of the following.

☑ Risk of engulfment or entrapment by a free-flowing solid (such as sand and fine soils).

☑ Nature of the excavation (deep and narrow) and the ground in which it is dug that could result in the accumulation of a naturally occurring gas (such as hydrogen sulphide (H_2S)).

☑ Asphyxia, due to the nature of the ground. (Peaty soils absorb oxygen from the atmosphere so the bottom of a trench dug in peat is unlikely to have a sufficient level of oxygen.) The action of chemicals in the soil on brownfield sites can also alter the oxygen content in an excavation. Soil which is high in limestone can produce carbon dioxide if it is contaminated with acidic rainwater.

☑ Substances used (such as LPG) which is heavier than air.

☑ Carbon monoxide (CO) from internal combustion engines located within the excavation. Though slightly lighter than air, it may build up in the excavation and take time to dissipate (clear).

☑ Nature of the substances released from any underground services that have to be broken into.

All of these factors can potentially have the effect of reducing the percentage of oxygen in the air and/or introducing toxic gases into the air. Control measures on the risk assessment may include forced, fresh-air ventilation or, as a last resort, appropriate RPE.

For further information refer to Chapter D27 Confined spaces.

D
25

D
25

26

Underground and overhead services

What your employer should do for you
1. Obtain and provide the licence and authority for works on roads and highways.
2. Ensure no works are carried out in roadways without the proper authority and licence.
3. Provide training for supervisors and operatives to enable works in highways and roadways (New Roads and Street Works Act (NRSWA) Chapter 8).
4. Provide training to enable the identification of underground services.
5. Contact all relevant bodies and ensure all underground services are identified before excavations start. Obtain plans and drawings.
6. Arrange for the disconnection of all underground services, where possible, and obtain certificates of disconnection.
7. Where underground services are not disconnected ensure all interested parties know those services are live.
8. Locate, identify and indicate the location of all underground services before excavation starts. Carry out a site survey and scan for services.
9. Produce a safe system of work for performing excavation works. Inform, instruct and train operatives in the safe system of work for excavations, including a permit to work and permit to break ground (permit to dig) and permit to work procedures.
10. Produce a procedure for the discovery of unidentified, underground services or objects and train staff in those procedures.
11. Where overhead cables are present, consult the power supply company to establish if the power can be isolated, or the minimum safe working distance from which a safe system of work can be developed.
12. Erect goal posts and barriers and introduce control measures (isolators on plant) to ensure that nothing and no-one encroaches into the exclusion zone.

D
26

What you should do as a supervisor

Checklist	Yes	No	N/A
1. Ensure works are authorised by obtaining a copy of the licence and authority for the works on roads and highways.			
2. Ensure no works are carried out in roadways without proper authority and licence.			
3. Ensure all staff employed on works in roadways (including yourself) are trained and licensed to carry out works in roadways (NRSWA Chapter 8).			
4. Ensure all relevant bodies are contacted and all underground services are identified before excavations start.			
5. Ensure all underground services are disconnected, where possible, and obtain certificates of disconnection.			
6. Where underground services are not disconnected ensure all interested parties know those services are live.			
7. Locate, identify and indicate the location of all underground services before excavation starts.			
8. Implement and follow the safe system of work procedure for performing excavation works. Ensure operatives are informed, instructed and trained in the safe system of work for excavations, including a permit to work and permit to break ground (permit to dig) and permit to work procedures.			
9. Follow and implement the procedure for the discovery of unidentified, underground services or objects and train staff in those procedures.			
10. Maintain records of services in the excavated area and contact and advise owners and operators of underground services, as required.			
11. Follow procedures for reporting any strikes or damage immediately to the appropriate body and make sure workers are trained in these procedures.			
12. Where overhead cables are present, make sure the power supply company has been consulted and has isolated the supply or provided the minimum safe working distances work for working near cables.			
13. Ensure goal posts and barriers are in place and inform workers of all control measures to ensure that nothing and no-one encroaches into the exclusion zone.			

D
26

Introduction

Every year people are injured and some are killed due to accidental contact with underground and overhead services, such as gas pipes and cables.

For more information on working near overhead and underground cables, download the free HSE leaflet *Avoiding concealed services and overhead power lines* (Busy Builder series).

Underground services

All underground services have the potential to cause harm. There are many injuries and deaths each year caused by accidental contact with underground services.

If the work involves penetrating the ground surface the following six steps should be taken before the work commences.

Six steps to safety
1. Obtain and understand current utilities companies' drawings.
2. Arrive, observe the site and work area and plan the survey.
3. Locate underground services using a suitable device such as a cable avoidance tool (CAT) and generator (genny).
4. Mark up cable routes (using appropriately coloured spray paint).
5. Hand dig trial holes (where possible, avoid using pickaxes, forks or bars).
6. Ensure compliance with *Avoiding danger from underground services* (HSG47).

The services you are most likely to find and their relevant colours are shown below. Please note this list is not exhaustive.

Service	Colour
Electricity (all voltages)	Black or red.
Water	Blue, black or grey.
Gas	Yellow.
Communications	Grey, white, green, purple or black.

Underground services (drainage pipes passing over a gas main)

Plan – Locate – Dig

Before digging – plan

The client should provide any information they have on the location of underground services. Where they do not know or they are unsure, they must allow the contractor time to identify the services for themselves.

The contractor must always plan the operation and check with the owners of other services to see if they have underground services in the area of the planned excavation. If service providers are planning to open the ground around the same time, it may be possible to carry out all of the work during a single opening.

The local electricity or gas company will give advice by telephone. British Telecom operates a similar service. Utilities companies will also visit the site and give advice where they see that it is necessary (for example, sensitive apparatus, such as high voltage, high pressure and fibre optics).

Types of marker posts commonly found to indicate the location of underground services

Existing service drawings do not always indicate the exact location of a service pipe or cable and, on occasions, services are moved without authority or consent. It therefore pays to look out for indicator posts, manholes, valve covers, differences in surface colour (fresh or new tarmac patches or tracks) and so on as clues to the route of underground services in the area in which you plan to work. Regardless of other indicators, a survey for underground services should be carried out to locate underground cables and services.

Cables and services – locate

There is a wide range of instruments designed to detect underground services, which can detect cables, pipes and metal objects. The most common are hand-held cable avoidance tools (CAT), which are easy to use, but it is essential that operatives are properly trained and use the correct instrument for the job.

It will not be possible to detect non-metallic objects using conventional detectors unless an end of a service can be exposed, and a sonde (type of transmitter) can be used in conjunction with a generator to trace the route. Even the most skilled operator using the best equipment will not find every pipe or cable every time. In unskilled hands, the instrument may not find anything.

A cable avoidance tool and generator

 A cable locating tool may not identify all services.

D
26

Brightly coloured plastic tape or mesh, sometimes with a metal insert, may be left about 300 mm above an underground service in the backfill. The absence of such a marker does not indicate that there is no underground service, so care must be taken when excavating.

The development of hand-held ground-penetrating radar, which has the capability to locate changes in density of the material below the transmitter, has enabled trained operators to detect non-metallic objects (such as plastic or earthenware pipes and even air-filled voids).

For larger areas ground-penetrating radar surveys can be commissioned to detect services, underground obstructions and unexploded ordnance (UXO). UXO is still a risk on some construction sites today and this risk should be mitigated by using a professional surveying company. If a risk is identified, specialist advice will be required (most likely from a bomb disposal unit) in how to deal with the device.

Excavation – dig

Depending upon the potential hazards, it may be necessary to use a permit to work system before commencing any digging. On some sites a specific **permit to break ground** or **permit to dig** system may be used.

Mark all the located services in the area with appropriately coloured survey spray.

Before starting any excavation or where existing services cross or come close to the route of the excavation, always dig **trial holes** by hand to establish where the services are located across the full width of the proposed excavation.

Never assume that a pipe or cable will run in a straight line between any two holes.

Do not use power tools or excavators within 500 mm of services; hand digging must be adopted, using insulated tools and avoiding the use of picks, forks, spades or other sharp tools. Excavate alongside the service rather than directly above it. Final exposure of the service by horizontal digging is recommended, as the force applied to hand tools can be controlled more effectively.

Do not use power tools directly over the indicated line of a service, even when it has reportedly been made dead. Steps must be taken to avoid damage.

Checklist

☑ Always assume that services are present and that they are live.

☑ Before starting, establish what type(s) of service are present.

☑ Always check with service providers or landowners.

☑ Use detectors and look for signs of marker tapes.

☑ Where possible, ensure that services have been isolated or disconnected before starting work.

☑ Services enclosed in concrete must be isolated if the work involves breaking them out.

☑ Obtain a permit to dig if such a system is in use.

☑ Be prepared for services that are either not where you expect them to be or not at the expected depth.

☑ Be wary of displaced tapes, tiles or slabs. Use shovels rather than spades, forks and pickaxes, and carefully lever out rocks, stones or boulders.

☑ Where possible the final exposure of underground services should be carried out in a way that prevents any damage (such as using a vacuum excavator or compressed air lance).

☒ Do not use excavators, especially when near underground services.

☒ Do not over-penetrate with power tools.

 Never assume that a service is dead – always treat it as live until confirmed otherwise.

Damage to underground services

Damage to underground services **must** be reported to the owner or occupier immediately. When such damage causes an emergency situation, call the **police – fire – ambulance** services as necessary.

Gas

Contact the police, fire brigade and gas supply company immediately.

 For gas emergencies phone the Gas Emergency Services on 0800 111 999.

If there is a dangerous situation and the emergency services have not arrived, try to evacuate the immediate area, including if necessary, the occupants of nearby properties to an upwind position. As far as possible, prevent anyone from smoking and keep traffic clear of the area.

 If the gas escape catches fire, do not attempt to extinguish the flames.

The normal minimum **depth of cover** for gas mains operating in the low and medium pressure ranges is the following.

☑ 600 mm in footways or verges.

☑ 750 mm in carriageways.

These figures may vary since each gas company can have its own standards.

Electricity

The depth at which electricity cables or ducts are usually installed in the ground is determined by the need to avoid undue interference or damage. Depending on the type of cable and the power that it may be carrying, the depth of cover may vary from 450 – 900 mm.

Never assume that services will always be at the recommended depth

D
26

Electrical services can be found at any depth. It is not uncommon for them to have little or no cover.

In all cases where the **depth of cover** is likely to increase or decrease, the service owner must be consulted.

Avoid contact with any damaged cable or apparatus. If you are operating a machine do not attempt to disentangle any equipment. If safe and possible to do so, jump clear of the machine, ensuring that you do not make contact with the vehicle and ground at the same time.

If this is not possible, stay exactly where you are. Shout for help. As far as possible, do not touch any metallic part of the vehicle, such as the steel parts of the cab or door. If you are able, inform the electricity company or ask someone else to do so. Keep people away.

For electricity emergencies phone the National Grid 24-hour electrical emergency service on 0800 404 090.

Other services

Leave any damaged service well alone and inform the owner immediately.

Backfilling

Never tip hardcore or rock onto an underground service in an attempt to fill the hole more quickly. Use selected backfill, settle and compact carefully, avoiding damage to the pipe or cable. Place warning tapes or tiles approximately 300 mm above the service.

In the case of water or gas mains, seek advice from the utility company on backfill methods.

Working in the roadway

Unless you are a licensed utility company, you may not work in the footway, carriageway or any verge. If you are working in the roadway, you must comply with the New Roads and Street Works Act.

There are two main Acts that govern works on the highway: the New Roads and Street Works Act and the Highways Act.

New Roads and Street Works Act

The New Roads and Street Works Act applies to works carried out in a street by an undertaker (such as a utility company) exercising a statutory right to inspect, place and maintain pipes, cables, sewers or drains, which are laid in the carriageway or footway. The term **undertaker** also covers holders of street works licences.

When a Local Authority acts as an agent to an undertaker or contractor to carry out work for an undertaker, the execution of the works is governed by the New Roads and Street Works Act.

Highways Act

The Highways Act applies to all work on the highway. The Highway Authority (or Roads Authority in Scotland) must be consulted and grant permission for works to be carried out. This applies to any works for road construction or maintenance purposes. These are covered by the provisions of the Highways Act and are the responsibility of the Highways Authority.

This Act also makes provision for licences for skips and scaffolds and places responsibility for safety with the Highway Authority.

Contractors must obtain permission before working on the highway.

Plan – the work to be done.
Locate – the services before digging.
Dig – using a safe method of work.

For further information refer to the excavations chapter and underground and overhead services chapter in Section D and the street works and road works chapter in Section F of GE 700 *Construction site safety*.

For further information refer to the HSE publication *Avoiding danger from underground services* (HSG47).

Overhead services

Every year people are killed or seriously injured when they come into contact with overhead electricity power lines. These incidents are often due to poorly planned working activities that result in contact with power lines.

If there is contact with a power line, or even if a piece of equipment gets too close to it, the electricity can be conducted to earth, which can cause fire, an explosion and shock or burns to anyone touching the machine or equipment.

Overhead lines can be difficult to spot, particularly in foggy or dull conditions. Often, people just fail to look up.

Overhead cables carrying electricity are generally uninsulated. You must be mindful of the following.

☑ Electricity will flow through any conductor that comes into contact with it (such as a metal ladder, a scaffold pole or a raised excavator bucket).

☑ Electricity may jump through the air (arc) to anything nearby that will conduct electricity.

The siting or use of cranes, lifting appliances or any conductor near to overhead power cables is dangerous and calls for extreme care. Particular care must be taken with the positioning of any crane, piling rig, hiab, lorry loader, tipper truck and so on. The higher the voltage in the cables, a greater safety distance from the cable is required.

The power supply company must always be consulted before siting or using any plant or conductor adjacent to overhead power cables. They will advise on the voltage of the supply and the minimum safe distance.

Where overhead cables are within premises it may be possible to arrange with the owner or occupier to temporarily isolate the power. If the cables are part of the national power distribution network, isolation of the supply may not be possible or there may be strict time limitations.

Isolation alone will not make a cable dead. It must be established if the cable in question is part of a backup or standby supply and, if so, the site or another competent person must isolate the back up supply before the main supply.

**D
26**

If it is not possible for the power to be isolated, the power supply company must be consulted to establish the minimum safe working distance from which a safe system of work can be developed. This will often involve erecting barriers and possibly introducing other control measures to ensure that nothing and no-one encroaches into the exclusion zone.

Find out who owns the installation first and talk to them **before** you start work. Is it possible to isolate or insulate?

For further information refer to the underground and overhead services chapter in Section D of GE 700 *Construction site safety*.

☑ Cranes and other items of plant should only pass under live cables where goal posts have been set up, in accordance with the HSE leaflet *Avoiding danger from overhead power lines* (GS6) or by the criteria set down by the local electricity supply company.

☑ Information on construction site safety and working near power lines is available on the HSE website.

 Overhead power line electrocution

A construction company was prosecuted after a crane operator suffered an electric shock when the equipment he was using came into contact with overhead power lines. The sub-contractor was using the crane to move sections of steel. As they started to lift a section of steel using the crane, the hook block came into contact with an 11 kV power line and he suffered an electric shock. The sub-contractor was resuscitated but now suffers from long-term memory loss. The electricity company had warned the contractor about the presence of the overhead power cables, and had received advice on the removal of the power supplies running across the site. However, no measures were put in place by the company to prevent plant and equipment accessing the area beneath the power lines or for the power supply to be diverted or isolated. The company was fined £20,000.

The HSE said: 'This terrible incident could have been avoided had the company placed physical barriers on site so that no plant or equipment could gain access to either side and directly below the overhead power lines, or if the high voltage cables were diverted or isolated'.

27

Confined spaces

What your employer should do for you
1. Have in place confined space procedures and safe systems of work for confined space operations, including selection of workers, gas testing, permit to enter and permit to work, and rescue procedures.
2. Ensure that managers, supervisors and employees are aware that confined space working should be avoided, if possible, and if not avoidable, planned before entry.
3. Train staff in the organisation's safe system of work procedures for confined space operations.
4. Provide the correct access equipment, isolating equipment, gas monitoring equipment, respiratory protective equipment (RPE) and other personal protective equipment (PPE), and make sure that operatives are trained in the equipment provided.
5. Ensure that the work team who are to enter confined spaces are trained, competent and medically fit.
6. Ensure that a suitable rescue plan, with trained rescuers and suitable rescue equipment, are provided and available.

D
27

What you should do as a supervisor

Checklist	Yes	No	N/A
1. Be aware that confined space working should be avoided, if possible. If it cannot be avoided, make sure work is planned before entry.			
2. Ensure that the work team are trained (in line with the requirements of the regulations and company procedures) and are aware of the different hazards of confined spaces.			
3. Ensure there is a site and task specific safe system of work, including isolation procedures, gas testing and monitoring, access and egress procedures and provision for emergencies (whether or not confined space related), including a site specific rescue plan.			
4. Ensure that the safe system of work is properly communicated and understood by all interested parties, including the permit to enter and permit to work procedures.			
5. Ensure that a competent and trained supervisor and a competent and trained confined space attendant are present.			
6. Ensure that the correct PPE, RPE and rescue equipment is available and issued.			
7. Supervise the work to ensure that a rescue plan has been prepared and practised prior to entry.			
8. Check that the work team who are to enter confined spaces are trained, competent and medically and physically fit.			
9. Ensure the work team are properly briefed on the safe system of work, raising the alarm and rescue procedures, and that they understand the pre-entry caution statement regarding nausea, headaches and drowsiness.			
10. Remain present for the duration of the works, if required by the findings of the risk assessment.			
11. Ensure all systems and services are isolated and made dead (drained and depressurised) as far as is practicable. Perform pre-entry gas tests, where required, and ensure other required permits have been issued and issue a permit to enter.			

D
27

Introduction

Every entry into a confined space is potentially dangerous. Some confined spaces are easy to identify, while others are less obvious but may be equally dangerous.

A *confined space* has two defining features.

☑ **A space which is substantially, though not always entirely, enclosed.**

☑ **A place where a specified risk exists, or there is a reasonably foreseeable risk of a specified risk arising (being created).**

The Confined Spaces Regulations place a duty on employers and persons in charge of premises (which could include site management) to ensure that no person enters a confined space to carry out work if it is possible to do that work without having to enter the confined space (for example, using CCTV or a robotic camera to carry out a visual inspection of a tank or pipework).

If it is necessary for someone to enter a confined space then the entry and the work must be carried out in accordance with a safe system of work, which must be produced by a competent person (assisted by other competent persons, if necessary).

The starting point for the safe system of work is a suitable and sufficient risk assessment, which must consider the place of work, the task to be done and the nature of the confined space itself (for example, is it a trench, a deep excavation, a tank or vessel, a roof space or other void). Following the risk assessment the competent person(s) should draw up a method statement looking at the following.

☑ How and when the confined space will be accessed.

☑ How it will be isolated, drained, purged, cleaned and vented.

☑ Depending on the confined space and the work to be done, the number of people required in the work team and their competencies and skills (such as welder, electrician and pipe fitter).

☑ What plant and equipment will be needed for the task and to access the confined space.

☑ What work and protective equipment may be required (such as gas monitors, air movers, ventilation equipment and communication equipment).

☑ What PPE and RPE may be required.

The work team must be trained and familiar with the equipment to be used. The method statement should consider the need to control the works and entry to the confined space, possibly by means of a permit to enter or permit to work, and whether other permits (such as hot-work permits) are required. The competent person(s) must consider the possibility of an emergency arising within the confined space or elsewhere, whether related to any of the specified risks or not, and have an appropriate (emergency) rescue plan, which should not be reliant on the emergency services.

Definition of a confined space

A confined space is any place where there is a reasonably foreseeable risk or a **specified risk**.

Examples of specified risks are given below.

☑ Serious injury from fire or explosion.

☑ Unconsciousness as a result of excessive body heat.

D
27

☑ Unconsciousness or asphyxia from gas, fumes or vapours, or a lack of oxygen.

☑ Drowning in liquid

☑ Asphyxia, burial, engulfment or entrapment by a free flowing solid (FFS). FFS include any material that freely flows and behaves as a liquid (for example, sand, gravel or fine soil).

Examples of confined spaces

Listed below are some confined spaces that may be encountered during construction activities.

☑ A cellar or an inadequately ventilated basement room.

☑ A boiler, boiler flue or chimney.

☑ A manhole, sewer or drain.

☑ A ceiling void or duct.

☑ A caisson or cofferdam.

☑ An excavation.

☑ A loft or roof space.

Any room or enclosed space with poor ventilation can become a confined space (for example, painting a room or power floating in a large hangar using petrol-powered equipment).

A worker died after inhaling toxic fumes while carrying out restoration work in a bathroom at a flat in South West London. The worker was using an industrial paint and varnish remover to strip resin coating from the bath. The room had insufficient ventilation and the 55 year old victim was overcome by the fumes. He died at the scene and was discovered by the occupant of the flat.

There are many more examples of confined spaces and the hazards vary with the location, the type of work being carried out, and the equipment or substances used.

Lofts, enclosed or unventilated rooms or similar areas can be or can become confined spaces, depending on the space and the work being done

D
27

For further information refer to the HSE's *Safe work in confined spaces* (L101), which includes a flowchart to help employers identify if an area is a confined space.

Hazards in confined spaces

Oxygen deprivation and suffocation

The air that we breathe contains around 21% oxygen and, at that level, people can work without difficulty. If the oxygen level falls to 19%, ill effects start to be felt, including the loss of co-ordination and concentration, together with accelerated fatigue. Should the oxygen level fall to 10%, it will cause severe breathing difficulties and unconsciousness. An oxygen level of less than 6% will result in respiratory arrest, and possibly death.

Oxygen deprivation may be the result of the following.

☑ The displacement of oxygen by gas leaking in from elsewhere, or the deliberate introduction of purge gas (that has not been adequately vented off).

☑ The displacement of oxygen by a naturally occurring gas (such as hydrogen sulphide (H_2S)).

☑ Oxidisation, rusting or bacterial growth using up the oxygen in the air.

☑ Oxygen being consumed by people breathing or work processes (such as hot work).

☑ Any process of combustion (such as welding and other hot works).

☑ The prior discharge of a fire-extinguishing system containing oxygen-dissipating or -displacing characteristics (especially where it has not been adequately vented off).

Toxic atmospheres

However much oxygen is present in the atmosphere, if there is also a toxic gas present in sufficient quantity it will create a hazard. Some of the many toxic gases that may be encountered include:

☑ hydrogen sulphide, usually from sewage or decaying vegetation

☑ carbon dioxide from any fermentation or naturally evolved in soil and rocks

☑ fumes and vapours from chemicals (such as ammonia, chlorine and sodium), and from petrol and solvents.

 Atmospheric testing

At Carsington Reservoir in Derbyshire, four young, physically fit men, aged between 20 and 30, died at the bottom of an open-topped inspection shaft. Naturally evolved carbon dioxide had displaced the oxygen, but no tests were made before the first man entered. He collapsed and the three other men in turn climbed down, attempting to rescue their colleagues. They were overcome by the lack of oxygen and subsequently died.

Whenever a toxic gas (or any gas, fume or vapour that may be hazardous to health) is thought to be (or known to be) present, an assessment of the risk to health must be made under the provisions of the **Control of Substances Hazardous to Health Regulations** and the appropriate control measures must be put into place to eliminate or control the risk.

For further information refer to the control of substances hazardous to health chapter in Section B of GE 700 *Construction site safety*.

D
27

Petrol and diesel engines create carbon monoxide, which is an extremely toxic gas. The use of any form of internal combustion engine within a confined space should be prohibited, unless a specifically dedicated exhaust extraction system is used.

Test the atmosphere before and during confined space entry

Flammable and explosive atmospheres

Some gases need only be present in small quantities to create a hazard. A few of the major sources of explosive and flammable hazards are shown below.

☑ Petrol or liquefied petroleum gas, propane, butane and acetylene. These are explosive in the range of 2% in air upwards. The hazard is normally created by a spillage or leakage.

☑ Solvents, acetone, toluene, white spirit, alcohol, benzene, thinners and so on. These are explosive in the range of 2% in air upwards. The hazard generally results from a work process and/or spillage.

☑ Methane and hydrogen sulphide, which are naturally evolved from sewage or decaying organic matter. These are explosive in the range of 4% in air upwards.

☑ Hydrogen and other gases evolved from processes such as battery charging.

☑ Airborne dust clouds.

In any atmosphere, a toxic or suffocating hazard may also exist (such as hydrogen sulphide, which is an extremely toxic gas that is also flammable).

Hostile environments

Apart from the hazards dealt with above, other dangers may arise from the use of electrical and mechanical equipment.

Extremes of heat can have adverse effects and may be intensified in a confined space. High humidity levels can be a major problem as they can interfere with the body's natural cooling mechanism, preventing sweat from evaporating. Excessive sweating will cause the body to lose vital salts. Further danger exists due to the difficulty of getting into, or out of, and working in, a confined space, which may involve working at height. The potential hazard of an inrush of water, gas, sludge and so on, due to a failure of walls or barriers, or leakage from valves, flanges or blanks, must all be considered at the risk assessment stage.

D
27

Information, instruction and training

The need for comprehensive training prior to any involvement in confined space working cannot be stressed too highly. The number of deaths that have occurred in confined spaces in recent years, many of them as a result of an attempted improvised rescue of a casualty, is testimony to the extreme hazards that can be present in confined spaces.

The fact that many deaths occur during improvised rescues is indicative that the entry was not properly planned or resourced. The Confined Spaces Regulations require that provision for rescue is considered as part of the safe system of work and that all necessary rescue equipment is on hand (and set up) prior to the entry being effected.

A person should never enter a confined space unless they are trained, competent and authorised to do so and a suitable and sufficient procedure is in place.

Not only should operatives who have to enter confined spaces be trained, but also anyone involved in:

- ☑ planning and supervising confined space work
- ☑ communication between those inside and outside the confined space
- ☑ rescue activities.

The content of the training required will vary according to circumstances and the type of space being entered (for example, in some circumstances training in the use of atmospheric monitoring equipment or the use of escape or full breathing apparatus may be required).

The training of anyone who might have to enter a confined space (for example, workers, supervisors or rescuers) must include a significant amount of practical work in addition to the theory.

Safe working

Risk assessments

An early decision must be made as to whether it is necessary for someone to enter the confined space or whether an alternative method for carrying out the work is practical.

Care must be taken when entering a confined space

The risk assessment is essential to the planning, resourcing, execution and management of any confined space work. The findings of a risk assessment will determine the safe system of work that will be:

- ☑ supported by a method statement or another form of documented procedure, which must include suitable and sufficient provisions for emergency rescue, whether or not the emergency rescue is related to a specified risk

- ☑ controlled, and in many cases limited in scope, by a permit to work

- ☑ backed up by an emergency plan.

The risk assessment, from which the method statement (or other documented procedure) will be developed, must consider the following.

- ☑ An assessment of the possible hazards present and those that are reasonably foreseeable (such as an increase in the level of liquid).

- ☑ Appropriately trained staff.

- ☑ Atmospheric monitoring **before** entry and continuously whilst work is carried out.

- ☑ PPE, including RPE.

- ☑ A trained rescue team and appropriate rescue plan.

- ☑ A suitable means of communication between those in the confined space and those outside.

- ☑ Pre-entry notification of the emergency services.* (This is particularly important where there are likely to be a high number of entrants, deep or large working areas, several access points, or it is known that smoke logging could be a particular problem.)

* The HSE stress that people who plan work in confined spaces must not regard the pre-notification of the emergency services as a substitute for developing adequate emergency arrangements.

 Plan for rescue

When an engineer collapsed in a sewer, a rescuer entered without breathing apparatus and was overcome. Another person then tried to reach the victims. When the fire brigade arrived, they had to remove the two bodies before they could get to the engineer – this delayed the rescue and he died too. The deaths could have been avoided if there had been a properly thought out plan, including the provision of a properly equipped rescue team.

 Some types of RPE are not appropriate for entry into or work in confined spaces, as they may not adequately protect against the risk of being overcome. For example, some RPE does not provide adequate protection against high concentrations of gases and vapours and respirators should never be used in oxygen-deficient atmospheres.

 For further information on respiratory protective equipment refer to Chapter B10 Personal protective equipment.

D
27

Worker exiting a confined space wearing escape breathing apparatus

 For further information on the principles and practical aspects of carrying out risk assessments refer to Chapter A04 Risk assessments, method statements and permits to work.

Where a risk assessment is being prepared for work in a confined space in which there will, or may be, toxic gases or other hazardous substances, the risk assessment must satisfy the requirements of the following.

☑ Management of Health and Safety at Work Regulations with regard to the general principles of risk assessment.

☑ Control of Substances Hazardous to Health Regulations with regard to the specific threat to health from harmful substances.

Selection of workers

Not every worker is suitable for working in a confined space.

☑ Facial hair can reduce the effectiveness of respiratory protection considerably, by not providing an effective airtight seal between the mask and the face. Everyone required to wear RPE must be face-fit tested.

☑ The need to wear spectacles also has the potential to be a problem when combined with the need to wear RPE. It is possible to get prescription spectacles that can be worn inside respirators and breathing apparatus. However, they tend to be expensive and they must be pre-fitted, which is not always possible when escape breathing apparatus is provided. For this reason, people who have severe visual impairment are generally not considered suitable as confined space entrants but, if appropriately trained, could serve as attendants.

Rescue

The extent of arrangements necessary for emergency rescue will depend upon:

☑ the risks identified

☑ the physical nature of the confined space.

Rescue equipment will often include a lifeline, a tripod and hoist (over the entry point), full or working duration breathing apparatus and first-aid equipment.

 Where the risk assessment has identified asphyxia as a potential risk, suitable and sufficient resuscitation equipment must be provided and operatives must be trained in its use.

For further information refer to the confined spaces chapter in Section D of GE 700 *Construction site safety.*

A tripod and hoist in use

Permit to work

A permit to work system is a formal written system and is usually required where there is a reasonably foreseeable risk of serious injury when entering or working in a confined space.

The permit to work procedure is an integral part of the safe system to work, not a replacement for it.

The use of a permit to work system does not, by itself, make the job safe. It supports the safe system, providing a ready means of recording findings and the authorisations required to proceed with the entry. A permit to work should also contain information on, for example, time limits on entry, results of the gas testing, and other information that may be required during an emergency and which, when the job is complete, can also provide historical information on original entry conditions.

A permit to work system is appropriate to ensure the following.

☑ People working in the confined space are aware of the hazards involved and the identity, nature and extent of the work to be carried out.

☑ There is a formal check undertaken confirming elements of a safe system of work are in place. This must take place before people are allowed to enter or work in the confined space.

☑ Other people and their activities are co-ordinated or excluded, using controlled and formal procedures, where they could affect work or conditions in the confined space.

☑ If the work requires the authorisation of more than one person or there is a time limit on entry. It may also be needed if communications with the outside are other than by direct speech, or if particular RPE or PPE is required.

Interactive examples of a permit to work and a permit to dig can be found on the GE 700 companion website.

D
27

28

Environmental management

What your employer should do for you
1. Identify the environmental risks and control measures for the project and implement an environmental management plan.
2. Make sure that all environmental licences, discharge consents and authorisations are in place with the environmental regulators.
3. Ensure that everyone is aware of their environmental responsibilities and put in place the correct communication channels.
4. Ensure sub-contractors and suppliers have considered appropriate environmental controls in their method statements.
5. Ensure that staff are competent to carry out their environmental responsibilities.
6. Ensure that suitable protection arrangements are put in place for sensitive areas.
7. Ensure that suitable procedures and arrangements are put in place for the effective management of waste.
8. Provide suitable and sufficient spill-kit facilities and ensure everyone is aware of emergency reporting arrangements.
9. Ensure that site inductions and briefings include the key project environmental issues and any specific measures for their control, including resource efficiency.
10. Ensure that the project environmental performance is regularly monitored, discussed, reported and communicated.
11. Deal with any environmental problems reported to them.
12. Lead by example in environmental best practice.
13. Put measures in place to monitor the management of water and energy conservation.

E
28

What you should do as a supervisor

Checklist	Yes	No	N/A
1. Ensure you are aware of your environmental responsibilities for the area under your supervision.			
2. Ensure your manager has informed you of the arrangements for the following.			
■ Water discharges and consent requirements.			
■ Protection of sensitive areas (for example, trees, vegetation, wildlife, and historic or archaeological sites).			
■ Oil storage and refuelling.			
■ Waste management, storage and disposal (skips, waste carriers and so on).			
■ Emergency spill procedures.			
■ Noise and vibration (working hours, screening and so on).			
■ Dust controls (wetting down and road sweeping).			
3. Ensure water and energy management and conservation measures are followed.			
4. Ensure your workforce understand the environmental risks and the arrangements to control them.			
5. Carry out regular inspections of the works.			
6. Report any problems to your manager.			

E
28

Introduction

Environmental management is about protecting the environment by avoiding, minimising and controlling the impacts that may arise and the damage that could be caused by and during the project. Building and construction site activities will have some impact on the environment. The objective of an environmental management plan is to reduce the impact to the absolute minimum.

 The environment **can be defined as any physical surroundings (consisting of air, water, land, natural resources, flora, fauna, humans and their interrelationships) in which an organisation operates.**

A company's environmental performance can significantly affect public perception of a company that, in turn, may influence clients in their choice of contractors. Many well-managed companies will have an established environmental policy in place, alongside their health and safety policy.

Benefits of environmental management

The main drive of environmental legislation is to prevent damage or harm to human life. This includes protecting people's health, their senses, their quality of life or their property, and limiting damage to wildlife and living organisms or avoiding pollution of habitats that can arise from the release or emission of any substance.

Effective environmental management can result in the following benefits.

☑ **Meets legal requirements.** There is extensive legislation covering the environment, most of which is formed in line with the **'polluter pays'** principle. Failure to comply may result in companies or individuals being fined or imprisoned for causing damage to the environment. There are other compliance requirements that the company can choose to implement or that clients can request to be implemented.

☑ **Makes business sense.** As clients become more aware of environmental management, it is often expected as standard; it will enhance the company's reputation, demonstrate social responsibility and give a better public image.

☑ **Saves money.** Good site management, including waste management, will reduce the amount of damaged and surplus materials, skip hire and associated landfill tax, and initiate the reuse and recycling of materials.

Before development starts, principal designers, designers, principal contractors and contractors should, together with the client and any relevant regulators, establish the likely environmental impacts that the project or work activities may have. They should make provisions to eliminate, as far as practicable, any sources of environmental damage or pollution, and establish sufficient control measures to minimise the negative environmental effects of construction activities.

There are significant opportunities at the design stage to reduce environmental impacts (for example, specifying environmentally friendly materials, materials with recycled content or manufacturing components off site for simple assembly on site, reducing rework and waste).

Environmental damage

Construction can damage the environment in a number of ways. The construction industry therefore has a major role to play in protecting natural resources and ensuring that they are passed on, in good order, to future generations, adding to their quality of life and for their enjoyment. Construction activities with the potential to cause environmental damage are listed below.

☑ Environmentally damaging designs or poor choice of materials.

☑ High water and energy usage (and consequent greenhouse gas emissions).

☑ The use of materials from inappropriate, unsustainable sources.

☑ Ill-conceived developments having little regard for reducing local environmental impacts (for example, building on floodplains).

☑ The construction process itself.

Clients, principal designer, designers and specifiers can eliminate many of these damaging activities by taking the impacts into account when a project is first considered.

Contractors and developers can also play their part in reducing the impact of their work, and it is important that environmental matters are incorporated within company risk assessment and management processes.

Damage to the environment may arise from construction site activities, which may include, but are not limited to, any of the following.

Atmosphere	Land	Water
▪ Asbestos	▪ Asbestos	▪ Silt
▪ Dust	▪ Concrete and chemicals	▪ Concrete and chemicals
▪ Radiation	▪ Lead	▪ Contaminated water
▪ Exhaust emissions	▪ Litter	▪ Run-off
▪ Gases or vapours	▪ Oils and fuels	▪ Effluent
▪ Noise	▪ Spillage of materials	▪ Oils and fuels
▪ Smoke	▪ Waste materials	▪ Hazardous solid matter
		▪ Slurry

It is important that one solution to environmental pollution does not divert the problem to another area (for example, a solution to air pollution must not lead to water or ground contamination).

Environmental impact assessments

Environmental impact assessments (EIA) are a formal, systematic process used to assess the effects that a proposed development may have on the environment.

The process of environmental assessment is used to collate information for the use of the developer and planning authority in deciding if the development should go ahead. The following projects always require environmental impact assessments.

☑ Construction of motorways, express roads, lines for long distance railway traffic and some airports.

☑ Some waste-disposal installations.

E
28

☑ Long distance pipelines.

☑ Certain factories and manufacturing plants.

☑ Large quarries and open-cast mines.

Other projects (such as the following) are subject to environmental impact assessments if there is significant effect on the environment.

☑ Extraction of some types of mineral.

☑ Construction of roads, harbours, airfields, dams or other water storage structures.

☑ Industrial estate developments.

☑ Yacht marinas.

☑ Urban developments, including shopping centres and car parks, sports stadiums, leisure centres and multiplex cinemas.

☑ Tramways.

☑ Coastal works (dykes, jetties, breakwater or other sea defence work).

☑ Motorway service areas.

While some projects are required to have a formal EIA completed, many others have an environmental statement that summarises the findings of the EIA, outlining the measures that are to be put into place during construction.

 The principal contractor should be aware of and review the EIA or environmental statement, where available, before commencing any works.

Managing the project environmental issues

The principal contractor or contractor (on single contractor projects) will have overall responsibility for ensuring that the right environmental controls are put in place with input from the client, regulators, principal designer, designers, suppliers, sub-contractors and other site personnel. There are **five** key steps to ensure that environmental issues are effectively managed on site.

Step 1. Identify the project environmental requirements
The client's specification, together with other documentation (such as the planning conditions for the project) will define what moral, legal and other environmental requirements need to be met.

Step 2. Identify the project environmental risks
Having identified the project's environmental requirements in Step 1, the next step is to determine important environmental risks for the project and the actions to be taken explaining how they can be overcome on site. Emergency situations should also be considered.

Step 3. Define responsibilities for managing the environmental risks
Having identified the project's environmental risks in Step 2, the principal contractor (or contractor) will define what responsibilities and lines of communication are needed to manage the environmental risks effectively, including who will produce and manage the various environmental plans.

Step 4. Implement the controls for managing the environmental issues
Various documents and plans will draw together the project's environmental requirements, risks and controls and responsibilities for managing them. For supervisors, this is usually in the form of a construction environmental management plan (CEMP).

E
28

Other documents that could be included or referenced include the site waste management plan, water management plan, noise management plan, site and task risk assessments and method statements.

Step 5. Implement a monitoring and inspection regime

A monitoring system will need to be put in place to ensure that the requirements of the construction environmental management plan and specific control measures are being managed effectively. Site supervision will play a key part in this process and will involve checking and inspecting site controls for the following.

☑ Protection of sensitive areas (such as archaeology, habitats and flora).

☑ Oil, fuel and chemical storage.

☑ Waste facilities and housekeeping.

☑ Water discharges.

☑ Energy and water management and conservation.

☑ Spill and emergency response equipment.

☑ Dust management.

☑ Noise management.

Any problems should be reported to your senior management so that they can be rectified.

Pollution prevention

There are several hundred major pollution events from construction and demolition sites every year, many leading to prosecution. Common causes of pollution are poor work practices, accidents and incidents, illegal discharge, surface water run-off (rain), fire-fighting water run-off, deliberate discharge by vandals and vandalism.

The following common substances impact the environment.

☑ Silt.

☑ Oils, petrol and diesel.

☑ Concrete and cement.

☑ Dust and smoke.

☑ Sewage.

☑ Grout.

Good planning is the key to minimising the risk of a pollution event by considering whether an activity can impact on one or more of the five key receptors: **air, water, humans, animals or land**.

By following three simple steps, measures can be put into place to allow you to control and manage the issues.

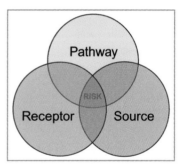

Step 1. Identify the activities (sources) likely to cause pollution, as well as the pathways and receptors on which it can impact. For example, diesel storage leaks (source) may be transported via a pathway that could be the ground or a stream.

☑ If the pathway is the ground, the receptor could be an aquifer used for drinking water. This would lead to humans being a further receptor.

☑ If the pathway is the stream, then fish and other organisms could be additional receptors.

Step 2. Plan and put in place controls identified in the construction environmental management plan, and for any other likely event, documenting the actions to be taken. Make someone responsible for the area and conduct regular inspections to make sure that procedures are being followed (for example, locate a diesel tank in a bund away from any drains and make sure it is kept locked and there is a key holder responsible for it).

Step 3. Communicate the plans to the workforce. The site team should know what mitigation measures are in place, why they are there and what to do in an emergency (for example, for a diesel spill, contain the spill, report it to site management and clean up the spill).

In planning for pollution control, take account of the location of the site, its surroundings, its geography, location and identification of drains (foul or surface water), and local residents and neighbours (such as schools or other businesses).

Concrete washout water needs to be controlled

Managing noise and vibration, dust and air pollution

Nuisance is often a result of poor site practices and procedures and can lead to poor neighbourhood relations and even suspension of the works by the Local Authority.

Nuisance through noise, dust, vibration, light, smoke or vermin can have a major impact on people's quality of life. The creation of nuisances may be minimised in the following ways.

☑ Ensure powerful sources of lighting are directed away from residents or other sensitive receptors and switch them off when the work is complete. If they are required for security purposes, give special consideration to the location and how they or their operation may affect other residents.

☑ Enforce site speed limits.

☑ Dampen down site roads and regularly sweep local roads to prevent the spread of dust.

☑ Consider the use of wheel-washing equipment at site exits to avoid slippery surfaces or dust.

☑ Minimise dusty operations by damping down or enclosing the operations within sheeting.

☑ Locate crushing plant away from sensitive areas.

☑ Form holes in slabs when casting rather than cutting them out later.

☑ Ensure noisy operations are carried out during normal working hours.

☑ Substitute noisy operations, noisy equipment or plant with quieter options or fabricate off site if possible.

E
28

☑ Ensure equipment is properly maintained to eliminate loose parts, fit mufflers or safely fix materials that will reduce the noise and/or vibration.

☑ Provide acoustic enclosures, curtains or screening.

☑ Locate equipment as far away as possible from sensitive receptors.

☑ Use an auger instead of driven piling.

☑ Use electric motors instead of internal combustion engines.

☑ Avoid using reversing sirens or bleepers by the use of one way routes if possible.

☑ Shut down plant and equipment when not required.

Traffic and deliveries can cause congestion, noise and disruption on local roads and should be programmed to avoid queuing outside of the site. The contractor can apply for, or the Local Authority might request, a Section 61 agreement (prior consent) that sets out measures to control noise nuisance from your site. If the conditions of the Section 61 Consent (or local limits) are breached then the Local Authority can issue a Section 60 Abatement Notice.

If it is believed that noise will be a consideration, then the application for a Section 61 notice is advisable. The Section 61 notice offers a level of protection against a Section 60 notice which, if issued, can delay a project and incur additional costs.

Maintain good neighbourhood relations by sweeping roads regularly

Managing site discharges and drainage

Where there is a possibility that effluent from any construction work might pollute drainage systems, watercourses or rivers and streams, an application for a permit or consent to discharge must be made to the relevant authority. The issuing authority will depend on where the discharge is made.

For trade effluent, the company will need to obtain a trade effluent consent to discharge from the water authority or sewerage company.

If a discharge is going to be discharged to surface water (rivers, streams, estuaries, lakes and so on) or to groundwater (water that has seeped into the ground and is stored in cracks and gaps known as aquifers), the company may need an environmental permit from the relevant Environment Agency. Small quantities or temporary discharges of some liquid wastes may be discharged under an exemption (in England and Wales) or general binding rules (in Scotland). Contact must be made with the relevant Environment Agency before commencing work to seek clarification.

E
28

As a general rule, any work on or near a watercourse will require consents or permits. Specific environmental permits in England and Wales called 'flood risk activities' cover work on, above, below or near (generally within 10 m, although there may be local variations) the following locations.

- ☑ A main river.
- ☑ A flood defence structure.
- ☑ A flood plain.
- ☑ A sea defence.

The following agencies issue permits.

- ☑ **England:** Environment Agency or Local Authority.
- ☑ **Northern Ireland:** Rivers Agency.
- ☑ **Scotland:** Scottish Environment Protection Agency (SEPA).
- ☑ **Wales:** Natural Resources Wales or Local Authority.

An up to date and accurate site drainage plan is essential to identify the location of all drains and sewers in and around the site and where they lead. When a discharge to a drain is made it is essential to check that the connection is made to the correct system.

- ☑ Sewage and trade effluent (trade effluent is any liquid waste created at premises being used for business, trade or industry) should be discharged to the foul sewer (identified red).
- ☑ Clean, uncontaminated water should be discharged to the surface water drainage system (identified blue).

It will help to colour code manhole covers, gullies and grills by painting them in accordance with a recognised system: blue for surface water drains and red for foul water drains.

Excavations need to be considered in terms of the need to dewater and discharge. Silty water will need to be treated in settlement tanks, lagoons, filtration systems or by using flocculent prior to discharge. The size of the tank or lagoon should be adequate for the settlement time required and the rate at which the water is pumped into and drained from it.

An environmental permit is not normally required for a temporary discharge of uncontaminated water from an excavation to surface water, provided certain conditions are met. An example would be where the discharge is temporary for an overall period of less than three consecutive months and is more than 500 m from a protected area (such as a site of special scientific interest). Many other sites are designated as having high local value for wildlife.

Muddy water should not be discharged into surface water drains

Concrete washout areas should be designated and located away from watercourses and other sensitive areas and **at least** 10 m away from drains and watercourses. Water from concrete washout is highly alkaline and should be disposed of to foul water systems or disposed of cost-effectively elsewhere.

A robust monitoring system should be put in place to regularly check that controls are in place and required discharge quantities and contaminant thresholds are not exceeded.

Fuel and chemical storage and management

Oil and diesel spills can have a major impact on surface waters and drainage systems. There are regulations in place requiring certain types of oil storage to be in secondary containers (bunds). Guidance from oil storage regulations states that secondary containment within multiple fixed tanks, mobile bowsers or intermediate bulk containers (IBCs), must have a capacity that is equal to whichever is the greater of the two measurements below.

- [✓] One-quarter of the combined capacity of all the containers.
- [✓] 110% of the capacity of the largest container.

Further information on oil storage and pollution prevention regulations can be accessed online.

Store all fuels and liquids in bunded areas or on drip trays, away from drains, and have spill-kit clean up materials (such as absorbent pads and booms) located in each area.

Many sites have a designated area for the safe storage of chemicals and hazardous substances to minimise the environmental risks.

When storing solvents, paints and chemicals consideration should be given to the following.

- [✓] Their control of substances hazardous to health (COSHH) safety data sheets.
- [✓] The floor area used for storing or decanting chemicals (this must not be permeable).
- [✓] Old or corroded drums, as these will cause more problems than those in good condition.

The following measures can be taken to minimise ground contamination.

- [✓] Purchase chemicals in the appropriate sized containers to avoid the need to transfer liquids from one container to another (decanting).
- [✓] Where decanting is necessary, have safe procedures that avoid any spillage and that are carried out within a protected area.
- [✓] Provide relevant information, instruction, training and supervision to employees.
- [✓] Dispose of all products in the correct way.
- [✓] Provide clear procedures and training for operatives to deal with accidental spillages.
- [✓] Make drip-trays available for plant in case it leaks environmentally damaging fluids.
- [✓] Have set procedures for the refuelling and replenishing of plant so that any spillage cannot permeate into the ground.
- [✓] Install bunding around all storage areas, even temporary fuel stores on construction sites.

E
28

- ☑ Maintain equipment or storage vessels in good condition.

- ☑ Follow procedures for the storage and use of minimal quantities of each product. Only store such products in areas with impermeable floors without drain gullies.

- ☑ Maintain good housekeeping procedures and avoid the accumulation of litter or rubbish.

- ☒ Do not bury waste materials – this is strictly prohibited.

An emergency and incident response plan, appropriate to the size of the site and chemicals being used, should be in place in case of any spillages or pollution alerts.

 A spill involving just one litre of oil can contaminate one million litres of water.

Be prepared – a site pollution response poster, spill kit and drip tray

Dealing with environmental incidents

While good planning can minimise the risk of an environmental incident, you should have a plan of what to do in the event of an emergency. Consider the emergency scenarios and incidents which may occur on a construction site and what, in the surrounding environment, may be impacted. Types of incident include fires, spills and leaks.

For each one of these types of incident several different parts of the environment may be affected. (For example, a fire will release products of combustion into the atmosphere and contaminated water, used to extinguish the fire, may enter the watercourse, trade effluent or surface water sewers and also percolate into the ground.)

Such a plan should include the following steps.

- ☑ **Stop.** How to stop pollution in the first place.

- ☑ **Contain.** How to keep the pollution in the area and stop it spreading any further.

- ☑ **Notify.** Who should be informed. This should include site management, the emergency services, the regulatory agencies and senior company management.

- ☑ **Clean-up.** How to clean-up the pollution and what to do with the waste. The regulatory agencies may provide direction or instruction as to how this will be done.

- ☑ **Train.** Make sure the site team know their roles and responsibilities and replenish the spill kit material.

- ☑ **Test.** Conduct drills, to test and reinforce the response needed.

- ☑ **Report.** You should report all environmental incidents to site management as soon as possible.

Environmental incidents can also be reported to the Environment Agencies via the Hotline.

If there is an incident on your site, environmental regulators have extensive powers to interview people, review documents (including computer records) and take copies. Regulators have been given powers to impose civil penalties for some minor offences, rather than initiating criminal proceedings through the courts. If you find yourself being investigated you should fully co-operate with the regulators and seek professional, legal support and advice.

Managing transport

Vehicle movements and the transport of materials and people represent resources being used. It is important that vehicle movements are handled, programmed and managed. This will lead to more efficient use of resources and a reduction in costs.

Good logistics with prompt, efficient arrivals and departures for materials being off-loaded in the right locations will result in the following benefits.

- ☑ Reduction to nuisance, noise, dust and congestion.
- ☑ Avoidance of double handling of materials and waste.
- ☑ Minimal inconvenience.
- ☑ Reduced fuel consumption (lower carbon emissions and cost savings).

Traffic management planning

A good traffic management plan will give consideration to the following factors.

- ☑ Local traffic conditions, peak flows and congestion hot spots.
- ☑ Delivery and departure routes, and sequencing and times for all site vehicles.
- ☑ Using a construction consolidation centre to reduce deliveries.
- ☑ Lay down and delivery areas.
- ☑ On-site traffic routes and the protection of pedestrians.
- ☑ Signage and directions on site.
- ☑ Hold areas for vehicles waiting to off-load or depart the site.
- ☑ Communication between vehicles and the logistics manager on and off site.
- ☑ Wheel-wash locations, dust suppression and mud sweeping.
- ☑ Receiving and responding to complaints.
- ☑ Consultation processes with emergency services, local residents, schools, public facilities and businesses.

Construction consolidation centres (CCCs) and sharing of transport

The use of off-site consolidation areas and the sharing of transport will reduce the number of vehicle movements to and from site. Vehicle sharing can be planned by site staff. Project suppliers may permit the use of their parking areas as car pooling points.

For further information on construction consolidation centres, visit the WRAP website.

E 28

Parking and lay down areas

☑ On-site parking for staff, contractors and visitors needs to be clearly identified.

☑ Delivery vehicle and waste removal parking also needs to be identified.

☑ Vehicle off-loading and lay down areas should be clearly identified.

Plant and vehicles

Ensure that plant and vehicles are properly maintained to ensure efficiency of operations.

On-site traffic management (safe routes, dust suppression and wheel wash)

☑ Use wheel washes to prevent mud and any contaminated materials getting onto local roads.

☑ Water bowsers can be used for dust suppression.

☑ Road sweepers can be used to remove any mud accumulations.

Materials

Construction uses huge amounts of natural resources and in the UK accounts for 25% of all raw materials used. Historically construction has been an inherently inefficient process, arising from the individual nature of on-site construction. For example, it has been common practice to over-order by 5-10% to allow for site wastage from damage, spillage and theft. This not only wastes a lot of money, it produces high levels of waste materials and causes excess material extraction to replace those materials that have been lost through inefficient use.

The aim of modern construction is to move to the top of the waste hierarchy (prevention) and away from where it has been traditionally placed, at the bottom (disposal).

 The waste hierarchy diagram can be found in Chapter E29 Waste management.

Practical ways for improving resource efficiency and reducing waste are shown below.

☑ **Design.**

– Incorporating recycled materials.

– Using standard product sizes, avoiding on-site cutting and allowing for the pre-assembling of components off site.

– Allowing a cut/fill balance and by utilising surplus materials in site features (such as landscaping).

– Specifying non-hazardous and low environmental impact materials.

☑ **Procurement.**

– Selecting suppliers with a good environmental track record.

– Requiring sub-contractors to have a waste management policy.

– Not over-ordering materials.

– Reducing the amount of packaging.

– Ordering materials at the size required, to avoid off-cuts.

☑ **Delivery and storage.**

– Unloading carefully to avoid damage.

– Refusing to take delivery of damaged goods.

E 28

- Not taking delivery of incorrect deliveries (specification and quantity).
- Not delivering to inappropriate areas of the site.
- Avoiding damage or contamination from incorrect storage.
- Storing material stockpiles to avoid silt run-off and keep them away from drains and watercourses.
- Not exceeding the shelf life of materials.
- Storing waste in a designated area and in segregated waste streams.
- Keeping valuable items in a secure location.

☑ **Handling.**

- Using the correct equipment to lift or move materials to avoid damage.
- Avoiding multiple handling of materials.

There are many benefits to using recycled aggregates and these help to reduce the demand for virgin materials, including lower embodied energy and less transport if produced on sites where the recycled aggregates will be used. On-site processing of demolition aggregates may be classed as a waste operation and may require a permit or exemption notice.

 For further information refer to the waste management chapter in Section E of GE 700 *Construction site safety*.

Water consumption

There are a variety of techniques that can be used to increase water efficiency.

On larger construction projects, where high volumes of water are being used, the first action is to establish an approach to measuring and monitoring water usage so that it can be managed. This may involve the use of water meters at appropriate locations and the use of water balances to account for water usage. Water reduction targets can be set based on known volumes of water usage and progress monitored.

Collecting rainwater for reuse

Significant savings can be made by using rainwater harvesting systems to collect rainwater from roofs and other flat surfaces. Early installation of suitable collection systems would need to be investigated at the design stage. Harvested water can be used for dust suppression, flushing toilets and wheel washes, avoiding the need to draw water from the mains or abstraction from surface water.

E
28

Monitor water use during site tours and deal with any obvious leaks or running taps. The use of triggers on hoses will prevent hoses from running whilst unattended.

Vehicle wheel washes are now available with water recycling and recirculation systems fitted. These will reduce the volume of water used and have the potential to save money. These systems work by providing a solids settling area, sometimes combined with the use of flocculants to further promote the settlement of solids. The solids that are collected must be periodically removed to an appropriate waste management facility.

Site accommodation can be fitted with waterless urinals, push taps and rainwater harvesting for toilet flushes. Harvested water and mains water must be kept totally separate (for example, two independent systems). Due consideration must be given to the increased risk of legionella and other bacteria collecting in harvested water reservoirs, especially where such water is used as a spray or mist, which may be inhaled.

Waterless urinals

Energy use and climate change

Many governments, including the UK, have taken action by introducing laws and regulations that specifically influence how we use energy (such as building regulations and the need for high levels of insulation in new builds).

Some clients and construction companies now have to measure and report on their energy and fuel use and carbon emission through assessment schemes (such as BREEAM (Building Research Establishment Environment Assessment Method), and CEEQUAL, the sustainability assessment, rating and awards scheme for civil engineering). Site management and supervisors should observe and promote good energy efficiency practices (such as switching equipment off when not in use), monitoring and reporting on fuel, electricity and gas consumption.

The Strategic Forum for Construction, together with industry leaders, has set out an action plan with a number of priorities that can be undertaken by companies to help reduce their energy and carbon emissions, such as the following.

A dripping tap will waste enough water to fill around 50 wash basins in one month

- ☑ Ensuring sites connect to the electricity supply as early as possible to reduce the need for equipment, such as generators, which run on fuel oil (diesel).

- ☑ Installing energy efficient site accommodation.

- ☑ Efficient use of construction plant, appropriate for the task (turning off when not required).

- ☑ Practise good energy management on site, including the following.
  - Planning transport/haulage to reduce part loads.
  - Avoiding double handling or delivery to wrong areas.
  - Effective control of lighting/heating in welfare facilities.
  - Setting up of car sharing or crew bus schemes.

- ☑ Making use of consolidation centres to reduce transport and handling of materials.

- ☑ Fuel efficient driving through driver training.

- ☑ Practising good energy management in company offices.

Quality and workmanship

As building regulations and air tightness standards for new and refurbished buildings become more demanding, the quality of the materials and the workmanship required to install them has a significant impact on energy efficiency. It is therefore important that all site personnel understand how energy efficient construction can be used to deliver good energy performance in reality.

- ☑ **Insulation quality.** Gaps as a result of poor fitting of insulation cause heat loss, significantly reducing the energy efficiency of a building.

  Note: poorly fitted cavity wall insulation board can result in >300% heat loss than design values.

- ☑ **Air tightness.** Air gaps caused by poor design details, unsealed service penetrations and poorly fitted doors and windows will allow more air penetration, increasing heat loss or gain and demand for additional energy for heating or cooling.

  Note: the lower the air tightness testing, resulting in $m^3/(hr.m^2)$, the lower the unintended heat loss/gain will be. Performance greater than 10 times the Building Regulations' minimum standard has been achieved on many UK construction projects.

- ☑ **Cold bridging.** Significant heat loss can be caused through cold bridges, produced by poor design, changes in the build details from the design and poor workmanship. This heat loss can create condensation issues and damp when the building is in use. Installing insulation to provide a continuous barrier, particularly at junctions of walls, roofs, floors and around windows, is important in avoiding this.

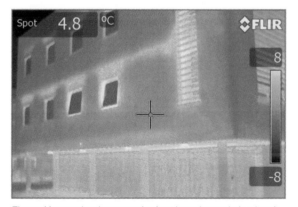

Thermal image showing excessive heat loss above window heads and at second floor level, highlighting poor continuity of thermal insulation (Image supplied by Willmott Dixon)

E
28

Plants and wildlife

Damaging, disturbing or removing protected species can result in prosecution under a range of environmental legislation. Wildlife is also held in high regard by the general public.

Construction activities have the potential to impact on the ecological environment. These impacts can be in the form of the following.

- ☑ Disturbance of birds, bats, badgers and other protected species.
- ☑ Removal or damage of habitats.
- ☑ Disturbance to aquatic wildlife and water quality.
- ☑ Disturbance to wildlife from noise and vibration.
- ☑ Damage to trees and hedgerows.

Before starting on site

The first step in dealing with any wildlife issues is to determine whether the client has identified any designated sites, protected species or invasive plants, together with any particular protection requirements.

This information should be in the pre-construction information package supplied by the client. Where a formal environmental impact assessment has been carried out under planning requirements the resulting CEMP will highlight any protected species, habitats and areas, and any other environmental issues that may be relevant to the site. Contract or planning conditions may state, for example, that certain trees must remain undamaged.

Before any work commences all sensitive areas should be identified and fenced off, or have access to them restricted, to prevent accidental damage. These issues should be addressed in the project's CEMP and communicated to site personnel through induction briefings, toolbox talks and work method statements.

Protected species and plants

On large projects, licensed ecologists will carry out surveys that will be included in the environmental impact assessment as part of the planning process before the project will be given the go-ahead.

You should familiarise yourself with the resulting construction environmental management plan (CEMP) so that you understand what environmental issues need to be considered.

Protection and mitigation actions will be found in the CEMP and should be followed to safeguard the protected species and avoid prosecution. If additional protected species are encountered on site you should inform the site manager, who will arrange for a licensed ecologist to complete a further survey and determine the best course of action.

Great crested newt

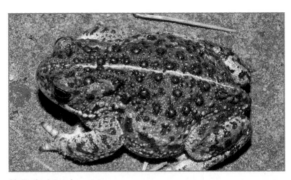

Natterjack toad

Bats

Projects will have to work around any bats and nesting birds as the roosts of bats and birds' nests, eggs and immediate habitat are protected. This could mean scheduling works around hibernation and breeding seasons and having to wait for the chicks of nesting birds to fledge and leave the nest.

Examples of some protected species include those listed below.

☑ All wild birds.

☑ Great crested newt.

☑ Water vole.

☑ Natterjack toad.

☑ Bat.

☑ Otter.

☑ Smooth snake.

☑ Dormouse.

☑ Adder.

☑ Slow worm.

☑ Badger.

☑ Large golden ringed dragonfly.

Protected plants include those listed below.

☑ Fen orchid.

☑ Bluebell.

☑ Shore dock.

Please note these lists are not exhaustive.

An early survey should identify the presence of protected plants such as the bluebell

E
28

Invasive plants

Species of plants that do not naturally occur but have been introduced are known as **non-native** species. A number of these non-native species have become invasive, taking over the native species that are unable to compete against these bigger, faster growing, more aggressive plants.

It is an offence to plant or otherwise cause to grow in the wild the following plants.

- ☑ Giant hogweed.
- ☑ Japanese knotweed.
- ☑ Himalayan balsam.
- ☑ Rhododendron.
- ☑ Floating pennywort.
- ☑ Parrot's feather.
- ☑ Australian swamp stonecrop.

Giant hogweed

Japanese knotweed
(Image supplied by Bridget Plowright)

Himalayan balsam

E
28

The CEMP for the project will highlight any concern for non-native species. If these are present and are not included within the CEMP then advice should be sought from specialists who will provide further details on how to best treat and dispose of these plants in each instance.

Careful planning should take place to ensure that work on areas of vegetation destined for removal is done outside of any breeding or nesting season to avoid damage or disturbance to any protected species.

A regular inspection regime should be put in place to ensure that all protection to sensitive areas is being maintained in a satisfactory condition without damage or encroachment by the construction works.

Archaeology and heritage

Archaeological remains and the historic built environment provide a valuable record of a nation's history and identity and are an irreplaceable part of its national heritage. For these reasons archaeology and built heritage form a key element of planning policy and must be considered early in any construction project, particularly those which require a formal environmental impact assessment.

Suitable controls to manage archaeology and heritage should be included in the project as early as possible for the reasons below.

☑ Ensure buildings are designed to avoid the disturbance of remains or historic features.

☑ Avoid disturbance during the construction process itself.

☑ Enable designers to incorporate historic features of the site in the final development.

☑ Comply with legal requirements relating to scheduled monuments, listed buildings, conservation areas and protection of the historic environment.

Protection of historic sites, artefacts and remains

There are different types of historic environments that are given legal protection, including the following.

☑ **Scheduled monuments.** These require scheduled monument consent prior to work on them or in their vicinity.

☑ **Human remains and burial grounds.** Unexpected remains must be reported to the coroner and permissions must be in place prior to work being carried out on disused burial grounds.

☑ **Treasure.** This includes coins at least 300 years old, objects containing at least 10% gold or silver and any object found in the vicinity of known treasure.

☑ **Listed buildings.** These are given greater protection to maintain their architectural value and/or as a record of historical events.

☑ **Conservation areas.** These have special architectural or historical character. The Local Authority should be contacted prior to carrying out any work.

Before starting on site

The environmental statement and planning conditions for the project provided by the client should identify any obligations for the management of archaeology and heritage. These requirements should be incorporated into the CEMP, the pre-construction information package, the construction phase plan and method statements. It may be a condition of the planning consent to prepare an archaeological management plan, which may include the employment of a qualified archaeologist as a watching brief during excavations, dismantling activity or other relevant construction work.

E
28

Areas of known archaeological or historic interest should be protected from damage. This can include boarding up windows, or covering areas with impact-resistant materials, dust sheets and fencing to prevent encroachment. Scaffold poles should be fitted with end caps and suitably tied to the structure to avoid unnecessary damage to masonry.

It will also be important to agree appropriate methods of working adjacent to sensitive areas. Vibration from excavation, piling or tunnelling work may cause damage, so vibration monitoring equipment may be required to ensure vibration levels are not exceeded.

De-watering schemes may have an impact on archaeological features, causing differential settlement or damage to materials previously protected by being waterlogged. Appropriate methods of de-watering should be agreed in advance of the works taking place.

Unexpected finds

If any unexpected finds are encountered, work should stop in the affected area and be fenced off to protect it.

Where there is no archaeological watching brief employed by the project, you should contact the Local Authority archaeological officer for advice on how to proceed. If human remains are found it will be necessary to stop work and report this to the coroner. For authorisation to continue, approval will need to be given by the Home Office.

Land use and contamination

Building and construction work often involves the redevelopment of land previously used for commercial or industrial activities. These are often called brownfield sites. The surface of the ground and the ground beneath the surface may be contaminated by materials that have been used in a manufacturing process, stored, spilt, buried, dumped or abandoned on the land in previous years.

This may include the residue, waste or by-products from some industrial processes and the ashes from fires. Both solid and liquid waste may have permeated into the ground to a considerable depth.

Sites with previous industrial occupation should be assumed to be polluted, and tests undertaken to ascertain the types of pollutant and their concentration.

The assessment of contaminated land is complex and should be carried out by competent persons. Everyone involved in work on such land must make an assessment of potential risks to human health and the environment, and implement any protective measures that need to be taken.

Dealing with a contaminated land risk is a three-stage process.

Step 1. Identify the risks by reviewing the source contaminants, pathways and receptors.

Step 2. Decide upon the most appropriate remediation strategy to deal with the contamination.

Step 3. Implement the remediation works on site, including appropriate protection measures (such as sheeting contaminated material and installing wheel-washing facilities).

Clients have a duty under the Construction (Design and Management) Regulations to provide all contractors with relevant health and safety information on the project. This will include details of the previous use of the land (going back historically as far as is practical) and details of any buildings or structures (existing or demolished) that were built upon it.

 If working on a site and you come across unusually coloured soils, liquids, sludge or encounter any unusual smells or odours – stop work immediately, evacuate the area and seek professional advice.

E
28

Declaration of a clean site

The management responsible for workings on the site will formally decide when a site is free from contamination, and declare this so any necessary fencing and decontamination facilities previously provided can be removed. This may be in consultation with the Local Authority or Environment Agency, particularly where there may be a planning condition to meet regarding remediation of the site.

Occupational health considerations

The health of workers on contaminated sites can be affected through one or more of the following ways.

- ☑ Asphyxiation.
- ☑ Inhalation.
- ☑ Gasing.
- ☑ Skin absorption.
- ☑ Ingestion.
- ☑ Skin penetration.

Suitable personal protective clothing and approved respiratory protective equipment must be worn at all times when work is carried out on contaminated land sites.

Personal hygiene

The level of risk to health by any contaminants will determine the scale of any hygiene facilities needed, but certain precautions (such as the provision of a drench shower) should always be considered when working on a contaminated site.

- ☑ A dirty area is required for workers to discard dirty or contaminated clothing. Such clothing should be bagged and identified within the area before being dispatched to specialist cleaners.

- ☑ A clean area is required for workers to put on clean and non-contaminated clothing. Access to and exit from this clean area must be to the clean part of the site. It is essential that the entry/exit point of the clean area is in the clean part of the site.

☑ Toilets, showers and washing facilities should be positioned between the dirty and clean areas, so that workers may wash or shower in order to remove any contaminant from their bodies.

For further information refer to the waste management chapter in Section E of GE 700 *Construction site safety.*

E
28

E
28

29

Waste management

Waste management

What your employer should do for you
1. Employ a competent member of staff who is familiar with waste management legislation and requirements, and will be responsible for waste on the project.
2. Liaise with the waste regulators as appropriate and apply for relevant waste management permits and exemptions.
3. Engage the design team to take steps to minimise waste during the design process if relevant.
4. Prepare a site waste management plan (SWMP), where appropriate, identifying the project wastes and how they will be minimised and managed.
5. Ensure that sub-contractors and suppliers are aware of the project waste requirements and that they contribute to the SWMP (if being used).
6. Ensure that all relevant staff receive a SWMP induction/briefing (if being used) so that they are aware of the correct on-site procedures for handling, storing and recording waste.
7. Ensure that all proposed disposal facilities have a valid waste management permit or licence.
8. Ensure that all proposed waste carriers have a valid waste carrier licence.
9. Maintain records of associated waste transfer documentation – two years for non-hazardous waste and three years for hazardous waste.
10. If in Wales, and the project is expected to produce more than 500 kg of hazardous waste, register the site as a hazardous waste producer.

E
29

What you should do as a supervisor			
Checklist	**Yes**	**No**	**N/A**
1. Liaise with all sub-contractors and suppliers under your control to ensure the site waste requirements are being fulfilled.			
2. Ensure that all work areas under your control are safe and free of debris.			
3. Ensure that all skips and containers are properly identified for the waste they are allocated.			
4. Regularly monitor waste containers and skips to ensure they contain the correct materials.			
5. Engage in regular site tours and inspections with site staff and contractors to review current waste practices and performance.			
6. Notify any waste infringements to the relevant personnel.			
7. Deliver regular toolbox talks and briefings on waste as and when appropriate.			
8. Arrange for skips and containers to be regularly emptied.			
9. Ensure that waste transfer documentation is being completed correctly before the waste leaves the site.			
10. Ensure that waste transfer documentation is returned to the site office for inclusion in the SWMP/site records.			

E
29

Introduction

The construction industry is the single biggest consumer of resources in the UK and consumes around 420 million tonnes of materials per year. The industry also generates a huge amount of waste – around 120 million tonnes a year; about 20 million tonnes still goes to landfill.

Site notice encouraging good practice for waste

The poor management of materials and resources on a construction project can lead to excessive amounts of waste, which is costly, bad for the environment and can be unsafe. Waste can be generated in a number of ways, including poor design, incorrect or over-ordering, poor workmanship, incorrect storage and poor management.

The following points are covered within this chapter.

☑ The improper disposal of waste is illegal and can lead to prosecution and even imprisonment.

☑ Producers of waste must correctly identify their waste as inert, non-hazardous or hazardous with reference to the appropriate European Waste Catalogue (EWC) code.

☑ In Wales, producers of 500 kg or more of hazardous waste (such as oils or asbestos) must register their premises with Natural Resources Wales.

☑ Producers of waste have a legal duty of care to ensure that it is passed on to an authorised person with the correct technical competence.

☑ All contractors who carry or collect waste should have a waste carrier's licence.

☑ All waste disposal facilities should have a waste management permit (England and Wales) or licence (Northern Ireland and Scotland) unless they have a registered exemption from the Environment Agency, Natural Resources Wales, Northern Ireland Environmental Agency or Scottish Environment Protection Agency.

E
29

☑ All waste transfers must be supported by the correct documentation.

☑ For waste classified as inert (non-active) and non-hazardous (active) you will need to complete a waste transfer note.

☑ Waste classified as hazardous (active) requires a completed consignment note.

☑ In Scotland, hazardous waste is called special waste.

☑ Site waste management plans (SWMPs), used by major contractors to support efficient processes on site and reduce waste and associated costs.

Waste regulation authorities

In England the Environment Agency (EA) is the main authority for enforcing waste legislation and issuing permits and exemptions. In Wales it is Natural Resources Wales, in Northern Ireland it is the Northern Ireland Environment Agency and in Scotland it is the Scottish Environmental Protection Agency.

Local Council Authorities also have some waste enforcement powers, such as the stop and search and seizure of vehicles suspected of waste crime (such as fly tipping) and for lesser offences (such as littering). Local Authorities are also responsible for issuing waste permits involving air pollution control (such as mobile crushing equipment).

Waste responsibilities

There will be a number of personnel involved in a construction project who have key responsibilities for waste management. For a typical construction project using a SWMP, the following table provides an example of the waste responsibilities for the project team.

E
29

Waste management

Project member	Waste management responsibility
Client	■ Set waste standards and targets in the project specification. ■ Where using a Site Waste Management Plan (SWMP), ensure it is started before the works commence. ■ Regularly review and sign off changes to the SWMP.
Principal contractor's or single contractor's contract/project manager	■ Ensure that a suitably competent person is employed, who is familiar with waste management legislation, waste management requirements and procedures. ■ Ensure that the SWMP is started as early as possible in order that waste can be minimised through design and procurement. ■ Set an expectation of high waste management standards. ■ Ensure that the project team and contractors are engaged in the development and implementation of the SWMP by ensuring its implications are embedded in sub-contracts and method statements, discussed in meetings with sub-contractors and the site team, is a topic of focus on site inspections/walk rounds and is appropriately policed. ■ Provide necessary leadership to ensure the SWMP's implementation, and ensure co-operation from the rest of the team. ■ Produce and promote the site waste rules in co-operation with the person in charge of the SWMP. ■ Take responsibility for having all required waste-related documentation.
Principal designer	■ Contribute to measures to design out waste. Help to co-ordinate design with construction, to ensure that waste minimisation plans are sustained and implemented.
Commercial manager	■ Contribute to waste minimisation and waste management actions and ensure quantities reflect the waste minimisation actions.
Procurement manager	■ Ensure that relevant actions for waste minimisation and recycling are included in relevant tender documents and contracts. Ensure that all contractors are invited to submit their own ideas for waste minimisation.
Construction supervisors	■ Contribute to waste minimisation and waste management actions. Ensure co-ordination of construction process so that all waste minimisation and management actions are implemented.
Site staff	■ Support the construction supervisors with the above actions, particularly with work packages they oversee or are involved in.
Contractors	■ Be fully engaged in site waste management.

E
29

Understanding and describing waste

Waste generally means a substance or object which the holder discards, intends to discard or is required to discard, although many court cases in the UK and Europe highlight that whether or not the substance is a waste may be subject to review in each particular case. This is because a material can be classed as waste even if it has a use or someone is prepared to pay for it. Another simple definition of waste could be a substance or object that a company or organisation no longer wants, needs or can use.

Waste that can be sent to landfill can be broadly divided into three categories.

☑ **Inert (inactive).** Waste that will not decompose to produce greenhouse gases (such as bricks, concrete, tiles, ceramics and glass). This is relevant to any waste sent to landfill.

☑ **Non-hazardous (active).** Waste (such as timber, food and paper) that will decompose but does not contain hazardous substances.

☑ **Hazardous (active).** Waste that contains hazardous substances and is dangerous to human health or the environment, as stated in the European Waste Catalogue (EWC).

It is the waste procedure's responsibility to:

☑ decide what is and is not waste

☑ record and retain details (in the SWMP if applicable).

Cardboard and shrink wrap packaging waste. Consider using reusable or returnable packaging to avoid cost of waste removal

Waste transfer documentation must contain information that properly describes the waste so that waste disposal sites know what type of waste they are accepting. European Waste Catalogue (EWC) codes should be used on any waste transfer note or hazardous waste consignment note (known as the special waste consignment note in Scotland). The EWC is covered in more detail in a later section 'Disposal of waste off site' (see page 380).

 It is not acceptable just to enter 'muck away' or 'general waste' on the waste transfer note as it is a legal requirement to include a description and the six-digit waste code.

E
29

Waste priorities – reduce, reuse and recycle

When thinking about how to deal with waste there are a number of options, with each option having different levels of environmental benefit. The waste hierarchy, shown in the diagram *(right)*, identifies the various options from prevention (most preferred) to disposal (least preferred). The well-known phrase 'reduce, reuse or recycle' relects the various levels within the waste hierarchy.

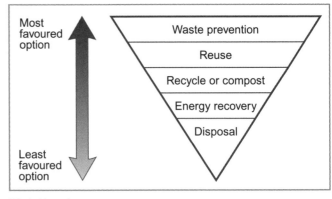

Most favoured option

Least favoured option

Waste prevention

Reuse

Recycle or compost

Energy recovery

Disposal

Waste hierarchy

The following table includes examples of waste minimisation principles at different stages of a construction project.

Design	Procurement	On-site processes
▪ Use a smaller number of component types (for example, standardised doors and windows). ▪ Avoid unnecessary material use. ▪ Use set dimensions to minimise off-cuts. ▪ Design to enable maximum application of procurement and on-site waste minimisation principles. ▪ Integrate demolition and build into one project and maximise the reuse of demolition material.	▪ Manufacture off site with reusable packaging of all delivered units. ▪ Eliminate packaging. ▪ Avoid unnecessary layers of packaging. ▪ Reduce thickness of packaging. ▪ Take-back of packaging, excess product and damaged product. ▪ Take-back of pallets. ▪ Include contractual clauses to penalise waste production/incentivise waste reduction or require waste-reducing activities. ▪ Recycle/reuse clauses included in contracts.	▪ Repair pallets or use plastic, reusable pallets so no new pallets arrive on site. ▪ Arrange bulk deliveries (but be aware of handling implications). ▪ Arrange just-in-time deliveries. ▪ Provide a good, recognised storage area for reusable products on site. ▪ Maximise segregation.

E
29

10 million tonnes of new, unused building products go to landfill every year. The typical cost of waste on a project is around 5% of the build cost.

Waste duty of care

Under the common law duty of care all waste must be properly stored (to prevent escape or release) and must be transferred and ultimately disposed of in a responsible manner. All transfers of waste must be made to properly authorised persons holding the relevant permit or licence.

A building contractor or anyone else who carries waste (such as a plumber, carpenter, bricklayer or decorator) must be registered as a carrier even if they only carry their own waste. They must have the necessary documentation to consign the waste to a licensed site who will, in turn, acknowledge receipt and give details in writing of where and when the waste is to be disposed of.

 Remember: you must register as a waste carrier if you transport construction or demolition waste in your own vehicle.

Legislation requires that waste must be transferred to a waste transfer station or disposal site holding the right permit or licence, together with appropriate documentation in the form of a waste transfer note for inert and non-hazardous waste or a consignment note for hazardous waste.

 Carrying surplus materials back to your workshop or stores for sorting and reuse does not constitute the carriage of waste.

Waste management permits, licences and exemptions

Permits, licences or exemptions may be required where work activities on site result in the reuse or treatment of contaminated or demolition materials.

Examples include mobile treatment of contaminated land for reuse, and mobile crushing plant for recycled aggregate. Where these activities are required, checks should be made to ensure that the local waste regulators (either the relevant Environment Agency or Local Authority) have been contacted and the appropriate licences, exemptions or permits are in place.

 If you believe you require an exemption or permit then you should speak to your local waste regulator at the earliest opportunity.

 The detailed regulations and guidance are freely available on the regulators' websites.

Managing waste

Before starting on site

It may be necessary to arrange some of the aforementioned exemptions or permits from the regulator, as they can take some time to obtain. Early discussions can prevent unexpected delay.

It is good practice to carry out the following steps at the start of the planning phase for any construction work.

E
29

Waste management

- [✓] Obtain the contact details of the waste regulator and Local Authority in whose area you will be working.

- [✓] Contact the waste regulator and discuss as appropriate any plans for the treatment and recovery of any on-site materials.

- [✓] Discuss how and where you intend to move the waste, who will be moving it and how.

- [✓] Consider options for handling the materials as non-waste.

- [✓] Investigate and share options for on or off site treatment plans.

- [✓] Check that any waste carriers are licensed and listed on the public records.

- [✓] Check any waste transfer, treatment, recovery or disposal sites are correctly permitted and listed on public records.

- [✓] Review the need for any waste exemptions or permits that might be needed.

- [✓] Where required, a SWMP for the project should be completed as far as practicable before the commencement of work.

Site waste management plans

SWMPs can play an important role in managing and reducing waste and associated costs and it is good practice to have a SWMP for all but the very smallest of projects. The purpose of the plan is to reduce the amount of waste on site, encourage reuse and recycling, and prevent fly-tipping.

A SWMP will typically:

- [✓] enable consideration of waste generation and options before a project starts

- [✓] document how waste has been designed out of a project

- [✓] identify who is responsible for resource and waste management on the project

- [✓] show what types of waste will be produced

- [✓] detail how the waste will be managed (reduced, recycled, reused or disposed of)

- [✓] identify which contractors will be used to handle the waste

- [✓] set out how the waste quantities will be measured.

Implementing a SWMP can bring a number of business benefits

- [✓] Wastes can be identified early and minimised through design and procurement practices before construction starts.

- [✓] Queries from the waste regulator can be answered simply and easily.

- [✓] It helps to avoid prosecution by ensuring that all wastes being disposed of end up in the right place.

- [✓] It shows how waste is managed and helps to reduce costs.

- [✓] Materials and waste are managed responsibly and are therefore of less risk to the environment.

- [✓] It helps to provide valuable information for future projects on the costs and quantities of waste produced. This information can be used to set targets for reduction.

Managing hazardous (or special) waste

Hazardous waste (special waste in Scotland) contains substances in sufficient quantities that make it hazardous to human health or the environment.

Hazardous to the environment sign

The following controls should be adopted to comply with the hazardous or special waste regulations.

- ☑ Different types of hazardous wastes should be segregated as there is a clear need to identify the quantities and types of hazardous waste on the consignment notes.

- ☑ Mixing of different types of hazardous waste should be avoided as this may inadvertently create an explosion or fire risk, particularly in warm weather.

- ☑ Mixing of hazardous waste with non-hazardous waste to dilute the material below the threshold concentration is prohibited.

- ☑ Packaging or containers contaminated with hazardous substances should be treated as hazardous waste unless it can be shown that the concentration (including the packaging) is below the threshold limits.

Where individual products are combined to form a substance (for example, adhesives and resins), then each component should be considered for its hazardous properties and disposed of accordingly. Resins are often inert when set so leaving materials to dry before disposal may make them non-hazardous.

Handling and storage of waste

This can be achieved on construction sites, in practical terms, by setting up appropriate segregation skips and separating out (sorting) any wastes that can be reused or recycled, or which will change the characteristics of the original waste stream. This will aid in facilitating the handling of the waste, enhancing recovery of the waste and further reducing the volume of waste destined for landfill.

 Hazardous wastes are required to be stored and disposed of separately from non-hazardous wastes.

 A colour coding scheme can make the accurate segregation of waste easier.

Segregated waste streams

E
29

Use of skips or containers

When deciding on the type and number of containers required, consider the type of waste that will be produced (this should be done at SWMP stage).

- ☑ Would a compactor skip be better than an open one?

- ☑ Would a compactor skip cut down on the number of skips you require?

- ☑ Would a tailgate skip be easier to use than a fixed one?

- ☑ Is the skip the correct size and will it hold all your wastes (prevent wind-blown litter, scavenging or leaking)?

- ☑ How many skips will you need and how often will they need to be emptied?

- ☑ How many different types of waste will you produce and will it be hazardous or non-hazardous waste (for example, most chemicals, oils and greases would fall into the hazardous waste category)?

  Examples of the types of waste-specific skips you may require are listed below.

  – Brick rubble, concrete and cement.

  – Gypsum or gypsum-related products.

  – Empty paint tins, adhesive tins or drums.

  – Wood, cardboard, paper and carpeting.

  – Scrap metal (such as pipes or wires).

  – Various chemicals, oils and greases.

  – PVC window mouldings, gutters and downpipes.

Dispose of waste appropriately

Remember

- ☑ Place skips where contractors or your carrier's lorries can reach them easily.

- ☑ Keep access to skips clear.

- ☑ Do not overload any skip; if you do, your carrier has every right to tell you to unload it, or even refuse to take it away.

- ☑ Do not load the skip above the height of the sides.

- ☑ Make sure that all waste is stored in the skip and not spilled around it.

- ☑ Do not light fires in skips.

- ☑ Never allow anyone to climb into or ride in a skip (it is a dangerous practice and could result in waste being inadvertently tipped on top of them).

E
29

☑ Consider whether any, or all, of the skips need to be covered to prevent filling with water and limit the potential for contaminated water run-off.

☑ Avoid storing more than 50 m³ capacity at any one time; above this amount, you may have to register for an exemption or permit.

Managing waste electrical and electronic equipment

Waste electrical and electronic equipment (WEEE) (such as computers, fridges and phones) are the fastest growing waste streams and come under the WEEE Regulations. If you are considering the disposal of waste electrical equipment, the following actions must be taken.

☑ It must be segregated from other types of waste for disposal.

☑ If the waste electrical equipment was purchased before 13 August 2005, and is being replaced with new equivalent equipment, then ask the producer for details of their producer compliance scheme and collection arrangements.

☑ If the waste equipment is not being replaced with new equivalent equipment, or the producer compliance scheme cannot be traced, then you must pay to transfer the waste equipment to an approved authorised treatment facility that can accept waste electrical equipment (for example, an authorised transfer station, approved by the waste regulation authority to receive such waste).

☑ If it was purchased after 13 August 2005, refer to the producer compliance scheme and collection arrangements or contact the supplier for details.

☑ Any waste transferred to an authorised collector or waste carrier must meet all of the normal requirements of the duty of care, such as a waste carrier's licence, transfer notes and licensed treatment facilities (a waste transfer station approved by the waste regulation authority to receive such waste).

Managing waste batteries

The construction industry is a large user of batteries in many types of vehicles, plant and equipment.

The regulations deal with three types of battery.

Automotive batteries – used for starting, or the ignition of, a vehicle engine, or for powering the lights of a vehicle.

Industrial batteries – used for industrial or professional purposes (such as the battery used as a source of power and propulsion to drive the motor in an electric forklift).

Portable batteries – that are sealed, can be carried in the hand and are neither an automotive battery or accumulator nor an industrial battery. Examples of a portable battery include the AA or AAA batteries used to power a small hand-torch or the battery used to power a laptop or mobile telephone.

Where do your batteries go?

E
29

A producer of **industrial batteries** is obliged to provide for the take-back of waste industrial batteries free of charge from the end user in the following circumstances.

- ☑ Where the producer has supplied new industrial batteries to that end user.

- ☑ If, for any reason, the end user is not able to return waste industrial batteries to the producer who supplied the batteries, providing the waste batteries are of the same chemistry as the batteries the producer places on the market.

- ☑ If the end user is not purchasing new batteries and a battery with the same chemistry as the one being returned has not been placed on the market for a number of years, then the end user's entitlement is to be able to contact any producer to request take-back.

The regulations also require that **automotive battery** producers collect, on request, waste automotive batteries free of charge, from businesses such as garages, scrap yards, end-of-life vehicle authorised treatment facilities or civic amenity sites (such as Local Authority waste recycling centres).

Producers do not have a duty to collect waste automotive batteries from individual end users.

The burning of waste

There are few situations where the burning of waste is permitted or legal on a construction site. Over and above government legislation, some companies may also prohibit site fires. Activities that may be allowed are associated with demolition materials or the burning of invasive plants. The appropriate Local Authority should be consulted before lighting any bonfires.

For further information on bonfires on site refer to Chapter C17 Fire prevention and control.

Difficult wastes

Although not legally defined, there are some types of waste that need to be handled in a different way. This is because there are specific legal controls in place for that waste or that the handling of it at the landfill site might be problematic (for example, dusty materials).

Plasterboard and gypsum

Plasterboard, gypsum-based and high sulphate wastes should be collected separately and must not be mixed with biodegradable waste. Many suppliers of plasterboard now offer recycling services and these should be considered ahead of landfill.

Other difficult wastes include the following.

- ☑ **Invasive plants.** Waste materials, both soil and plant matter contaminated with Japanese knotweed or Giant hogweed, can only be disposed of at sites that are specifically licensed to receive them.

- ☑ **Contaminated soil.** That which is a mixture of soils, stones, rubble containing polluting substances that could be a range of things left over from former use of the site or as a consequence of illegal tipping.

Disposal of waste off site

Step 1. Classifying the waste

It is a legal requirement for waste disposal sites to have a clear description of any waste they are accepting. This should be explained on the duty of care waste transfer note or the hazardous waste consignment note, the description of waste can be identified from a list of wastes in the European Waste Catalogue (EWC).

E
29

Under the EWC, each waste has a six-digit code – the first two digits refer to the activity that produced the waste, the second two digits refer to the sub-chapters for the different waste types and the final pair of digits corresponds to the individual waste stream.

17 01 02 is the LOW/EWC code for bricks.

☑ **17 refers to construction and demolition waste.**

☑ **01 refers to concrete, bricks, tiles and so on.**

☑ **02 refers to bricks.**

Any waste code listed within the EWC and marked with an asterisk (*) is potentially a hazardous waste and should be managed accordingly.

When you carry waste for disposal, or contract a carrier to dispose of it for you, you must give an honest description of the waste, including the six-digit waste code.

Step 2. Handing over the waste
Under the duty of care you must pass on your waste to an appropriately authorised person. You must check the following.

☑ That the person collecting or transferring your waste holds a valid waste carrier licence.

☑ That the landfill site or transfer station where the waste is being taken holds a valid environmental permit or licence.

For clarity you must make these checks even if you are taking the waste to the landfill or transfer station yourself.

Waste transfer documentation
Whenever you pass the waste on to someone else (even if you carry your own waste) it must be supported by a waste transfer note (for inert and non-hazardous wastes) or a consignment note (for hazardous waste).

A waste transfer note must provide the following information.

☑ Identify the producer of the waste.

☑ Give a description of the waste, including the six-digit EWC code.

☑ State the quantity.

☑ State how the waste is contained, whether loose or in a container and, if in a container, the kind of container.

☑ Give the place of transfer from your ownership into the waste site management.

☑ State the date and time of transfer.

☑ Contain your signature and the signature of the authorised person receiving the waste.

Step 3. Disposal of waste
At the point of disposal (such as the waste transfer station or landfill site) the receiving facility will sign the waste transfer note or consignment note and will issue a receiving ticket. For traceability purposes regular checks of this documentation should be made to verify the destination that was originally identified when the waste left site. This information will also be useful for completing the SWMP and other monitoring requirements, particularly where the project is being assessed under BREEAM.

E 29

In England and Wales whenever waste is passed on to someone else, the producer will have to declare on the waste transfer note, or consignment note for hazardous waste, that they have applied all reasonable measures to apply the waste management hierarchy. It is also a requirement to include the appropriate 2007 Standard Industry Classification (SIC) code on all waste transfer notes. In Scotland, special waste consignment note codes are obtained from SEPA (for the relevant fee). A three day prenotification period is required for the consignment of special waste, which must then be moved within one month of the expected removal date.

Removal of contaminated waste

Where contaminated waste and other materials are to be removed from a site, protective sheeting for skips and lorries will be necessary.

All skips or vehicles must be completely sheeted within the dirty area of a site. Care must be exercised by those carrying out the sheeting operations to ensure they do not come into contact in any way with contaminated materials.

Vehicle drivers should not sheet their own vehicles, except to finally tighten sheet ropes, which should only be done in the clean area of the site.

Facilities must be available to thoroughly wash all vehicles leaving a contaminated site. Detailed records must be kept of the disposal of hazardous or contaminated waste.

·

Other means of disposal

It is illegal to dispose of any liquid waste, including paint and solvent residues, by pouring it into drains or allowing it to soak into the ground. The environmental impact of such an action is likely to be significant. Such wastes are likely to be classed as hazardous and must be disposed of in accordance with the waste disposal legislation at the time of generation.

Mixed, solid waste (such as brick rubble, off-cuts of roofing felt and other scrap materials) must not be buried. The different types of waste should be segregated into separate skips.

From the perspective of site tidiness and health and safety, waste materials should not be allowed to accumulate. As well as posing slip, trip and fall risks, sites where waste is allowed to accumulate have an increased fire risk. Waste must be cleared up and deposited in the appropriate skips at regular intervals. A clean-as-you-go policy should be implemented and enforced.

The Construction (Design and Management) Regulations place legal duties on the employer, the self-employed and any other person who controls the way in which construction work is carried out, and this includes the management of waste.

For further information refer to the waste management chapter in Section E of GE 700 *Construction site safety.*

30

Street works and road works

What your employer should do for you

1. Provide detailed information about any known hazards, including information on the surrounding area (such as schools and transport issues).

2. Provide detailed drawings and layouts from the utility companies outlining services and apparatus located in the vicinity of the work.

3. Make sure that the relevant people have received new roads and street works training and their cards are up to date and registered with the accredited body.

4. Provide suitable welfare resources and facilities.

5. Ensure that a permit from the Local Authority has been issued to open or close the public highway.

6. Devise a construction phase plan for the work and ensure an F10 notification of the construction project is in place, if applicable.

7. Provide suitable barriers and signage to make sure there is safe passage through the works and that access to the site is secure from unauthorised access.

8. Make specific security arrangements for particular pieces of plant, if required.

9. Make sure there are suitable parking arrangements for visitors, contractors and staff.

10. Create and communicate a programme of the schedule of works and material deliveries.

11. Provide details of emergency contacts, in case of any breakages or site incidents.

12. Provide suitable personal protective equipment (PPE), including the correct class of hi-visibility clothing.

F
30

What you should do as a supervisor

Checklist	Yes	No	N/A
1. Induct the workforce on their initial arrival on site, and induct all site visitors.			
2. Provide safe routes of passage through the work for both pedestrians and vehicles.			
3. Make sure all signage is erected and clearly displayed, as required, throughout the programme of work, and amend as required.			
4. Make sure the site is secure at all times, especially when left unattended.			
5. Make sure any traffic control equipment is operating correctly, including out of hours.			
6. Check that all operatives are trained, competent and have the necessary certification for the tasks they are to undertake.			
7. Make sure that visitors to the site are aware of any hazards and are either accompanied or know where to go and what to do.			
8. Check that there are suitable welfare provisions for the workforce, either on or off site.			
9. Make sure materials are stacked and stored appropriately, and hazardous materials are kept secure.			
10. Provide banksman and manual operation of traffic control when traffic movement, affected by the work, becomes an issue.			
11. Make sure all operatives are wearing the correct PPE.			

F
30

Introduction

The New Roads and Street Works Act (NRSWA) provides a legislative framework for road works (including work carried out by public utility companies). Road works will normally bring operatives carrying out construction work in close proximity to vehicles (both construction plant and passing traffic).

The safety of the workers, pedestrians and vehicle drivers will depend on a well-planned and organised site set up throughout the work, carried out by trained and competent workers and by controlling the movement and behaviour of passing traffic.

With the exception of Scotland, compliance with the Code of Practice is a legal requirement and failure to comply is a criminal offence.

Before starting work

The following information and documentation will be required before work starts.

- ☑ A Section 50 street works licence, issued by the Local Authority responsible for the public highway, will be needed if the project requires the placement of new apparatus (for example, pipes, cables and ducts) within the carriageway, footway or verge.

- ☑ A construction plan produced by the principal contractor.

- ☑ A traffic management plan outlining the positioning of signs, barriers, cones and traffic controls.

- ☑ A set of utility drawings and documents outlining the position of any known apparatus that is in the vicinity of the work.

- ☑ Contact details of all the local utility companies.

- ☑ Copies of street works training and street works qualifications register (SWQR) cards for supervisors and operatives carrying out the work.

- ☑ Copies of training for specific tasks (such as plant operation, banksman, manual handling and changing abrasive wheels).

- ☑ Risk assessments and method statements for the work to take place.

- ☑ Use of a permit system, controlled by the supervisor, prior to any excavating in the carriageway, footway or verge.

- ☑ A copy of *Safety at street works and road works – A Code of Practice* (the red book).

 The Code of Practice can be freely downloaded from the Department for Transport's website.

Site set up

- ☑ Plan the location and set up of welfare, either on or off site.

- ☑ Make sure the workforce have access to toilets, somewhere to take a break, drinking water, a means of washing their hands and somewhere for drying clothes (such as the use of a small, self-contained unit, often used with a portable generator for power).

- ☑ Make sure all operatives are wearing the appropriate personal protective equipment (PPE) for working in the highway.

- ☑ Plan initial temporary traffic management and laying out of traffic management in line with the Code of Practice.

- ☑ Set up barriers and a safe route for pedestrians.

- ☑ Ensure any signs are properly weighted down.

- ☑ Make sure signage is duplicated on either side of the road.

- ☑ The set up must include a works area, working space and safety zone.

- ☑ The safety zone should include a lead-in taper, longways clearance, sideways clearance and exit taper.

- ☑ Make sure traffic control systems are set up correctly, including stop/go boards managed by trained operatives, and communication devices are working correctly.

- ☑ Traffic lights should be operating correctly and details of the supplier should be available. Make sure training in manual use has been carried out.

- ☑ A first-aid kit, trained first aider and fire extinguishers must be available on site at all times.

- ☑ A cable avoidance tool (CAT) should be available on site. This must have been calibrated within the previous 12 months and checked prior to use. Use a signal generator (genny) if there are non-energised cables and ducts that need to be traced. Somebody should be trained in the use of the CAT and genny.

- ☑ Identify the location and controls for overhead cables, including erecting goalposts, barriers and displaying signs.

- ☑ Ensure the segregation and safe disposal of waste.

- ☑ Make sure that lighting in the area is adequate, with flashing beacons on cones and additional floodlights to highlight signage during hours of darkness. Temporary street lighting may be required.

- ☑ Lights should be positioned to avoid glare to drivers and to prevent nuisance to local residents. If lighting is powered by mains supply then a back up battery-operated lighting system may be required.

- ☑ Work vehicles moving through the working space must be a conspicuous colour and have a flashing amber beacon or light.

- ☒ Never work in, or store materials in, the safety zone. It is there to protect the workforce from the traffic, and the traffic from the work activities.

Notify before starting work

Footpath diversion showing the safe route for pedestrians

F
30

Signs should be properly secured

On motorways and high speed dual carriageways (50 mph and above), the following extra precautions are necessary.

- ☑ Class 3, long sleeved high-visibility clothing must be worn.

- ☑ Advanced warning signage should be duplicated in the central reservation.

- ☑ A registered traffic management contractor must be employed.

- ☑ Flashing beacons on work vehicles should be switched on at least 200 m before accessing the work.

Workers wearing PPE to Class 3 standard

Site activities

- ☑ Use a floor saw or abrasive wheel to cut the surface. Make sure equipment is checked prior to use and the abrasive wheel is only replaced by a competent person.

- ☑ Operatives must wear appropriate PPE, including ear defenders, eye protection (to BS EN 166), and FFP3-rated respiratory protective equipment (RPE).

- ☑ Vibration levels of equipment need to be obtained from the manufacturer and trigger times monitored, in line with HSE guidance. Operatives should wear gloves.

- ☑ All cutting must be dust suppressed, either by using a water system or by on-tool extraction methods.

- ☑ Underground cable routes should be identified using a cable avoidance tool (CAT) and their exact location confirmed through hand-dug trial holes using insulated tools.

- Other means include using vacuum excavation with water or high-velocity air jetting. They do have limitations and will not work in all ground conditions.

- If cables, pipes and ducts are uncovered they will need to be supported or even diverted if there is a risk of damage now that they are not supported.

- Open trenches need to be assessed by a competent person and support installed if there is potential for collapse.

- When using excavators, make sure that they cannot swing into the live carriageway.

- Backfill any excavations with specified material and compact with suitable equipment. Vibration from the equipment has to be assessed from the manufacturer's information and monitored for usage time.

- Complete a daily check of all signs and barriers to make sure they are in good order.

- Direct pedestrians and traffic, as required.

- Make sure the site is always secure from unauthorised access, especially when it is going to be left unattended.

- Make sure all tools and equipment are locked away and plant is isolated and secured when not in use.

- Make sure the storage of hazardous materials is secured in suitable containers or cages.

- Make sure there is an information sign displayed, with details of who to contact in an emergency or if the traffic controls fail to work correctly.

- [X] Do not excavate within 500 mm of known cables using excavators or powered equipment.

All sides of an excavation where a pedestrian may gain access must be fenced off

Water main renewal notice

F
30

Removing temporary traffic management

When the works are complete remove the temporary traffic management in reverse of the installation.

☑ Remove all surplus materials and waste.

☑ Use competent persons to carry out the work or a registered traffic management contractor.

☑ Operatives must wear the required class of hi-vis clothing.

☑ Remove all signage that is not required. There is a legal duty to remove it.

**F
30**

31

Demolition

What your employer should do for you

1. Develop, maintain, review and communicate a construction phase plan that details the demolition sequence and techniques to be used.

2. Develop a method statement that identifies the correct demolition sequence to prevent accidental collapse.

3. Identify connected services and arrange for these to be isolated or disconnected before demolition begins, or confirm that they have already been isolated or disconnected.

4. Identify hazardous materials (such as asbestos containing materials, chemicals, toxic fumes, silica and other dusts) that may be generated from work activities, and implement a safe system of work to prevent exposure.

5. Provide you with information from asbestos refurbishment and demolition surveys and provide you with, as a minimum, asbestos awareness training.

6. Protect you and members of the public from the risk of falling materials and dust by establishing exclusion zones and hard hat areas, marked with barriers and hoarding and providing dust suppression.

7. Protect you from falls from height, by ensuring edges and openings are protected and that fragile surfaces have been identified and access to these areas prohibited or a safe system of work has been agreed.

8. Develop a traffic management plan to protect you from moving, slewing, reversing or turning vehicles.

9. Ensure the correct plant is supplied, inspected and maintained.

10. Manage your exposure to noise and introduce hearing protection and exclusion zones.

11. Manage your exposure to vibration and use low vibration equipment.

12. Inform you about any hot-work permits that may be required.

13. Develop a fire safety plan and monitor escape routes to ensure you can leave the building in the event of an emergency.

14. Ensure all arrangements are communicated to everyone working on site and visitors.

What you should do as a supervisor

Checklist	Yes	No	N/A
1. Ensure all workers and visitors under your control receive a site induction, which includes details of the site layout, emergency and evacuation procedures, including muster point and designated first-aid personnel.			
2. Check operatives are competent to undertake the demolition work and operate and use the required tools, personal protective equipment (PPE) and plant.			
3. Check the progress and sequence of the work and ensure it complies with the construction phase plan.			
4. Ensure equipment and plant is maintained and inspected.			
5. Ensure access and egress routes are properly maintained and workers are protected from falls from height.			
6. Ensure signs are displayed and are clearly visible to warn of hazardous areas and activities.			
7. Check the agreed safe system of work for demolition is being followed.			
8. Ensure the site is kept tidy and free from piles of combustible materials and rubbish.			
9. Monitor the fire plan and ensure a means of access is provided for all areas at all times.			
10. Check operatives are wearing their PPE as required.			
11. Ensure employees undertake health surveillance as required.			

F
31

Introduction

Demolition can be a hazardous activity. It should only be carried out by appropriately trained, supervised and competent people. It includes the complete removal of buildings and structures or partial removal of building elements (such as internal walls or a chimney breast).

Whether demolition is required for a small building or structure, or for a complex industrial, commercial or residential site, everyone on site must be aware of the hazards and risks. These need to be identified, assessed and effectively controlled to avoid danger and remove or reduce the potential for injury to persons and damage to adjacent property, as far as is reasonably practicable.

 Information, planning, resources and the responsible implementation of controls are the essential elements for safe and successful demolition projects.

All demolition and refurbishment work, including partial demolition work, must comply with the requirements of the *Code of Practice for full and partial demolition* (BS 6187:2011). If temporary works are required, for façade retention, propping, and so on, then such works must be carried out in accordance with the *Code of Practice for temporary works procedures and the permissible stress design of falsework* (BS 5975:2008).

Only people with the necessary training, knowledge, skills and experience should carry out demolition work. This generally means workers who have a CSCS card for Certificate of Competence of Demolition Operatives (CCDO), and a CPCS card for demolition plant.

Demolition work should be planned and demolition methodologies identified by demolition engineers and workers with the training, knowledge, skills and responsibilities commensurate with their experience. Demolition engineers should be members of the Institute of Demolition Engineers (IDE) and hold a valid CSCS professionally qualified person card as a demolition engineer.

 For further information about the demolition engineer card visit the IDE website.

Many demolition projects, particularly within buildings constructed prior to 1999, may contain asbestos. A demolition and refurbishment survey, in accordance with the requirements of the **Control of Asbestos Regulations** and *Asbestos: the survey guide* (HSG264), must be carried out. This should be provided by the client as part of their pre-construction information. Demolition works must not start before a survey has been undertaken and the results of that survey received. Additional surveys that could be required to identify hazards prior to demolition work commencing are listed below.

- ☑ Structural survey.
- ☑ Lead (paint) survey.
- ☑ Dilapidation survey, for near or adjoining properties and highways.
- ☑ Environmental surveys *(refer to Chapter E28 Environmental management).*
- ☑ Bio hazard surveys (can include the removal of sharps and drug-related materials, human excrement and animal remains).

F
31

Legislation

Section 80 of the **Building Act** requires persons intending to carry out the demolition of a structure or part-structure greater than 1,750 ft³ (approximately 50 m³) to give six weeks' notice to the Local Authority Building Control Department. A Section 81/82 counter notice is usually issued, providing conditions that apply to the work or a refusal.

The **Construction (Design and Management) Regulations** (CDM) require that all demolition or dismantling work must be planned and carried out safely. A plan, which covers how the demolition or dismantling work will be carried out, must be written down before the work starts. This could be included in the construction phase plan, which is required for all construction projects.

If more than one contractor is engaged then a principal designer and principal contractor must be appointed.

The **Provision and Use of Work Equipment Regulations (PUWER)** cover all equipment used at work, including equipment used in demolition. PUWER requires that an employer supplies work equipment which is safe, correct and suitable for the job and that equipment is maintained, inspected, and that records of inspections and examinations are kept. Staff must be informed, instructed and trained in the use of the equipment.

Examples of other legislation which may need to be complied with include the following: Working at Height Regulations, Lifting Operations and Lifting Equipment Regulations, Control of Noise at Work Regulations, Control of Vibration at Work Regulations, Clean Air Act, Control of Substances Hazardous to Health Regulations, and the Control of Asbestos Regulations. This legislation is covered in other chapters of this publication.

Management of demolition work

The **client** must make suitable arrangements for managing a project; they must appoint duty holders who are competent and adequately resourced and must provide pre-construction information that can be reasonably obtained.

The client must also ensure adequate welfare facilities are provided and suitable arrangements for managing health, safety and welfare are in place, before the work starts.

The **principal designer** must plan, manage, monitor and co-ordinate the pre-construction phase, and pass all relevant information to the principal contractor, so that they can produce a construction (deconstruction or demolition) phase plan.

The **principal contractors** must co-ordinate and manage health and safety during the demolition works. They must ensure that workers understand the control measures and precautions that must be taken. If there is only one **contractor** on site (the demolition contractor) the responsibility for health and safety during the construction, demolition and post demolition phases will rest with the demolition contractor until the site is returned to the client. All contractors, including the utility companies, must comply with relevant parts of the construction phase plan.

All demolition work must be **supervised**. The level of supervision will depend on the risks to health and safety and the training, knowledge, experience and skills of the workforce, remembering that young or inexperienced workers may require close supervision. Other factors to consider are the individuals' education, physical agility, literacy and attitude.

All persons involved in planning, managing and carrying out demolition work must be competent (have the right blend of training, knowledge, experience and skills), and be subject to the correct level of supervision.

F
31

A card scheme for the Certification of Competence of Demolition Operatives (CCDO) is managed by the National Demolition Training Group.

Competent people should hold one of the appropriate CCDO cards listed below.

White card
☑ NDTG approved trainer: five year renewable.

Yellow card
☑ Demolition site visitor: five year renewable.

Green card
☑ Demolition labourer L1 equivalent: five year renewable.

Red cards
☑ Demolition apprentice: two year non-renewable.

☑ Demolition and refurbishment operative: three year non-renewable, NVQ required.

☑ Demolition topman: three year non-renewable, NVQ required.

☑ Demolition chargehand: three year non-renewable, NVQ required.

☑ Demolition supervisor: three year non-renewable, NVQ required.

☑ Demolition manager: three year non-renewable, NVQ required.

Blue cards
☑ Demolition and refurbishment operative NVQ L2: five year renewable.

☑ Demolition topman NVQ L2: five year renewable.

Grey card
☑ Demolition chargehand NVQ L3: five year renewable.

Gold card
☑ Demolition supervisor NVQ L3+: five year renewable.

Black card
☑ Demolition manager NVQ L6: five year renewable.

Planning for demolition

Before any demolition work starts the following factors need to be considered.

☑ The age of the building and previous use.

☑ Type of construction and materials used.

☑ The type of demolition required, partial or full demolition.

☑ Separation points and anticipated load paths.

☑ Consideration of any hazardous substances (for example lead, asbestos, Japanese knotweed and contaminated land).

☑ Environmental considerations (such as historic value, nesting birds, protected species, surface and/or groundwater).

☑ Adjoining neighbours, businesses and highways.

☑ The type of waste that will be produced.

☑ How waste will be managed and disposed of.

☑ Land reclamation.

☑ The types of permits and licences that may be required.

Much of this information should be included in the pre-construction information.

Suitable measures must be taken to prevent unauthorised access, protect the public and segregate the demolition work

Associated risks

All work should be properly planned, with the required risk assessments and method statements in place.

The risk assessments and method statements should be communicated to the workers. The workers should then be encouraged to make suggestions and provide feedback on the suitability of the control measures suggested. Some of the risks are covered in more detail below.

Waste

Before commencing work it is recommended that a site waste management plan is produced. Waste should be evaluated for being reused, reclaimed or recycled, in that order, with disposal being the last option. Site management should ensure that the correct waste licences, permits and exemptions are in place.

For further information refer to Chapter E29 Waste management.

The demolition industry has developed demolition and refurbishment information data sheets (DRIDS) to help identify waste streams and explain how and where waste can be reused or recycled.

For further information regarding DRIDS visit the National Federation of Demolition Contractors (NFDC) website.

Falls from height and injuries from falling materials

All work at height should be planned in accordance with the Work at Height Regulations. Where possible, working at height should be avoided. Remote, mechanical demolition (such as a high reach breaker) will remove the need for contractors to work at height. Where working at height cannot be avoided, mobile towers or proprietary systems can be used. Collective and passive means of fall protection (such as edge protection, safety nets and other soft-landing systems) should be used in preference to individual protection (such as harnesses and fall arresters), which require the active participation of the operative (for example, they must anchor themselves).

Workers should not work above each other and care must be taken to ensure that debris does not drop into occupied areas. Any openings must be adequately protected. If using window openings to remove debris these must be protected to prevent operatives from falling. Debris landing zones must be clearly identified and completely protected.

The removal of non-structural fixtures and fittings (soft strip) must be planned and controlled, to prevent the release of asbestos fibres and prevent injuries from falling objects and falls from height.

F
31

Demolition

For further information refer to Chapter D24 Working at height.

Uncontrolled collapse

All steps must be taken to prevent and reduce danger to any persons. All temporary supports must be designed correctly and installed and maintained to withstand the loads placed on them to prevent any uncontrolled collapse.

Exclusion zones

BS 6187:2011 covers exclusion zones and safe working spaces for the safety of those persons on the site and others who may be affected by the work.

For further information refer to the NFDC guidance *Demolition exclusion zones*.

Connected services

Licences and permits should be considered and agreed before work starts, and utility companies must be contacted to discuss the planned demolition work.

Allow time for the complete physical disconnection or isolation of any utility services, as required. These requests should be made in good time and acknowledged in writing, with confirmation that the isolation and physical disconnection has been made.

Traffic management

For further information refer to Chapter C21 Site transport safety.

Hazardous waste and materials

There are many hazardous materials that may be present (for example, asbestos and lead).

Asbestos was widely used in the UK until it was banned in late 1999; disturbance of the fabric of any building built before this time has the potential to expose asbestos. Asbestos surveys must be undertaken before contractors are invited to tender. If asbestos is found the necessary planning, actions and notifications must be implemented.

Wherever paintwork or coatings are likely to be damaged or disturbed the Health and Safety Executive (HSE) advises that lead (paint) surveys should be carried out regardless of the age of the building.

A hazardous waste consignment note must accompany all such waste leaving site.

For further information refer to Chapter E29 Waste management.

Noise

If noise is likely to affect the general public it is advisable to apply to the Local Authority for a Section 61 agreement of the **Control of Pollution Act** (COPA), specifying working methods, working hours and noise levels. If approved, and the terms of the agreement are adhered to, this will protect the contractor against the issue of a Section 60 notice.

If the upper exposure action value (85 dB(A)) is exceeded, hearing protection must be worn and hearing protection zones clearly indicated.

Where the risk assessment indicates that employees are at risk due to noise exposure at work, health surveillance, including hearing checks, must be provided.

In addition, reference should be made to the *Code of Practice for noise and vibration control on construction and open sites – noise* (BS 5228-1:2009).

Dust

Precautions should be taken to reduce dust levels to a minimum, with particular consideration being given to respirable crystalline silica (RCS) dust and (airborne) asbestos fibres. Using damping techniques (such as water spray) can be effective in reducing nuisance dust that poses a risk to workers, and in helping to reduce or prevent dust from spreading outside the site boundary. Respiratory protective equipment (RPE) should be used in conjunction with most dust suppression techniques.

Managing dust and emissions by using a water cannon to spray a building being demolished

For further information refer to Chapter B13 Dust and fumes (Respiratory hazards).

Fumes

Cutting torches may produce a toxic gas, such as nitrogen dioxide. Phosphine can be produced if a phosphate coating is present. If a chlorinated solvent has been used, sulphides may be formed. Paint samples should be obtained prior to cutting and a control of substances hazardous to health (COSHH) assessment carried out. PPE, including respiratory protective equipment (RPE), should be used as necessary.

Vibration

Vibration from demolition activities can cause damage to adjacent properties and long-term health issues to people on site. Exposure to vibration must be controlled in accordance with the Control of Vibration at Work Regulations and reference made to the *Code of Practice for noise and vibration control on construction and open sites – vibration* (BS 5228-2:2009).

Fire and explosion

Where buildings or structures have been used to store or manufacture flammable liquids, any equipment or tanks must be purged (completely cleared) and tested for explosive gases prior to work taking place. The structure or vessel should be treated as a potentially explosive atmosphere and a hot-work permit should be issued as required.

Where it is necessary, for further investigation, to enter any tank or vessel that has contained a flammable liquid or other hazardous chemical, the tank or vessel should be treated as a confined space until it is proven that the atmosphere within is safe and non-hazardous. This type of work may uncover previously hidden and unrecorded asbestos, asbestos-containing materials, asbestos contamination and lead-painted fixtures and fittings.

F 31

Methods of demolition

Soft strip partial demolition is carried out prior to any structural demolition. This is usually done by hand and involves the removal of non-structural fixtures, fittings and finishes (such as doors, windows, partitions, ceilings, cables and pipework), which can be reclaimed, reused or recycled. It may also involve the use of mini machines (such as skid steers and/or mini excavators).

Prior to using or allowing the use of such machines, an assessment of the floor-loading capacity should be undertaken by a competent person (such as a structural engineer). The assessment should take into account the dead and live loads and any necessity for temporary works (such as propping, shoring and so on).

Progressive (top-down) demolition is carried out in the reverse order to construction, and often follows the soft strip phase.

High reach demolition machine in use

 The NFDC has produced guidance on demolishing multistorey structures of 18 m and above, and in the use of high and ultra high-reach demolition machines to improve user and procurer awareness.

Demolition by designed collapse mechanism is achieved by pre-weakening the structure, followed by explosive displacement, remote mechanical demolition, high reach demolition rig or crane or, occasionally, pulling it down with a wire rope. Explosive displacement requires a high level of expertise, planning, supervision and execution. As a result, only qualified explosive demolition engineers should be used for this type of work.

Hydro demolition is a concrete removal technique that utilises very high pressure water to remove deteriorated and sound concrete, as well as asphalt and grout. Where this work is to be undertaken, consideration should be given to the noise generated and the capture of the water run-off, which may be contaminated and could pose a threat of silting to natural waterways and man-made draining systems.

Manual demolition techniques are used when other methods of demolition are not suitable or possible. Some of the tools that can be used are listed below.

☑ Hand tools.

☑ Breakers, compressors or hammers.

☑ Concrete nibblers or hydraulic pulverisers.

☑ Stitch drilling.

☑ Drilling and hydraulic bursting.

☑ Drilling and expansive pastes.

☑ Oxy-propane cutting equipment.

☑ Diamond cutting and sawing.

When using these techniques lifting equipment may be needed to hold the structural element in place, whilst cutting takes place, to avoid sudden collapse.

It must be remembered that a safe place of work must always be provided. The top of a wall that is being demolished is not a safe place of work and therefore a working platform may be required. If scaffolding is being used, this must be dismantled as the building is demolished, and additional ties may also be needed at the low level as the ties above are removed.

Demolition

32

Working over or near to water

What your employer should do for you
1.   Avoid putting you to work over or near water, where possible.
2.   Where work over or near to water cannot be avoided, develop a safe system of work to eliminate the risk of you falling into the water.
3.   Where the risk cannot be eliminated, implement measures to minimise the consequences of the fall and entering the water.
4.   Establish a rescue plan and brief you on it.
5.   Provide the equipment for a rescue and any required information, instruction or training.
6.   Ensure that personal protective equipment (PPE) is compatible and does not hinder or restrict your ability to undertake your work safely.
7.   Train you in the correct use of PPE and the actions to take in the event of an emergency.
8.   Review the safe system of work and rescue procedures as the conditions on site change.
9.   Provide you with adequate welfare facilities.

What you should do as a supervisor			
Checklist	Yes	No	N/A
1. Ensure work is undertaken in accordance with the risk assessment and method statement.			
2. Ensure the workers are aware of the actions they should take in the event of an emergency or rescue.			
3. Ensure workers are supplied with the correct compatible PPE, that it fits and they know how to use it.			
4. Ensure rescue equipment is inspected and maintained.			
5. Ensure that a separate risk assessment is undertaken when mobile elevating work platforms (MEWPs) are working adjacent to waterways and assess whether the operative should wear a harness or flotation device.			

F
32

Introduction

Construction, demolition, inspection or maintenance work can take place over or near to water. In these instances additional control measures need to be taken to prevent people from falling into the water. In the unlikely event that someone does fall in, a rescue plan needs to be in place to prevent harm and to facilitate a quick rescue.

When planning for safe working over or near to water the work plan must consider the safety of the public and other users of the waterways.

Working over or near to water will often, although not always, involve working at height.

Risk assessment

The risk assessment must assess whether it is possible to eliminate the hazard of working over or near to water by doing the job another way, or doing some of the work off site. If this is not possible controls will have to be put in place to reduce the risk of falling into water.

The risk assessment should follow the hierarchy for working at height.

For further information on working at height refer to Chapter D24 Working at height.

When working over water, scaffolding will often be cantilevered off the structure. If you have scaffolding on your site you must ensure that it is:

☑ properly designed and fit for purpose

☑ erected, modified as necessary, and struck by competent persons

☑ inspected.

Consideration must also be given to ensuring safe access from dry land for people, materials and the emergency services.

The safe system of work developed as a result of doing the risk assessment must be communicated to the workforce.

Areas of risk

Hazardous work areas include the following.

☑ Quaysides, docks and wharfs.

☑ Locks.

☑ Canals and rivers, including bankside paths.

☑ Open sea (off-shore construction sites and installations).

☑ Lakes, reservoirs and ponds (natural and ornamental).

☑ Sewerage and slurry ponds.

☑ Water-filled pits.

☑ Water-holding tanks, including those located underground.

☑ Culverts and other storm-drainage channels.

☑ Swimming pools and aquatic sports facilities.

☑ Water features (such as fountains and rock pools).

It is essential that fall prevention measures are taken, as for any other type of construction work

Preventing accidental entry into water

Workers should be prevented from falling into the water by protecting them against the following.

☑ Falls from height following the hierarchy of control *(refer to Chapter D24 Working at height).*

☑ Slips and trips.

☑ Being knocked over the edge by moving objects or vehicles.

☑ Loss of balance (for example, from high winds, a rough sea, rising swells or swells from passing boats).

☑ Open edges, gaps in structures or barriers, holes or floor voids.

☑ Failure of ropes, lines or anchor points.

Every effort must be made to eliminate the risk of accidental entry into water

When using a MEWP next to or over water the risk assessment will need to identify whether the greatest risk of injury to the operator is from falling from the MEWP or from drowning. It may be appropriate to wear a harness to address the fall risk. A harness should not be worn when working over or next to water due to the risk of being dragged down if the MEWP falls into the water, or being trapped by the lanyard and being unable to surface, and the obvious risk of drowning.

 Self-inflating lifejackets or buoyancy aids, not harnesses, should be worn where there is a risk of drowning.

 For further information refer to the HSE information sheet *Preventing falls from boom-type mobile elevating working platforms* (MISC614).

F
32

Dangers from falling into water

Falling into water could result in a worker or member of the public suffering injury from the fall, going into shock, becoming fatigued or suffering from hypothermia, losing consciousness, drowning, or contacting leptospirosis (Weil's disease) or digestive illnesses from swallowing contaminated water.

Planning for rescue from water

Every effort should be made to prevent people from falling into the water. However, if someone does fall into water there are four important points.

- ☑ The person must be kept afloat.

- ☑ Their location must be immediately obvious, or tracked in flowing water.

- ☑ Rescue must be achieved as quickly as possible.

- ☑ A process must be in place to call the emergency services immediately, so that they can be on their way whilst others facilitate the rescue.

Methods of rescuing a casualty

- ☑ Reaching out from the bank or edge (if the casualty is near enough to the edge or bank). This should only be attempted if the rescuer has a firm footing and is anchored to the bank.

- ☑ Throwing a rescue aid out from the bank or edge. Rescuers should ensure they have a secure foothold and sufficient grip to counteract the weight of the casualty in the water.

- ☑ Wading out to reach the casualty. The rescuer must be able to keep their feet on the bottom and have suitable on shore assistance. An example of this would be that the rescuer must have a life preserver/jacket and be wearing a harness and line. The line must be anchored on the bank and attended by at least one other person.

- ☑ Using a rescue boat.

Everyone working on or near to water must be properly trained and be briefed on the documented rescue procedures to be followed. They should know what to do in the event of an emergency, know where the rescue equipment is stored and how it should be worn or used. It is a good idea to practise the rescue plan to ensure it works effectively and inspect the rescue equipment before each shift to ensure it is not damaged.

Rescue equipment

Anyone working over or near to water should wear either a self-inflating lifejacket or a buoyancy aid. The type and size will depend upon the individual, but must take into account the weight of the person, clothing, footwear and any other items they may be wearing or carrying (such as a full tool belt).

Lifejackets must be made to the relevant British Safety standard, be self-inflating and obtained from a reputable supplier. The primary aim is to support the unconscious person in the water by turning them face upwards.

Buoyancy aids provide a conscious person with extra buoyancy to stay afloat and achieve a reasonable floating position. They might not be designed to turn a person over from face down.

Where a **safety harness** is worn, while wearing personal buoyancy equipment, it is important to ensure the two devices are compatible.

The type of equipment used should be assessed against the work that the operative will be undertaking. This assessment may include the length of time a person could be in the water, the risk of injury, water temperature, current and the proximity of assistance.

Lifebuoys should be available where people are working on or over water. They should be placed at obvious places near to the edge of the water and should be equipped with a retrieval line.

Rescue lines can be used in the event of an emergency. The free end of the line is held and the bag is thrown (underarm) to the casualty.

A typical rescue line

Stop nets or lines may be suspended on or just above the water to allow a conscious person to hold on while they are waiting to be rescued or to pull themselves towards the bank.

Rescue boats must comply with the regulations and bylaws of the navigation authorities. The boat crew should be competent at handling the craft on the appropriate waterways. Consideration should be given to having manned boats in the water at all times when people are working over water, with the boats patrolling the likely fall areas.

Boat crews should be properly dressed for working on water, for example, they must wear life jackets and suitable water and wind proof clothing. Requirements will be subject to the location, weather conditions and findings of the risk assessment.

Powered rescue boats must be equipped with a **kill cord**, which will stop the engine if the driver falls overboard. The free end of the cord should be fitted to the hand, arm, wrist or the lifejacket.

A typical powered rescue boat, equipped with radio, throwing line, paddles, boat-hook and a first-aid box

Rescue nets clip to the fittings along the side of the rescue boat and can be used to haul the person in the water over the side of a rescue boat.

F 32

409